K12 Summit
CURRICULUM

Algebra 2
A Reference Guide

Book Staff and Contributors

Harold Lawrance   *Content Specialist*
Jill Tunick   *Senior Text Editor*
Kay McCarthy   *Text Editor*
Suzanne Montazer   *Creative Director, Print and ePublishing*
Stephanie Shaw Williams   *Senior Print Visual Designer, Cover Designer*
Julie Jankowski   *Print Visual Designer*
Meredith Condit, Charlotte Fullerton, Steve Mawyer   *Media Editors*
Susan Raley   *Senior Manager, Writers and Editors*
Abhilasha Parakh, Dan Smith   *Senior Project Managers*

Paul Thomas   *Senior Director, Content and Assessment*
Kelly Engel   *Director, Mathematics Content Specialists*
Michelle Kitt   *Director, Instructional Design*
Jason Golomb   *Senior Director, Program Management Product Development*
Christopher Frescholtz   *Senior Director, Program Management*

Lisa Dimaio Iekel   *Director, Print Production and Manufacturing*

About K12 Inc.

K12 Inc., a technology-based education company, is the nation's leading provider of proprietary curriculum and online education programs to students in grades K–12. K^{12} provides its curriculum and academic services to online schools, traditional classrooms, blended school programs, and directly to families. K12 Inc. also operates the K^{12} International Academy, an accredited, diploma-granting online private school serving students worldwide. K^{12}'s mission is to provide any child the curriculum and tools to maximize success in life, regardless of geographic, financial, or demographic circumstances. K12 Inc. is accredited by CITA. More information can be found at www.K12.com.

ISBN: 978-1-60153-511-5 (online book)
ISBN: 978-1-60153-505-4 (printed book)

Printed by Quad Graphics, Versailles, KY, USA, April 2017

Contents

Probability Distributions

Data Gathering and Analysis

Systems of Linear Equations and Inequalities

Radicals and Complex Numbers

Polynomials

Polynomial Functions

Rational Expressions

Exponential and Logarithmic Functions

Radians and Trigonometric Functions

Graphs of Sinusoidal Functions

More Function Types

Using Function Models

Sequences and Series

Appendices

K¹² Summit Curriculum

And remember:
The pages in your
book are also
online!

Go to the online course to look for these
digital resources in your lessons:

 **– second MATH**

Videos will introduce
you to each topic.

 **math CAST**

Visual learning with
animations and interaction
will help you master
key skills.

 **Worked EXAMPLE**

Solve problems with
the help of stepped
examples.

 **APPLY it!**

Use real-world
examples to practice
what you've learned.

Probability Distributions

Topic List

How unique is a white ladybug? Probability distributions can help you describe how unusual a value is and can help you compare different populations or values.

Creating Probability Distributions

Probabilities of all outcomes of a discrete random variable can be summarized in a table.

Creating Probability Distribution Tables

A study of a new treatment for high cholesterol undergoes testing. The results are summarized in this frequency table.

X	0–9	10–19	20–29	30–39	40–49
f	81	73	35	47	14

In this table, X stands for the number of points that the patient's cholesterol level decreased, and f stands for the number of patients. For instance, 73 patients had their cholesterol decrease between 10 and 19 points after the new treatment.

▶ **Remember** The letter X is often used to represent a discrete random variable. For example, when a coin is tossed, the variable X would represent the two outcomes: heads and tails. These outcomes are both discrete and random.

A patient wants to know the probability that the new treatment will lower his cholesterol from 20 to 29 points. Here, a **probability distribution table** would be useful because it shows the probabilities for all of the outcomes.

How to Create a Probability Distribution Table

Follow these steps to create a probability distribution table from a frequency table.

Step 1 Find the sum of the frequencies.

Step 2 Divide each frequency by the sum found in Step 1.

Step 3 Replace each frequency in the table with the ratio found in Step 2.

Step 4 Change the label f to P.

For the frequency table describing the clinical testing, the total number of frequencies is $81 + 73 + 35 + 47 + 14 = 250$. So 250 patients took part in the study. Here is the complete probability distribution table.

X	0–9	10–19	20–29	30–39	40–49
P	0.324	0.292	0.14	0.188	0.056

According to this table, the probability that the new treatment will lower a patient's cholesterol between 20 and 29 points is 0.14, or 14%.

▶ **Think About It** The sum of the probabilities in a probability distribution table always equals 1.

In a different study, patients are separated into four groups according to a spinner.

For the spinner, there are four different outcomes: Group 1, Group 2, Group 3, and Group 4. There are six sections overall.

Notice that some outcomes are more likely than others. For instance, there are two sections for Groups 1 and 2, but only one section for Groups 3 and 4.

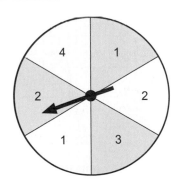

The probability distribution table shows that the chances of being in Group 1 or Group 2 are higher than the chances of being in Group 3 or Group 4.

X	1	2	3	4
P	$\frac{1}{3}$	$\frac{1}{3}$	$\frac{1}{6}$	$\frac{1}{6}$

Properties of Probability Distributions

There are two properties that every probability distribution table has.

▶ **Think About It** Every probability distribution for a discrete random variable must satisfy both properties.

This probability distribution table violates the first property because each probability is not a number between 0 and 1. So it is not a probability distribution.

X	1	2	3	4	5
P	0.5	0.1	0.3	0.4	-0.3

This probability distribution table violates the second property because the sum of all probabilities is not equal to 1. So it is not a probability distribution.

X	5	10	15	20	25	30
P	0.34	0.5	0.101	0.32	0.34	0.122

Graphs of Probability Distributions

A probability distribution table and a histogram can be used to interpret the likelihood of an event or outcome.

The developer of a test preparation class wants to know the efficacy of the class in improving test scores. Students took a practice test on the first and last day of the class, and the difference in their scores was recorded. The results are shown in the table.

X	≤19	20–29	30–39	40–49	50–59	≥60
f	22	54	62	38	18	6

In the table, X stands for the number of points the score increased after taking the prep class, and f stands for the number of students.

A student wants to know the probability that the prep class will increase her test score by 30 to 39 points. Here, a probability distribution table would be useful.

Step 1 Find the sum of the frequencies. For this frequency table, the total number of frequencies is $22 + 54 + 62 + 38 + 18 + 6 = 200$. Two hundred students took part in the study.

Step 2 Divide each frequency by the total found in Step 1.

Step 3 Replace each frequency in the table with the ratio found in Step 2.

Step 4 Change the label f to P.

Here is the complete probability distribution table.

X	≤19	20–29	30–39	40–49	50–59	≥60
P	0.11	0.27	0.31	0.19	0.09	0.03

According to the table, the probability that the class will increase a student's score by 30 to 39 points is 0.31, or 31%.

These data can also be graphed in a probability distribution histogram.

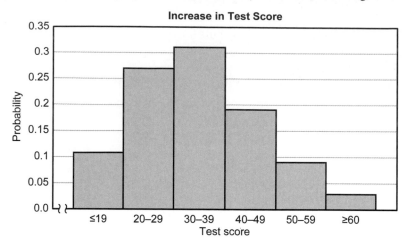

The third bar of the histogram represents a 30- to 39-point increase in test scores. The height of this bar is at the value $P = 0.31$. The probability of a student increasing his or her score by 30 to 39 points is 0.31, or 31%.

Interpreting Probability Distributions

The likelihood of many events can be summarized by a table or histogram.

Interpreting Probability Distribution Tables

A summer camp program director is planning activities for the summer. The probability distribution table shows the probability, P, that the age of a randomly chosen camper is X.

X	10	11	12	13	14
P	0.15	0.3	0.2	0.25	0.1

For the first activity, the program director selects a camper at random to read announcements. What is $P(X = 13)$, the probability that the camper selected is 13 years old?

According to the probability distribution table, when $X = 13$, the probability is $P = 0.25$. So $P(X = 13) = 0.25$.

In other words, the probability of selecting a 13-year-old camper at random is 0.25, or 25%.

Suppose the program director wants to determine $P(X \geq 13)$, the probability that a randomly selected camper is at least 13 years old.

This problem can be solved by adding individual probabilities.

$$P(X \geq 13) = P(X = 13) + P(X = 14)$$
$$= 0.25 + 0.1$$
$$= 0.35$$

There is a 35% probability of selecting a camper who is at least 13 years old.

Interpreting Probability Distribution Histograms

The program director now has to decide which staff members to assign to which activities. She is using the probability distribution histogram to help her make her decision.

In this histogram, X stands for the ages of individual staff members. P is the probability that if a single staff member is chosen at random, then the staff member will be that age.

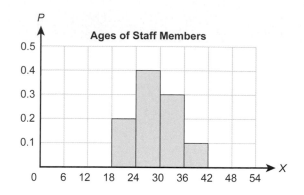

▶ **Remember** A histogram is a graph showing the frequency distribution of data.

For the first activity, the program director selects a staff member at random to lead the songs at dinner. What is $P(18 \leq X < 24)$, the probability that the staff member selected is at least 18 years old and less than 24 years old?

The first bar of the histogram represents $18 \leq X < 24$. The height of this bar is at the value $P = 0.2$. So the probability of selecting a staff member who is at least 18 years old and less than 24 years old is 0.2, or 20%.

Probability distribution histograms can help determine more than just single entries. Suppose the program director wants to determine $P(X \geq 30)$, the probability that a randomly selected staff member is at least 30 years old.

This problem can be solved by adding individual probabilities.

$$P(X \geq 30) = P(30 \leq X < 36) + P(36 \leq X < 42)$$
$$= 0.3 + 0.1$$
$$= 0.4$$

There is a 40% probability of selecting a staff member who is at least 30 years old.

Binomial Distributions

A table or graph can be used to represent outcomes of a variable that has a binomial distribution.

Determining Whether a Variable Has a Binomial Distribution

A doctor knows that for a certain type of adult migraine headache, Medicine Q works about 70% of the time. If the medicine is tried with two or more different patients who have this condition, the resulting probability distribution is a binomial distribution.

Binomial Distribution

A variable has a binomial distribution if it has these traits:

- There are a fixed number of independent trials.

- The outcome of each trial is success or failure.

- The probability of success for each trial is the same.

This situation meets all of the conditions for a binomial distribution.

- There are a fixed number of independent trials; there are two trials, and each patient taking Medicine Q is independent of the other.

- The outcome of each trial is a success or failure; for each patient, the medicine will either help the migraine (success) or it will not (failure).

- The probability of success for each trial is the same; there is a 0.7 probability of success when each patient takes Medicine Q.

Creating Binomial Distributions

Suppose the doctor is seeing two patients who have this type of adult migraine headache. You can create a binomial distribution table or graph to represent outcomes for these two patients.

The variable X can take on three different values: Medicine Q will work for none of the patients, one of the patients, or both patients. So the variable X is equal to 0, 1, or 2.

▶ **Remember** If A and B are independent events, then
$$P(A \text{ and } B) = P(A) \bullet P(B).$$

When $X = 0$, it means that Medicine Q failed to work for both patients. Since $P(\text{success}) = 0.7$, $P(\text{failure}) = 0.3$.

$$
\begin{aligned}
P(X = 0) &= P(\text{failure}) \bullet P(\text{failure}) \\
&= 0.3 \bullet 0.3 \\
&= 0.09
\end{aligned}
$$

When $X = 1$, it means that the medicine worked for one of the patients but not both.

$$
\begin{aligned}
P(X = 1) &= P(\text{success}) \bullet P(\text{failure}) + P(\text{failure}) \bullet P(\text{success}) \\
&= 0.7 \bullet 0.3 + 0.3 \bullet 0.7 \\
&= 0.21 + 0.21 \\
&= 0.42
\end{aligned}
$$

When $X = 2$, it means that the medicine worked for both patients.

$$P(X = 0) = P(\text{success}) \cdot P(\text{success})$$
$$= 0.7 \cdot 0.7$$
$$= 0.49$$

You can now use the probabilities that you calculated for each outcome to create a binomial distribution table and a binomial distribution histogram.

Binomial Distribution Table

X	0	1	2
P	0.09	0.42	0.49

Binomial Distribution Histogram

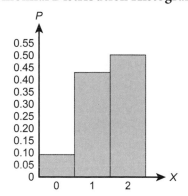

Interpreting Binomial Distributions

The doctor would be happy if the medicine was successful with at least one of the two patients. In the language of probability, the question becomes what is $P(X \geq 1)$?

The answer to this question is found by adding the appropriate probabilities in the table.

$$P(X \geq 1) = P(X = 1) + P(X = 2)$$
$$= 0.42 + 0.49$$
$$= 0.91$$

There is a 91% probability that Medicine Q will be successful with at least one of the patients.

Continuous Random Variables

Areas within probability distribution graphs can be used to compute probability.

Exploring Continuous Random Variables

An incubator is being used to hatch chickens. The incubator temperatures X, in degrees Fahrenheit, are distributed according to this probability distribution.

When all values of a random variable X are equally likely to occur, the resulting probability distribution is called a **uniform probability distribution**.

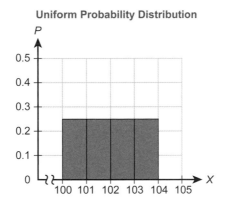

Uniform Probability Distribution

For the incubator, all of the values of X, from 100°F to 104°F are equally likely to occur. Because any temperature between these values, such as 101.5°F or 103.9°F, may occur, X, in this case, is considered to be a continuous random variable.

Using Area to Determine Probability

When X is a continuous random variable, the resulting probability distribution graph is a geometric shape with a total area of 1. The probability that $a \leq X \leq b$ will be the area of the shape bordered by the values a and b.

For instance, suppose the temperature of the incubator is taken at 10 a.m. What is the probability that the temperature is between 101°F and 103°F?

To answer this question, you can compute the area of the rectangular region where $101 \leq X \leq 103$, which is shown here.

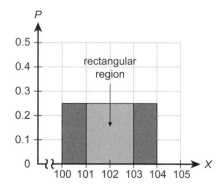

The area of the rectangular region is the product of the base and the height.

$$2 \cdot 0.25 = 0.5$$

There is a 50% probability that the temperature will be between 101°F and 103°F at 10 a.m.

Using Continuous Nonuniform Probability Distributions

Here is another continuous probability distribution that is not uniform and is in the shape of a triangle.

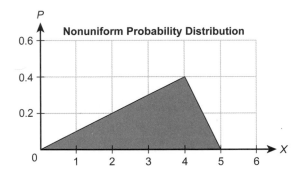

Suppose we want to know $P(1 \leq X \leq 4)$, which is the probability that X is between 1 and 4.

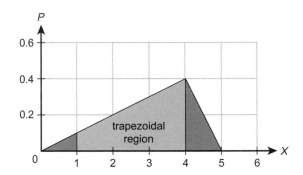

The region bounded by $X = 1$ and $X = 4$ is a trapezoid with base lengths 0.1 and 0.4. The height of the trapezoid is 3.

$$\text{area} = \frac{1}{2}h \left(\text{base}_1 + \text{base}_2\right)$$

$$= \frac{1}{2} \cdot 3 \left(0.1 + 0.4\right)$$

$$= 0.75$$

The probability that X is between 3 and 4 is 0.75, or 75%.

The Normal Distribution

A bell-shaped curve is often used for data analysis and probability.

Identifying Normal Distributions

Definition
A **normal distribution** is bell shaped and is centered around the mean.

If you were to collect many unopened boxes of the same cereal and weigh them, the weights would all vary slightly but would be centered around the mean weight of all boxes. Some boxes would weigh slightly less than the mean and some slightly more, but most would weigh closer to the mean, creating a bell-shaped curve, or a normal distribution.

Some distributions are not normally distributed. The years on coins, for example, are not normally distributed. Most coins will have more recent years, and few will have older dates. However, no coins can have dates that are greater than the current year, creating a distribution that is shaped more like a triangle. It is not bell shaped.

Using the Normal Distribution

When a data set has a normal distribution, a histogram that represents the data set is symmetric and has a bell shape.

When a curve is drawn through the tops of the bars, the curve is in the shape of a bell.

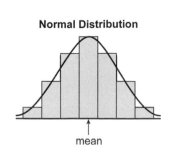

Normal Distribution

mean

Normal distributions have important properties that help us study data sets that are otherwise too large to study.

For example, the mean is always at the center of the distribution, so about half of the data set is above the mean and half of the data set is below the mean.

The standard deviation of a normal distribution also gives us useful information about the data set.

▶ **Think About It** In a normal distribution, the mean, median, and mode all have approximately the same value.

Properties of a Normal Distribution

If a data set has a normal distribution, then it has the following traits:

- About 68% of the data are within one standard deviation of the mean.
- About 95% of the data are within two standard deviations of the mean.
- About 99.7% of the data are within three standard deviations of the mean.

The properties involving standard deviation are illustrated in more detail in this diagram.

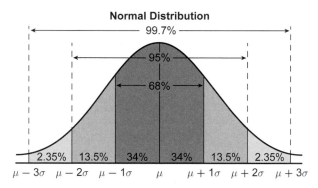

For example, you know that about 68% of the data are within one standard deviation of the mean. This means that about 34% are one standard deviation above the mean and 34% of the data are one standard deviation below the mean.

▶ **Remember** The Greek letters μ and σ are used to represent the mean and standard deviation of a data set, respectively.

Using Normal Distribution Properties

A pediatrician reads an article that states that the length of the flu incubation period is distributed normally with a mean length of 7 days and a standard deviation of 2 days. Afterward, she wonders what the probability is of the flu incubating for at least 9 days.

Assuming that flu incubation periods are normally distributed, a normal curve can be drawn to represent this situation.

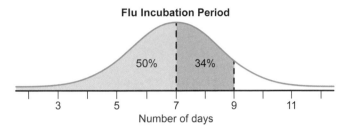

Nine days is one standard deviation above the mean of 7 days. So 34% of the data are between 7 days and 9 days. Also, 50% of the data are below the mean.

This means that 50% + 34% = 84% of flu cases have an incubation period of at most 9 days. By subtracting 84% from 100%, you can obtain the percent of cases that have an incubation period of at least 9 days.

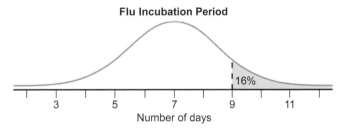

Therefore, the probability is about 16% that a flu case will have an incubation period of at least 9 days.

> ▶ **Remember** In a normal distribution, about 50% of the data are above the mean and about 50% of the data are below the mean.

What Data Are Normal?

Only certain data sets have a normal distribution. Looking at the graph of the data can help to determine if the data set is normally distributed.

Determining Whether a Data Set Is Normal

You can determine whether a data set has a normal, or approximately normal, distribution by creating a display of the data.

EXAMPLE

Here are the dates of 24 pennies found in a piggy bank. Explain whether the data are normally distributed.

1984, 2012, 2013, 1999, 2013, 2010, 2009, 1987, 2002, 1966, 1979, 2009, 2012, 2008, 1992, 1991, 1998, 2003, 2005, 2007, 1989, 1997, 2006, 2014

SOLUTION

The dates are widely spread, so a histogram is an appropriate display.

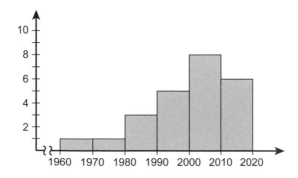

The graph is skewed left, so the data are not normally distributed. ■

Standard Deviation and Nonnormal Data

The mean of the penny data set is about 2000, and the standard deviation is about 12. If the data set were normally distributed, you could conclude that about 99.7% of the pennies, or nearly all the pennies, have dates between 1964 and 2036. Although it is true that all the dates in the data set are between 1964 and 2036, it is a misleading statement because the greatest date in the list is 2014.

Standardizing Data

A standard score tells us how far a data value is from the mean.

Converting Raw Scores into z-Scores

Antibiotics are strong medicines that are prescribed by a doctor and often used to treat infections. Once a patient begins taking an antibiotic, the length of time that it takes to cure the infection can vary.

Suppose that the time it takes a certain antibiotic to cure an infection is known to be normally distributed with a mean of 5.2 days and a standard deviation of 1.1 days.

To get an idea of how effective the new antibiotic is with certain patients, actual results can be converted into z-scores. A z-score tells us the number of standard deviations that a data value is from the mean of the data set.

When a data value (called a raw score) is greater than the mean, its corresponding z-score will be positive. When a data value is less than the mean, its corresponding z-score will be negative.

Converting Raw Scores into z-Scores

A **z-score** is the number of standard deviations that a data value is from the mean. Every data value in a data set has a corresponding z-score and is obtained by the formula

$$z = \frac{x - \mu}{\sigma}$$

where z is the z-score, x is the raw data value, μ is the mean of the data set, and σ is the standard deviation.

Suppose the antibiotic cures an infection in a patient in 3.8 days. What is the corresponding z-score?

Here, $x = 3.8$, $\mu = 5.2$, and $\sigma = 1.1$. These values can be substituted into the formula to find the corresponding z-score.

$$z = \frac{3.8 - 5.2}{1.1}$$
$$\approx -1.3$$

A z-score of -1.3 means that the antibiotic cures the infection in a time that is 1.3 standard deviations below the mean.

Converting z-Scores into Raw Scores

Suppose a patient takes the antibiotic and is cured of the infection according to a z-score of 2.3. This means that the patient was cured in an amount of time that is about 2.3 standard deviations greater than the mean cure time.

But suppose you want to know how many days it took the antibiotic to cure the infection in this patient. In other words, what is the raw score if the z-score is 2.3?

The z-score formula can be rearranged to create a formula for converting z-scores back into raw scores.

Converting z-Scores into Raw Scores

A z-score can be converted back into its original value, called a **raw score**, using the formula

$$x = z \bullet \sigma + \mu$$

where x is the raw score, z is the z-score, μ is the mean of the data set, and σ is the standard deviation.

Now convert the z-score of 2.3 back into a raw score. Using $z = 2.3$, $\mu = 5.2$, and $\sigma = 1.1$, you can find the value of the raw score, x.

$$x = 2.3 \cdot (1.1) + 5.2$$
$$\approx 7.7$$

In this patient, the antibiotic cured the infection in about 8 days—more than 2 days longer than the average cure time for this antibiotic.

Comparing Scores

Standard scores can be used to compare normal distributions.

Comparing z-Scores from Two Distributions

Black tea has been studied for its medicinal properties and for the amount of caffeine it contains (which can vary depending on the type of tea used and the amount of time brewed).

The amount of caffeine in single servings of tea is normally distributed. For a particular comparison, single servings of two different Ceylon tea mixtures are compared.

	Mixture A	Mixture B
Mean	$\mu = 55$ mg	$\mu = 52$ mg
Standard deviation	$\sigma = 4.1$ mg	$\sigma = 3.3$ mg

▶ **Think About It** Ceylon tea is a type of black tea grown in Sri Lanka.

Suppose you are given a serving of Ceylon tea that contains 50 mg of caffeine. Which mixture is the tea more likely to come from?

To determine whether the serving with 50 mg of caffeine is more likely to come from Mixture A or Mixture B, you can determine the z-score for each mixture.

Mixture A	Mixture B
$z = \dfrac{50 - 55}{4.1}$	$z = \dfrac{50 - 52}{3.3}$
≈ -1.22	≈ -0.61

For a normal distribution, any value that is closer to the mean will be a more likely outcome than any value farther away from the mean. Since -0.61 is closer to 0 than -1.22, Mixture B is more likely to produce a serving of Ceylon tea with 50 mg of caffeine.

> ▶ **Think About It** The z-score of the mean is 0.00 because it is zero standard deviations away from the mean.

Paulo is doing his own research about the caffeine content of these two Ceylon tea mixtures. The brew he makes with Mixture A has 57 mg of caffeine in a single serving. The brew he makes with Mixture B has 49 mg of caffeine in a single serving. Which result is more unusual?

To determine whether the serving with 57 mg of caffeine from Mixture A is more unusual than the serving with 49 mg of caffeine from Mixture B, you can determine the z-score for each mixture.

Mixture A	Mixture B
$z = \dfrac{57 - 55}{4.1}$ ≈ 0.49	$z = \dfrac{49 - 52}{3.3}$ ≈ -0.91

The z-scores for each mixture have different signs (one positive and one negative). However, we are only interested in knowing which z-score is farthest from 0.

Since Mixture A's z-score of 0.49 is closer to 0 than Mixture B's z-score of -0.91, the serving with 49 mg of caffeine from Mixture B is more unusual than the serving with 57 mg of caffeine from Mixture A.

Interpreting a *z*-Score in Two Distributions

Two normally distributed data sets can also be compared for the same *z*-score. For instance, in looking at the two mixtures of Ceylon tea, which mixture has more caffeine for a *z*-score of -3.00?

The *z*-score is -3.00, and you know the mean and standard deviation for each mixture. Use the appropriate formula to determine the actual amount of caffeine in a serving from each mixture.

Mixture A	Mixture B
$x = -3 \cdot 4.1 + 55$	$x = -3 \cdot 3.3 + 52$
$= 42.7$	$= 42.1$

At a distance of three standard deviations below the mean, the two mixtures have about the same amounts of caffeine. However, Mixture A has more caffeine compared to Mixture B.

▶ **Remember** $x = z \cdot \sigma + \mu$

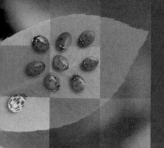

The Standard Normal Curve

The standard normal curve is used to analyze data.

When all of the data values of a normal distribution are turned into *z*-scores, the resulting distribution is called the standard normal curve.

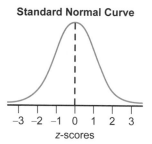

Standard Normal Curve

z-scores

Each value on the horizontal axis of the standard normal curve is a *z*-score, and the mean is always 0.

For instance, a data value with a *z*-score of 0.54 would correspond to 0.54 on the horizontal axis of the standard normal curve.

Properties of the Standard Normal Curve

The **standard normal curve** is a probability distribution with the following properties:

- The mean is 0.
- The standard deviation is 1.
- The total area under the curve is 1.

Using the *z*-Distribution Table

Because the standard normal curve is a probability distribution, it can be used to find probabilities. These probabilities correspond to areas under the standard normal curve.

Suppose a data value has a *z*-score of 0.54. What percent of the data values are less than this value?

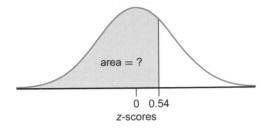

To answer this question, you can use the Table of z-Scores for Normal Distribution in the appendix. This table gives the areas under the standard normal curve that are less than a given z-score.

z	.00	.01	.02	.03	.04	.05
0.0	0.5000	0.5040	0.5080	0.5120	0.5160	0.5199
0.1	0.5398	0.5438	0.5478	0.5517	0.5557	0.5596
0.2	0.5793	0.5832	0.5871	0.5910	0.5948	0.5987
0.3	0.6179	0.6217	0.6255	0.6293	0.6331	0.6368
0.4	0.6554	0.6591	0.6628	0.6664	0.6700	0.6736
0.5	0.6915	0.6950	0.6985	0.7019	0.7054	0.7088
0.6	0.7257	0.7291	0.7324	0.7357	0.7389	0.7422

Using the z-distribution table, look for the area that corresponds to the row and column of a z-score of 0.54. You can see that $P(z < 0.54) = 0.7054$, which is about 71%.

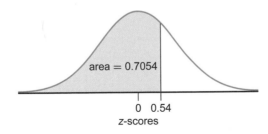

So about 71% of the data values are less than a value with a z-score of 0.54.

Using the Standard Normal Curve to Solve Problems

Suppose scores on a standardized test taken by future doctors are normally distributed with a mean of 10.5 and a standard deviation of 2.2. If 150 future doctors take the test, how many are likely to score between 12 and 15?

> ▶ **Remember** z-scores are obtained using the following formula:
>
> $$z = \frac{x - \mu}{\sigma}$$

The score 12 has a z-score of about 0.68, and the score 15 has a z-score of about 2.05. To help answer the question, you need to know the area that corresponds to $P\left(0.68 < z < 2.05\right)$.

The area under the standard normal curve less than $z = 0.68$ is 0.7517, and the area less than $z = 2.05$ is 0.9798.

So $P\left(0.68 < z < 2.05\right) = 0.9798 - 0.7517 = 0.2281$.

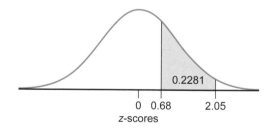

Multiply the area by the number of future doctors taking the exam.

$$0.2281 \bullet 150 \approx 34$$

So about 34 of the 150 future doctors taking the exam are likely to score between 12 and 15.

Finding Standard Scores

Areas under the standard normal curve can be used to find standard scores and percentiles.

Using Area to Find a *z*-Score

Although the straightforward way of reading the z-distribution table is to look up the z-score and then find the corresponding area under the standard normal curve, we can also read the table in the other direction.

Suppose that about 20% of the data in a data set are below a certain value. What z-score corresponds to this value?

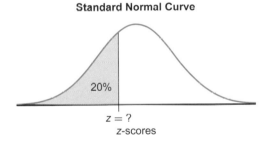

Standard Normal Curve

20%

$z = ?$

z-scores

▶ **Remember** z-scores are sometimes called standard scores.

Since 20% = 0.2, you want to find an area in the body of the z-distribution table that is closest to 0.2.

z	.00	.01	.02	.03	.04	.05
−1.4	0.0808	0.0793	0.0778	0.0764	0.0749	0.0735
−1.3	0.0968	0.0951	0.0934	0.0918	0.0901	0.0885
−1.2	0.1151	0.1131	0.1112	0.1093	0.1075	0.1056
−1.1	0.1357	0.1335	0.1314	0.1292	0.1271	0.1251
−1.0	0.1587	0.1562	0.1539	0.1515	0.1492	0.1469
−0.9	0.1841	0.1814	0.1788	0.1762	0.1736	0.1711
−0.8	0.2119	0.2090	0.2061	0.2033	0.2005	0.1977
−0.7	0.2420	0.2389	0.2358	0.2327	0.2296	0.2266

The area 0.2005 is closest to 20%. Use the row and column of the area to locate the corresponding z-score, which corresponds to a z-score of −0.84.

Determining Area Above a z-Score

Suppose that 15% of the data in a data set are above a certain value. What z-score corresponds to this value?

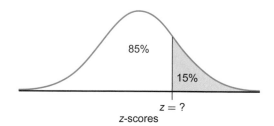

Since the z-distribution table only gives the areas that are below a particular z-score, you need to find the percent of data below the value: 100% − 15% = 85%. Since 85% = 0.85, you want to find an area in the body of the z-distribution table that is closest to 0.85.

z	.00	.01	.02	.03	.04	.05
0.6	0.7257	0.7291	0.7324	0.7357	0.7389	0.7422
0.7	0.7580	0.7611	0.7642	0.7673	0.7704	0.7734
0.8	0.7881	0.7910	0.7939	0.7967	0.7995	0.8023
0.9	0.8159	0.8186	0.8212	0.8238	0.8264	0.8289
1.0	0.8413	0.8438	0.8461	0.8485	0.8508	0.8531
1.1	0.8643	0.8665	0.8686	0.8708	0.8729	0.8749

The area 0.8508 is closest to 85%, which corresponds to a z-score of 1.04.

Understanding Percentiles

A **percentile rank** is the percentage of data that falls below a particular value. For example, if a student scores higher than 60% of the other students who took an exam, then the student's percentile rank is at the 60th percentile.

▶ **Remember** The *n*th percentile is the value (or score) below which *n* percent of the data may be found.

Scores on the math section of a standardized aptitude test are normally distributed with a mean of about 500 and a standard deviation of about 100. According to this information, what score would be at the 80th percentile?

Using the *z*-distribution table, you see that the area 0.8023 is closest to 80%, which corresponds to a *z*-score of 0.85. Use the appropriate formula to find the corresponding score.

$$x = z \bullet \sigma + \mu$$
$$= 0.85 \bullet 100 + 500$$
$$= 585$$

So a score of 585 on the math section of this standardized test is at the 80th percentile.

Data Gathering and Analysis

Topic List

How many bees are in this colony? How many of them are workers? How many are drones? It would be impractical to check every single bee, but, with sampling, apiarists (beekeepers) and entomologists can figure out quite a bit about a bee colony.

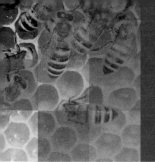

Sample and Population

If you can't study the entire group of objects that you are interested in, then study just some of them.

Distinguishing Between a Sample and a Population

A **population** is an entire set of members that you want to know something about. The set can be large or small, and it can be made up of people or objects. Here are examples of populations:

- every resident in the United States
- every library card holder in San Antonio, Texas
- every lion in a nature preserve
- every apple in an orchard

A **sample** is a subset of a population. It is common to study samples when a population is very large and studying each member would be impossible, costly, or time-consuming.

For example, a science professor is considering sending some of the university's science students on a field trip to another country. He wants to know how many of the 918 science students at his university would participate in such a trip. He surveys 83 of the science students and finds that 34 of them would participate.

Who makes up the population?

The 918 science students at that university make up the population. Ideally, the professor would be able to survey each of them, but his schedule does not allow him time to survey each student, especially those who have other professors.

Who makes up the sample?

The 83 students whom the professor surveys make up the sample.

> ▶ **Think About It** Every 10 years, the U.S. Census Bureau gathers basic information on every resident in the United States. Annually, the bureau gathers more detailed information from a sample of the population.

Finding and Using Sample Means

A group of biology students is studying Mexican free-tail bats in a local cave. They capture a dozen bats from the cave, record their wingspans in centimeters, and then release them. The wingspans are 31 cm, 36 cm, 34 cm, 32 cm, 33 cm, 33 cm, 29 cm, 35 cm, 30 cm, 34 cm, 35 cm, and 30 cm. Estimate the average wingspan of all the bats in the cave.

The sample mean is a good estimate of the population mean. To find the sample mean, divide the sum of the wingspans in the sample by the number of bats in the sample.

$$\frac{392}{12} \approx 32.7$$

Based on this sample, it is fair to estimate that the average wingspan of all the bats in the cave is about 33 cm.

> ▶ **Think About It** The accuracy of an estimate based on a sample depends largely on how the sample was produced and the size of the sample.

Finding and Using Sample Proportions: Fractions

A university prepares to send 520 biology test kits to overseas students. An assistant randomly inspects 40 of the kits and finds that 5 have outdated instructions. About how many kits in the shipment have outdated instructions?

Find the proportion of test kits in the sample with outdated instructions.

$$\frac{5}{40} = \frac{1}{8}$$

Because $\frac{1}{8}$ of the test kits in the sample have outdated instructions, it is fair to estimate that $\frac{1}{8}$ of the test kits in the entire shipment have outdated instructions—that is, $\frac{1}{8} \cdot 520 = 65$ test kits.

> ▶ **Remember** You can write a proportion as a fraction, decimal, or percent.

Finding and Using Sample Proportions: Percents

Sometimes it makes more sense to write the sample proportion as a percent.

After returning from a biology field trip, a professor asks a sample of the students whether they would return the following year. The table shows the results.

Response	Frequency
Yes	21
No	11
Unsure	6

A total of 80 students went on the trip. Estimate how many would say *No* if they were asked whether they would return the following year.

Find the percent of students in the sample that would not return. Divide the number who responded *No* by the total number in the sample.

$$\frac{11}{38} \approx 29\%$$

Find 29% of the population.

$$0.29 \cdot 80 = 23.2$$

Based on the sample, it is fair to estimate that about 23 of the 80 students would say *No* to returning the following year.

Statistics and Parameters

You can use data for one of two purposes: to summarize or to draw conclusions.

Distinguishing Between Descriptive and Inferential Statistics

Descriptive statistics are used to numerically summarize or represent a set of data. Here are some examples:

- A student's grade point average is 3.27.

- The median home value in a city is $259,000.

- The ducks in a zoo have a mean weight of 1.2 kg, with a standard deviation of 0.17 kg.

Inferential statistics are used to draw conclusions or make predictions. Notice in these examples that the purpose is to take the information gained from the sample and generalize it to the population it came from.

- A governor wants to know whether the residents in his state approve of his recent actions. In a poll, about 74% of those surveyed said they approved.

- Scientists caught 16 of the ducks in a lake, measured their lengths, and released them. They report, "Our findings indicate that the average length of the ducks in the lake is about 58 cm."

▶ **Think About It** In descriptive statistics, the numbers used to describe the data set are certain. In inferential statistics, the numbers used to describe the population are "best estimates."

Finding Parameters and Statistics

A **parameter** is a measurement that describes a population. A **statistic** is a measurement that describes a sample. Different notations make it easy to distinguish between parameters and statistics.

	Population	Sample
Mean	μ	$\overline{x}$
Standard deviation	σ	s
Proportion	p	$\hat{p}$

▶ **Think About It**

NOTATION The symbols μ and σ are the lowercase Greek letters mu and sigma. Read the symbol $\hat{p}$ as "p-hat."

At a zoo, 55% of the penguins are male. A researcher selects a sample of 5 of the penguins and notes that 3 are male. What are p and $\hat{p}$ for male penguins?

$$p = 0.55 \text{ because 55\% of the population is male}$$

$$\hat{p} = 0.6 \text{ because } \frac{3}{5}, \text{ or 60\%, of the sample is male}$$

The mean weight of the penguins at the zoo is 9.9 lb, with a standard deviation of 1.4 lb. The penguins in the researcher's sample weigh 9.7 lb, 10.4 lb, 11.5 lb, 8.6 lb, and 11.8 lb. Find μ, $\overline{x}$, σ, and s.

Because they describe the population, $\mu = 9.9$ and $\sigma = 1.4$.

Calculate to find the statistics.

$$\overline{x} = \frac{52}{5} = 10.4 \text{ and } s = \sqrt{\frac{6.9}{4}} \approx 1.3$$

Using a Table for a Simulation

In the zoo ponds, 20% of the goldfish are white. Use the Table of Random Digits in the appendix, starting at line 118, to simulate randomly selecting a sample of 40 goldfish and recording their color.

Because p is 20%, let 20% of the digits in the table represent selecting a white goldfish. For instance, let the digits 1 and 2 represent selecting a white goldfish and the digits 3, 4, 5, 6, 7, 8, 9, and 0 represent selecting a goldfish of another color.

116	84307	05017	79713	19252	39557	15608	90737	81430
117	43887	37323	47413	50487	23703	66932	09024	19395
118	01178	69415	09264	17728	58858	76330	57712	66411
119	36748	24247	75430	36452	95641	00723	22490	51418
120	66805	86573	49093	14317	20330	09825	36777	82572

The first five digits in line 118 are 0, 1, 1, 7, and 8, so the second and third fish selected were white. Continue reading across until you have selected 40 fish. You should have found that 10 of the 40 fish were white, so $\hat{p}$ is 25%.

▶ **Q&A**

Q Starting at line 118, what is $\hat{p}$ if you read by twos, letting the numbers 01 through 20 represent selecting a white goldfish?

A $\hat{p} = 27.5\%$ (11 out of 40)

Using a Table to Estimate a Probability

A dog successfully performs a trick 65% of the time. Use the Table of Random Digits in the appendix to estimate the probability that it will successfully perform the trick on at least 7 out of its next 10 attempts. Start at line 116 and perform 6 trials.

Let the numbers 01 through 65 represent a success. The first 10 two-digit numbers in line 116 are 84, 30, 70, 50, 17, 79, 71, 31, 92, and 52, representing 5 successes in 10 attempts.

Continuing along line 116, the next 10 numbers represent 6 successes in 10 attempts. Confirm for yourself that in the next 4 groups of 10 there are 6, 6, 7, and 7 successes. Out of the 6 trials, only 2 had at least 7 successes. Based on this simulation, the probability that the dog successfully performs the trick on at least 7 out of its next 10 attempts is about 33%.

Interval Estimates

In many practical situations, the population parameter is unknown.

Point and Interval Estimates

Point estimates are statistics, such as $\hat{p}$ and $\bar{x}$, that are used to estimate population parameters.

- The point estimate for p is $\hat{p}$.

- The point estimate for μ is $\bar{x}$.

> ▶ **Remember** p represents a population proportion, and $\hat{p}$ represents a sample proportion. μ represents a population mean, and $\bar{x}$ represents a sample mean.

An **interval estimate** is a range of values that contains the point estimate and, therefore, is likely to contain the population parameter. It is determined by the **margin of error**, the greatest likely difference between the point estimate and the parameter.

Find the lower limit by subtracting the margin of error from the point estimate. Find the upper limit by adding the margin of error to the point estimate. Look at the three ways you may see interval estimates described.

General form	Example
point estimate $\pm$ margin of error	14% $\pm$ 2%
between lower limit and upper limit	between 12% and 16%
(lower limit, upper limit)	(12%, 16%)

Using Interval Estimates: Proportions

A survey determined that the proportion, p, of voters in a city who support a local wildlife refuge is likely to be in the interval (0.62, 0.67). Write the interval estimate in the form *point estimate ± margin of error*.

The margin of error is half the difference of the upper and lower limits.

$$\frac{0.67 - 0.62}{2} = 0.025$$

To find the point estimate, $\hat{p}$, add the margin of error to the lower limit.

$$0.62 + 0.025 = 0.645$$

The interval estimate is 0.645 ± 0.025.

If 750 voters are randomly sampled, what is the best estimate for the number of voters who support the wildlife refuge?

Because $\hat{p}$ is the best estimate of p, then 64.5% of the 750 voters, or about 484 of the voters, are likely to support the refuge.

▶ **Q&A**

   Q What is the interval for the number of voters who are likely to support the refuge?

   A $(465, 503)$

Using Interval Estimates: Means

A study of a sample of two-toed sloths in a given area indicates that the mean weight of all the sloths in that area is between 16.8 lb and 17.6 lb. Write the interval estimate in the form *point estimate ± margin of error*.

Because $\frac{17.6 - 16.8}{2} = 0.4$, the margin of error is ± 0.4 lb and the point estimate $\overline{x}$ is 16.8 lb + 0.4 lb, or 17.2 lb. The interval estimate is 17.2 lb $\pm$ 0.4 lb.

Using Point Estimates: Proportions

In a random sample of 63 homeowners in a city, 15 homeowners said that they would support a ban on all nonnatural lawn fertilizers in an effort to protect the fish in the local waterways. The sampling method had a margin of error of $\pm$ 3.5%. Write the interval estimate for the proportion that would support the ban in the form (*lower limit, upper limit*).

First determine the point estimate.

$$\hat{p} = \frac{15}{63} \approx 0.238 = 23.8\%$$

Then subtract the margin of error from the point estimate to get the lower limit and add the margin of error to the point estimate to get the upper limit.

lower limit: 23.8% − 3.5% = 20.3%

upper limit: 23.8% + 3.5% = 27.3%

The interval estimate is (20.3%, 27.3%).

In a random sample of 120 homeowners in the city, how many homeowners would you expect to say they would support the ban? Give the answer as an interval.

Because 20.3% of 120 is about 24, and 27.3% is about 33, you would expect between 24 and 33 of the homeowners to say they would support the ban.

▶ **Think About It** The margin of error is affected by the size of the sample chosen. A surveyor can reduce the margin of error by increasing the number of members in the sample.

Using Point Estimates: Means

In a two-toed sloth study, the sloths in the sample had a mean body length of 63 cm. The study had a margin of error of $\pm$ 0.7 cm. Write the interval estimate for the mean body length in the form (*lower limit*, *upper limit*).

$$\text{lower limit: } 63 \text{ cm} - 0.7 \text{ cm} = 62.3 \text{ cm}$$

$$\text{upper limit: } 63 \text{ cm} + 0.7 \text{ cm} = 63.7 \text{ cm}$$

The interval estimate is $(62.3 \text{ cm}, 63.7 \text{ cm})$.

▶ **Think About It** The interval $(62.3 \text{ cm}, 63.7 \text{ cm})$ means that it is likely, but not certain, that the mean length of all the sloths in the area is between 62.3 cm and 63.7 cm.

Using Simulations

Simulations are used to model real-world probability events and can be used to draw conclusions about population parameters.

Using Simulations to Draw Conclusions

A **simulation** is a way to model random events. Simulations can be conducted to model the outcomes of real-world problems using methods such as flipping a fair coin, rolling number cubes, using a table of random digits, using a random number generator, and employing other methods.

The advantage of using a simulation is you can quickly gather data and use that information to draw conclusions about population parameters. You can also determine whether a statistical model is consistent with real-world results.

EXAMPLE 1

In a sample of grocery store customers who participated in a survey, 60% said that they use coupons on a regular basis. Based on nationwide market research, an analyst hypothesizes that the true population proportion is closer to 75%. To test whether this discrepancy is significant, he conducts a simulation assuming that the true population proportion is 75%. A random number generator is used to determine how many customers out of 10 would use coupons on a regular basis.

The line plot shows the results from 25 trials of the simulation in which the population proportion is 75%.

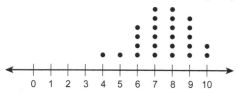

Number of Customers Who Use Coupons Regularly

A Does the range of the line plot suggest that the random number generator is fair? Explain.

SOLUTION

The results of the simulation are clustered fairly tightly in the interval from 6 to 9 customers, with 7 and 8 customers being the most common result. The entire range of simulation results is from 4 to 10 customers. It would not be very likely for the simulation to result in 0 to 3 customers if the population proportion is 75%, so it is not unusual that this situation never occurred in the 25 trials. The random number generator appears to be fair.

B Does it seem likely that a proportion of 60% could have been achieved in the sample if the true population proportion is 75%? Explain.

SOLUTION

Out of 25 trials of the simulation, a result of 6 or fewer customers occurred 6 times. This situation represents an experimental probability of 24%, so it seems fairly likely that a random sample of customers could result in a proportion of 60% when the true population proportion is 75%.

C Do the results of the simulation indicate that the true population could be 75% despite the survey sample results? Explain.

SOLUTION

Yes, it could be possible for the population proportion to be 75%. The simulation results show that if the population proportion were 75%, you could get samples ranging from 40% to 100%. However, because most of the samples would fall in the interval from 60% to 90%, it is very possible that the true population proportion could be 75% despite the survey results. ■

> ▶ **Think About It** The simulation or experiment only accounts for a small sample size of possible outcomes. When using simulations to draw conclusions about population parameters, it is beneficial to conduct a large number of simulation trials to obtain a more accurate understanding of the possible samples.

Using Interval Estimates for Population Proportions

Interval estimates for a population proportion can be determined from data that you have gathered. If you collect a range of data values through a simulation or from a sample of a population, you can use this range to determine the interval estimate for the population proportion.

To determine an interval estimate for a population proportion, use the mean of the sample as the point estimate. Then use half the range of the sample as the margin of error.

Using Half the Range
interval estimate for p: mean $\pm$ half the range

EXAMPLE 2

A wildlife conservation officer estimates that about 65% of the ash trees in a region will be lost to the emerald ash borer infestation. She uses a table of random digits to simulate what percent of the trees will be lost. Suppose the mean of the sample proportions is 0.62, the least sample proportion is 0.45, and the greatest sample proportion is 0.77. Use half the range to determine an interval estimate for p, the percent of trees that will be lost to the infestation.

SOLUTION

Determine the range of the simulated sample proportions.

$$\text{range: } 0.77 - 0.45 = 0.32$$

Divide the range by 2 to determine half the range.

$$\text{half the range: } \frac{0.32}{2} = 0.16$$

Use the mean of the sample proportions and half the range as the margin of error to determine the interval estimate.

$$\text{interval estimate: } 0.62 \pm 0.16 = (0.46, 0.78)$$

Using half the range to determine the interval estimate, the simulation predicts that the percent of trees lost will be between 46% and 78%. ■

You can also use the standard deviation to determine an interval estimate for a population mean. Use the mean of the sample as the point estimate and twice the standard deviation as the margin of error.

Using the Standard Deviation

interval estimate for μ: mean $\pm$ 2 × standard deviation

EXAMPLE 3

In a survey of 20 randomly selected members of a cycling club, members were asked how many miles they rode on the first day of a club riding event. The results were 22, 21, 28, 24, 23, 24, 20, 19, 25, 25, 22, 28, 28, 22, 27, 26, 28, 25, 24, and 25 mi. Use the standard deviation to determine an interval estimate for μ, the mean number of miles ridden by all of the club members.

SOLUTION
Use a graphing calculator or other technology to determine the mean of the sample.

mean: 24.3

Use a graphing calculator or other technology to determine the standard deviation of the sample. Round to two decimal places.

standard deviation: 2.74

Find the interval estimate for μ.

interval estimate: $24.3 \pm 2 \times 2.74 = (18.82, 29.78)$

Using the standard deviation to determine the interval estimate, the sample predicts that the mean number of miles ridden by members of the cycling club is between 18.82 and 29.78. ∎

Evaluating Reports

Many reports use data sets to support a point of view. If you are able to evaluate the data with a critical eye, you can determine how valid this point of view is.

The Reason for the Study

To critically judge a report that includes data, you must look at many factors. First determine who carried out the study and for what reasons.

EXAMPLE 1

The Olive Oil Society of the Americas reports that countries in which people consume olive oil daily have a lower rate of heart disease. Why did the organization release the report?

SOLUTION

Think about the name of the organization that produced the report. The Olive Oil Society of the Americas most likely wishes to promote the use of olive oil. The organization can achieve that goal if consumers believe that olive oil has tangible health benefits. ■

How Were the Data Collected?

A sample is **biased** if it is not representative of its population. For instance, a farmer wants to know the depth of the roots in a certain crop of plants. Because they are nearest to his house, he digs up 6 plants along the southwest corner of the field and inspects their roots.

> **Remember** We choose to study a sample only when we can't study the entire population.

The sample is likely biased because all the plants come from the same area of the field. This area may receive more or less sunlight than other areas. The amount of sunlight a plant receives affects the plant's growth and therefore its root system. Soil conditions may also differ in this part of the field. Also, 6 is a small number for a sample.

Bias may also arise from the question or questioning technique used. For example, a question may give only one side of the story. Compare these questions:

- **Biased toward a *No* response** Pesticides cannot be washed off of all foods, and pesticides leak into nearby waterways. Do you think our farmers should be allowed to put our health at risk by using pesticides?

- **Biased toward a *Yes* response** If our farmers cannot control pests effectively, our local food production could drop by 35%, creating a food shortage and economic recession. Do you agree that our farmers need to use pesticides?

Bias can also arise from questioning that is too personal, is too long and wordy, or has only a limited number of responses (because of multiple choice).

The Relevancy of the Data

Even a study that is well designed and carried out will have limitations on what can be learned from the study.

EXAMPLE 2

The Olive Oil Society of the Americas reports that countries in which people consume olive oil daily have a lower rate of heart disease. What can be concluded from this study?

SOLUTION

There is a difference between correlation and causation. Although it may be true that heart disease is lower in countries where olive oil is consumed daily, it does not necessarily mean that consuming olive oil causes this reduction in disease. You can only conclude that there may be a link between daily use of olive oil and a reduced risk of heart disease.

The olive oil report could be a stepping stone for further study. Which countries have lower rates of heart disease? Do the countries share a certain type of climate? Are there other dietary factors to consider? What about exercise or other health factors? Is there a scientific reason why the chemicals in olive oil would positively affect the human heart?

Statistics and data are useful for helping you understand many situations, but you need to be aware of how those data are collected and presented to gain a deeper understanding of reports. ■

▶ **Think About It** There are many factors that affect health and heart disease. Diet is just one of them.

Surveys, Experiments, and Observational Studies

Three methods used to collect data are surveys, experiments, and observational studies.

Surveys are used to collect information from a population by directly asking questions. They are administered in the form of a questionnaire or an interview. Surveys can be conducted over the phone, online, through the mail, or in person.

Experiments require defining a variable that you want to study and then randomly selecting a control group and an experimental group. Only the experimental group is manipulated in some way, and the control group receives no treatment. Both groups are monitored before and after the manipulation and any differences are analyzed.

Observational studies involve watching and recording the subjects of a study without influencing or manipulating the subjects.

Each data-collection method has strengths and weaknesses. Surveys are good for gathering data from a large population using a random sample but depend on people answering questions honestly. Experiments are controlled and useful for determining the effect of a single variable, but experimental outcomes can sometimes be affected by outside influences. Observational studies allow researchers to examine how someone or something behaves naturally, without any intervention. However, it is often difficult to randomly select the subjects who are to be observed.

Identifying Surveys, Experiments, and Observational Studies

Example of a survey: A trainer wants to know what percent of the 419 members of a gym would attend a personal training session if it were half price. The trainer randomly selects 30 gym members by first assigning each gym member a number from 001 to 419. She then uses a table of random, three-digit numbers to select the first 30 numbers from 001 to 419. She calls the 30 randomly selected gym members and records their answers.

Example of an experiment: A scientist wants to know if a new antibiotic is effective against a particular bacteria. She has 20 bacterial colonies, all with the same number of bacteria. She treats 10 colonies with the antibiotic and leaves the other 10 colonies untreated. After treatment, she counts the number of live bacteria in each colony and compares the two groups.

Example of an observational study: Researchers are watching blue whales in their natural habitat and recording their eating habits. The researchers are not manipulating the situation in any way. They are only writing down what they see.

EXAMPLE

A college student is asked a few questions to rate the effectiveness of an app he uses on his mobile device. Is he being asked to participate in an experiment, a survey, or an observational study?

SOLUTION

The student is not given any treatment, so he is not participating in an experiment. The student is also not being directly observed by a researcher, so he is not part of an observational study. Because he is asked to complete a questionnaire about the app he uses, he is being asked to participate in a survey. ∎

Systems of Linear Equations and Inequalities

Topic List

If a company has limited resources to make red, blue, yellow, and green paint, then how much should it make of each color to maximize profit? Mixture optimization problems are very common in business, and solving them can mean the difference between profit and loss.

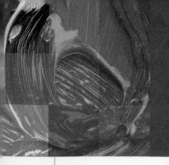

Systems of Linear Equations

When equations with the same variables are grouped together, a system of equations is formed.

Determining Whether a Given Ordered Pair Is a Solution to a System

Definition
A **system of equations** is two or more equations that contain the same variables.

A given ordered pair is a solution to a system if it satisfies all of the equations.

EXAMPLE 1

Determine whether each point is a solution to the system.

$$\begin{cases} 2x - 4y = 8 \\ y = 3x - 7 \end{cases}$$

A $(2, -1)$

SOLUTION

Substitute the coordinates of each point into each equation.

$$2x - 4y = 8 \qquad y = 3x - 7$$
$$2 \cdot 2 - 4 \cdot (-1) \stackrel{?}{=} 8 \qquad -1 \stackrel{?}{=} 3 \cdot 2 - 7$$
$$4 + 4 \stackrel{?}{=} 8 \qquad -1 \stackrel{?}{=} 6 - 7$$
$$8 = 8 \checkmark \qquad -1 = -1 \checkmark$$

The point $(2, -1)$ is a solution to the system because it makes both equations true.

B $(8, 2)$

SOLUTION

Substitute the coordinates of each point into each equation.

$$2x - 4y = 8 \qquad y = 3x - 7$$
$$2 \cdot 8 - 4 \cdot 2 \stackrel{?}{=} 8 \qquad 2 \stackrel{?}{=} 3 \cdot 8 - 7$$
$$16 - 8 \stackrel{?}{=} 8 \qquad 2 \stackrel{?}{=} 24 - 7$$
$$8 = 8 \checkmark \qquad 2 \neq 17$$

The point $(8, 2)$ is not a solution to the system because it does not make both equations true. ■

Solving Systems by Graphing

One way to solve a system of equations is to graph each equation to determine where they intersect. The point of intersection represents the solution to the system.

EXAMPLE 2

Solve the system by graphing.

A
$$\begin{cases} y = 3x - 2 \\ y = -\dfrac{1}{2}x + 5 \end{cases}$$

SOLUTION

Graph the two lines. The lines appear to intersect at $(2, 4)$.
You can check that $(2, 4)$ is a solution to both equations.

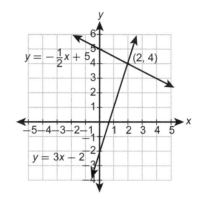

$y = 3x - 2$	$y = -\dfrac{1}{2}x + 5$
$4 \overset{?}{=} 3 \cdot 2 - 2$	$4 \overset{?}{=} -\dfrac{1}{2} \cdot 2 + 5$
$4 \overset{?}{=} 6 - 2$	$4 \overset{?}{=} -1 + 5$
$4 = 4 \checkmark$	$4 = 4 \checkmark$

B
$$\begin{cases} 10x - 4y = 24 \\ y = \dfrac{5}{2}x - 3 \end{cases}$$

SOLUTION

Find the x- and y-intercepts of the first equation.

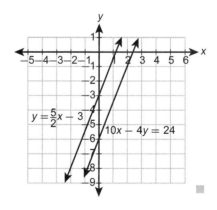

$10x - 4y = 24$	$10x - 4y = 24$
$10 \cdot 0 - 4y = 24$	$10x - 4 \cdot 0 = 24$
$-4y = 24$	$10x = 24$
$y = -6$	$x = 2.4$

Then graph each line. Because the lines are parallel,
they never intersect. This system has no solution.

Classifying Systems of Linear Equations

A system of two linear equations can have one solution, no solution, or infinitely many solutions. The table shows how linear systems are classified according to the number of solutions.

Classifying Systems of Linear Equations

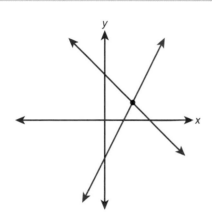

A linear system is **consistent and independent** if its graphs intersect at one point (one solution).

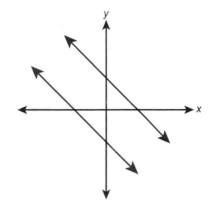

A linear system is **inconsistent** if the lines are parallel (no solution).

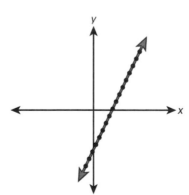

A linear system is **consistent and dependent** if the lines coincide (infinitely many solutions).

Solving Linear Systems by the Substitution Method

Algebraic methods, such as the substitution method, can be used to solve linear systems and often yield more accurate results than graphing.

How to Solve a System by the Substitution Method

Step 1 Solve one equation for one of the variables.

Step 2 Substitute the expression obtained from Step 1 in place of the corresponding variable in the other equation, and solve the resulting equation.

Step 3 Substitute the value of the variable from Step 2 into either of the original equations. Solve this equation to find the value of the other variable.

▶ **Think About It** You can always check your work by making sure that your solution satisfies both equations in the system.

EXAMPLE 3

Solve the system by substitution.

$$\begin{cases} -x + 4y = 6 \\ 3x - 12y = -18 \end{cases}$$

SOLUTION

Step 1 Both equations are in standard form, so solve one of the equations for x or y. It is easiest to solve the first equation for x.

$$-x + 4y = 6$$
$$-x = -4y + 6$$
$$x = 4y - 6$$

Step 2 Substitute the expression $4y - 6$ for x in the second equation.

$$3x - 12y = -18$$
$$3(4y - 6) - 12y = -18$$
$$12y - 18 - 12y = -18$$
$$-18 = -18$$

The equation $-18 = -18$ is true for all real numbers. This means that there are infinitely many solutions.

Step 3 Because there is no single value of y that is a solution, you don't have to complete Step 3.

So the system is consistent and dependent, and there are infinitely many solutions. ■

> ▶ **Think About It** When a system solved algebraically results in an equation that is true for all real numbers, the system has infinitely many solutions. When it results in an equation that is not true for any real number, the system has no solution.

Solving Linear Systems by the Linear Combination Method

Another algebraic method to solve a system is the linear combination method.

How to Solve a System by the Linear Combination Method

Step 1 Convert both equations to standard form.

Step 2 Multiply one or both of the equations by a real number so that the coefficient of one variable in one equation is the additive inverse of the coefficient of the same variable in the other equation.

Step 3 Add the equations, and then solve the resulting equation.

Step 4 Substitute the value of the variable from Step 3 into either of the original equations. Solve this equation for the second variable.

EXAMPLE 4

Solve the system by linear combination.

$$\begin{cases} 2x + 5y = 1 \\ y = \dfrac{3}{4}x - \dfrac{13}{4} \end{cases}$$

SOLUTION

Step 1 Convert the second equation to standard form by mutiplying through by 4 and subtracting $3x$ from both sides.

$$\begin{cases} 2x + 5y = 1 \\ -3x + 4y = -13 \end{cases}$$

Step 2 Multiply the first equation by 3 and the second equation by 2 so that the coefficients of x are additive inverses.

Step 3 Add the equations to eliminate x. Solve the result for y.

$$\begin{aligned} 6x + 15y &= 3 \\ -6x + 8y &= -26 \\ \hline 23y &= -23 \Rightarrow y = -1 \end{aligned}$$

Step 4 Substitute -1 for y in either of the original equations to find x.

$$2x + 5 \bullet (-1) = 1 \Rightarrow 2x - 5 = 1 \Rightarrow 2x = 6 \Rightarrow x = 3$$

So the solution to the system is $(3, -1)$. ∎

Solving a System of Three Equations with Three Variables

It is also possible to solve a system of three equations containing three variables. The solution of a system of three equations in three variables can have one solution, infinitely many solutions, or no solution. A system of three equations is solved by finding ordered triples that satisfy all of the equations.

How to Solve a System of Three Equations with Three Variables

Step 1 Convert each equation to standard form.

Step 2 Eliminate one variable from two of the equations.

Step 3 Using these two equations and substitution or linear combination, solve for one of the remaining variables.

Step 4 Substitute the value of the variable from Step 3 into either of the equations in Step 2. Solve this equation for the second variable.

Step 5 Substitute the value of the variables from Step 3 and Step 4 into any of the original equations.

▶ **Think About It**

NOTATION The solution of a system of three equations in three variables x, y, z is called an **ordered triple** and is written (x, y, z).

EXAMPLE 5

Solve the system.

$$\begin{cases} 2x + 5y - z = -8 \\ -x + y + z = -3 \\ -3x - y + 2z = -1 \end{cases}$$

SOLUTION

Step 1 The system has three equations in standard form. Eliminate the z variable from the first two equations by combining them.

$$
\begin{array}{rcl}
2x + 5y - z & = & -8 \\
-x + y + z & = & -3 \\
\hline
x + 6y & = & -11
\end{array}
$$

Step 2 Multiply the second equation by -2. Then combine the second equation with the third equation to eliminate the z variable.

$$
\begin{array}{rcl}
2x - 2y - 2z & = & 6 \\
-3x - y + 2z & = & -1 \\
\hline
-x - 3y & = & 5
\end{array}
$$

Step 3 Now you have a system of two linear equations with two variables. Combine the equations to solve the system.

$$
\begin{array}{rcl}
x + 6y & = & -11 \\
-x - 3y & = & 5 \\
\hline
3y & = & -6 \\
y & = & \mathbf{-2}
\end{array}
$$

Step 4 Use the value of y to solve for x in any of the two equations. Then substitute the value of x and y into one of the original equations to solve for z.

Solve for x: $x + 6 \bullet (-2) = -11 \Rightarrow x - 12 = -11 \Rightarrow x = \mathbf{1}$

Solve for z: $2 \bullet 1 + 5 \bullet (-2) - z = -8 \Rightarrow 2 - 10 - z = -8$

$\Rightarrow -8 - z = -8 \Rightarrow z = 0$

The solution to the system is $(1, -2, 0)$. ▪

▶ **Think About It** Check that your solution satisfies every equation in the system.

Inequalities in One Variable

You can represent an inequality by using an inequality symbol, interval notation, or a graph.

Definitions

A **bounded interval** is the set of all real numbers between two numbers, called **endpoints**; the endpoints may or may not be included.

An **unbounded interval** is the set of all real numbers on one side of a number, called an **endpoint**; the endpoint may or may not be included.

A **bounded closed interval** includes both endpoints. This bounded closed interval is the set of all real numbers between −2 and 2, including both −2 and 2.

A **bounded open interval** does not include either endpoint. This bounded open interval is the set of all real numbers between −2 and 2, excluding both −2 and 2.

A **bounded half-open interval** includes one and only one endpoint. This bounded half-open interval is the set of all real numbers between −2 and 2, including −2 but excluding 2.

Graphing Interval Notation

A simple inequality using $<, >, \le,$ or $\ge$ indicates an unbounded interval.

In interval notation, a bracket means the endpoint is included, and a parenthesis means the endpoint is not included.

> ▶ **Think About It** In interval notation, you can never put a bracket next to an infinity symbol because infinity is not a number that can be included in an interval.

Interval notation for $x > 4$ is $x \in (4, \infty)$. The ∞ symbol is read "positive infinity," and it means that the interval is unbounded to the right.

Interval notation for $x \le 1$ is $x \in (-\infty, 1]$. The $-\infty$ symbol is read "negative infinity," and it means that the interval is unbounded to the left.

The table shows the four cases of unbounded intervals.

Inequality notation	Graph	Interval notation
$x > a$		$x \in (a, \infty)$
$x \ge a$		$x \in [a, \infty)$
$x < a$		$x \in (-\infty, a)$
$x \le a$		$x \in (-\infty, a]$

In interval notation, the set of all real numbers is $(-\infty, \infty)$.

▶ **Think About It** In interval notation, always put the lesser number on the left.

EXAMPLE 1

Write the inequality in interval notation, and then graph.

A $x > 3$

SOLUTION

Interval notation for $x > 3$ is $x \in (3, \infty)$. The interval is unbounded to the right, and does not include the left endpoint.

B $m \leq 0$

SOLUTION

Interval notation for $m \leq 0$ is $m \in (-\infty, 0]$. The interval is unbounded to the left, and includes the right endpoint.

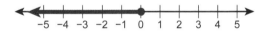

C $t > -2.5$

SOLUTION

Interval notation for $t > -2.5$ is $t \in (-2.5, \infty)$. The interval is unbounded to the right, and does not include the left endpoint.

Writing Interval Notation for a Given Graph

EXAMPLE 2

Write an inequality in interval notation for the graph.

A

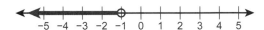

SOLUTION

The graph is unbounded to the left. It is a ray pointing toward "negative infinity." The open circle indicates that -1 is not included in the set.

$$x \in (-\infty, -1)$$

B

SOLUTION

The graph is unbounded to the right. It is a ray pointing toward "positive infinity." The closed circle indicates that 6 is included in the set.

$$x \in [6, \infty) \ \blacksquare$$

▶ **Think About It** The symbols ∞ and $-\infty$ do not denote real numbers. They simply denote unbounded intervals.

Solving an Inequality in One Variable with a Restricted Domain

When you solve inequalities, the domain of the variable may be whole numbers, integers, or real numbers.

EXAMPLE 3

Solve the inequality over the domain of whole numbers.
Graph the solution set.

A $\frac{x}{2} - 1 \leq 1$

SOLUTION

Solve an inequality as you would solve an equation, but reverse the inequality sign when you multiply or divide by a negative number.

$$\frac{x}{2} - 1 \leq 1 \qquad \text{Original inequality}$$

$$\frac{x}{2} \leq 2 \qquad \text{Add 1 to both sides.}$$

$$x \leq 4 \qquad \text{Multiply both sides by 2.}$$

$$x \in \left\{ 0, 1, 2, 3, 4 \right\}$$

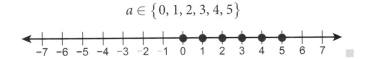

B $-2 < 4 - a$

SOLUTION

$$-2 < 4 - a \qquad \text{Original inequality}$$

$$-6 < -a \qquad \text{Subtract 4 from both sides.}$$

$$\frac{-6}{-1} > \frac{-1 \cdot a}{-1} \qquad \text{Divide both sides by } -1, \text{ reversing the inequality sign.}$$

$$6 > a$$

$$a \in \left\{ 0, 1, 2, 3, 4, 5 \right\}$$

EXAMPLE 4

Solve the inequality over the domain of integers. Graph the solution set.

A $\frac{n}{3} + 3 > 4$

SOLUTION

$\frac{n}{3} + 3 > 4$ Original inequality

$\frac{n}{3} > 1$ Subtract 3 from both sides.

$n > 3$ Multiply both sides by 3.

$$n \in \{4, 5, 6, \ldots\}$$

The graph is the set of points with coordinates that are integers greater than 3.

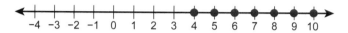

B $-7x \geq 3 - 2x$

SOLUTION

$-7x \geq 3 - 2x$ Original inequality

$-5x \geq 3$ Add $2x$ to both sides.

$\frac{-5x}{-5} \leq \frac{3}{-5}$ Divide both sides by -5, reversing the inequality sign.

$x \leq -\frac{3}{5}$

$$x \in \{\ldots, -3, -2, -1\}$$

The graph is the set of points with coordinates that are integers less than or equal to $-\frac{3}{5}$.

EXAMPLE 5

Solve the inequality over the domain of integers. Graph the solution set.

A $x + 6 \geq 3(x + 1) - 11$

SOLUTION

$x + 6 \geq 3(x + 1) - 11$ Original inequality

$x + 6 \geq 3x + 3 - 11$ Distribute 3.

$x + 6 \geq 3x - 8$

$x + 14 \geq 3x$ Add 8 to both sides.

$14 \geq 2x$ Subtract x from both sides.

$7 \geq x$ Divide both sides by 2.

$$x \in \{\ldots, -1, 0, 1, 2, 3, 4, 5, 6, 7\}$$

The graph is the set of points with coordinates that are integers less than or equal to 7.

▶ **Remember** $7 \geq x$ is the same as $x \leq 7$.

B $-9 - 3x > 3 - 5x$

SOLUTION

$-9 - 3x > 3 - 5x$ Original inequality

$-3x > 12 - 5x$ Add 9 to both sides.

$2x > 12$ Add $5x$ to both sides.

$x > 6$ Divide both sides by 2.

$$x \in \{7, 8, 9, 10, 11, \ldots\}$$

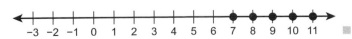

Real-World Inequalities

You can describe many real-world situations using inequalities. First, identify the unknown quantity. Next, write an inequality to model the situation and then solve.

EXAMPLE 6

Marcus is planning a deep-sea fishing trip. For boat rental, there is an initial fee of $150 plus $70 for each hour the boat is used. How many hours can Marcus rent a boat if he has $395?

SOLUTION

Marcus will be charged $70 times the number of hours, x, plus $150. This sum must be less than or equal to the amount he has, $395.

Write an inequality to describe the situation. Then solve for x.

$70x + 150 \leq 395$ Use x to represent the number of hours.

$70x \leq 245$ Subtract 150 from both sides.

$x \leq 3.5$ Divide both sides by 70.

Marcus can rent the boat for 3.5 h or less. ■

> ▶ **Think About It** If Marcus rents a boat for exactly 3.5 h, he will be charged $70(3.5) + 150 = 395$, or $395, which is the exact amount he has. He could rent the boat for fewer than 3.5 h and have money left over.

Compound Inequalities

When two statements are joined, they form a **compound statement**.

Definitions

A **conjunction** is a compound statement that uses the word *and*.

$$x < 0 \text{ and } x \geq -3$$

A **disjunction** is a compound statement that uses the word *or*.

$$x = 0 \text{ or } x = 5 \qquad x > 0 \text{ or } x < 23$$

A **compound inequality** is a pair of inequalities joined by the word *and* or the word *or*. A compound inequality is a type of compound statement.

Conjunction and Inequalities

The solution set of a conjunction inequality is the set of all numbers that satisfy both inequalities.

EXAMPLE 1

Graph the compound inequality, and then express it in interval notation.

A $x > 2$ and $x \leq 7$ (also written $2 < x \leq 7$)

SOLUTION

This set is of all numbers between 2 and 7, not including 2 but including 7.

$$x \in (2, 7]$$

B $x > 5$ and $x > 7$

SOLUTION

If a number is both greater than 5 and greater than 7, then it must be greater than 7.

$$x \in (7, \infty)$$

C $x > 0$ and $x < -2$

SOLUTION

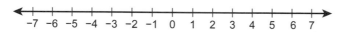

There is no number that is both greater than 0 and less than -2. There is no interval. The solution set is $\varnothing$, the empty set. ∎

The four general cases for conjunction inequalities, such as the one in Example 1A, are shown in the table.

Inequality notation	Graph	Interval notation
$a < x < b$		$x \in (a, b)$
$a \le x \le b$		$x \in [a, b]$
$a < x \le b$		$x \in (a, b]$
$a \le x < b$		$x \in [a, b)$

▶ **Remember** An open interval has neither endpoint included, a closed interval has both endpoints included, and a half-open interval (also called a half-closed interval) has one endpoint included.

Disjunction and Inequalities

The solution set of a disjunction inequality is the set of all numbers that satisfy either or both inequalities.

EXAMPLE 2

Graph the compound inequality, and then express it in interval notation.

A $x \leq -1$ or $x > 3$

SOLUTION

This set is of all numbers that are either less than or equal to -1 or greater than 3.

$$x \in (-\infty, -1] \cup x \in (3, \infty)$$

B $t > 4$ or $t > 9$

SOLUTION

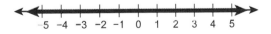

The set of all numbers that are either greater than 4 or greater than 9 is just the set of all numbers that are greater than 4.

$$t \in (4, \infty)$$

C $z > -2$ or $z < 1$

SOLUTION

The set of all numbers that are either greater than -2 or less than 1 is the set of all real numbers.

$$z \in (-\infty, \infty) \ \blacksquare$$

Writing a Compound Inequality and Interval Notation for a Given Graph

EXAMPLE 3

For the graph, write a compound inequality and interval notation.

A

SOLUTION

This set is of numbers between -3 and 3, excluding -3 but including 3.

$$\text{inequality: } -3 < x \le 3$$
$$\text{interval notation: } x \in \left(-3, 3\right]$$

B

SOLUTION

This set is of numbers that are either less than 1 or greater than 5.

$$\text{inequality: } x < 1 \text{ or } x > 5$$
$$\text{interval notation: } x \in (-\infty, 1) \cup \left(5, \infty\right) \ \blacksquare$$

Solving and Graphing a Compound Inequality in One Variable

EXAMPLE 4

Solve the compound inequality. Graph the solution set.

A $5 + x < 7$ or $-2x \le -10$

SOLUTION

Solve each inequality separately.

First Inequality $5 + x < 7$ or $-2x \leq -10$ **Second Inequality**

Subtract 5 from $x < 2$ or $x \geq 5$ Divide both sides
both sides.   by -2, reversing the
                                                         inequality sign.

> ▶ **Remember** To solve an inequality in one variable, find all values for
> the variable that make the inequality a true statement.

B $3x - 1 \geq 14$ and $6x \leq 48$

SOLUTION

Solve each inequality separately.

$$3x - 1 \geq 14 \text{ and } 6x \leq 48$$

Add 1 to both sides. $3x \geq 15$ and $x \leq 8$ Divide both sides

Divide both sides by 3. $x \geq 5$ and $x \leq 8$ by 6.

> ▶ **Think About It** The compound inequality $x \geq 5$ and $x \leq 8$ can be
> written as $5 \leq x \leq 8$.

C $4 \leq 2n + 10 \leq 18$

SOLUTION

$4 \leq 2n + 10 \leq 18$ Original inequality

$-6 \leq 2n \leq 8$ Subtract 10 from all expressions.

$-3 \leq n \leq 4$ Divide all expressions by 2.

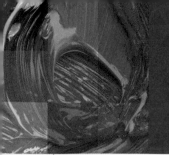

Inequalities in Two Variables

When the equals sign in a linear equation is replaced by an inequality symbol, the statement becomes a linear inequality.

Definition

A **linear inequality** uses terms with degree zero or one and an inequality symbol to relate two variables.

The graph of a linear inequality is a region of the coordinate plane. The region is determined by a line, called the boundary line. The boundary line is the graph of the related equation, which uses an equals sign.

$$\text{linear inequality: } y \geq \frac{3}{4}x - 3$$

$$\text{related linear equation: } y = \frac{3}{4}x - 3$$

The boundary line divides the plane into two **half-planes**. If the inequality is a nonstrict inequality (that is, it uses $\leq$ or $\geq$), then the boundary line is a solid line and the half-plane is a **closed half-plane**. If the inequality is a strict inequality (it uses $<$ or $>$), then the boundary line is a dashed line and the half-plane is an **open half-plane**.

Closed Half-Plane

$$y \geq \frac{3}{4}x - 3$$

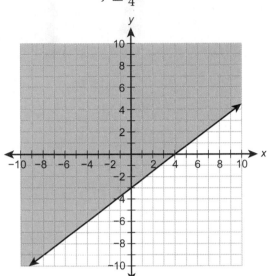

Open Half-Plane

$$y > \frac{3}{4}x - 3$$

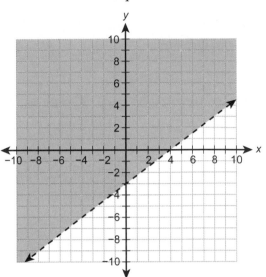

To determine which half-plane to shade, use a test point. You can choose any point that is not on the boundary line.

When the inequality is written in the form such that the related equation is in slope-intercept form, then the region to be shaded may be determined without using a test point. For $>$ or $\geq$, shade above the boundary line (where the y-values on the y-axis are greater than the y-intercept). For $<$ or $\leq$, shade below the boundary line (where the y-values on the y-axis are less than the y-intercept).

Any point in the shaded region is a solution of the inequality. A point on a solid boundary line is also a solution, but a point on a dashed boundary line is not a solution.

▶ **Think About It** The point (0, 0) is usually a good test point because it makes calculations simple.

Using the y-Intercept to Graph an Inequality in Two Variables

EXAMPLE 1

Graph $y < -2x + 1$.

SOLUTION

Step 1 Graph the related equation, $y = -2x + 1$. The y-intercept is 1, so first plot (0, 1). Use the slope of -2 to find another point on the line by moving down 2 units and right 1 unit from that point.

Step 2 Draw a dashed line through the points because $<$ indicates that the boundary line does not contain solutions.

Step 3 Since the related linear equation is written in slope-intercept form and the inequality symbol is $<$, shade below the boundary line.

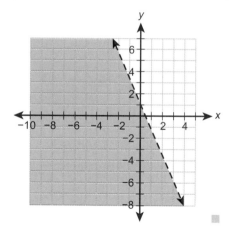

Graphing a Linear Inequality with One Variable

EXAMPLE 2

Graph $x \geq 1.5$.

SOLUTION

Step 1 Graph the related equation, $x = 1.5$. The line is a vertical line passing through $(1.5, 0)$.

Step 2 Use a solid line because $\geq$ indicates that the boundary line contains solutions.

Step 3 Choose a test point to determine which half-plane to shade.

$$\text{test-point: } (0, 0)$$
$$x \overset{?}{\geq} 1.5$$
$$0 \not\geq 1.5$$

The point $(0, 0)$ is not in the solution set; the half-plane that does not contain the origin is shaded. Shade to the right of the line.

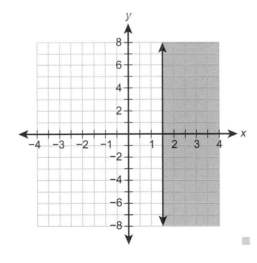

Using Intercepts to Graph an Inequality in Two Variables

EXAMPLE 3

Graph $2x - 5y > 10$.

SOLUTION

Step 1 Use intercepts to find two points on the graph of the related equation.

$$2x - 5y = 10 \qquad\qquad 2x - 5y = 10$$
$$2 \cdot 0 - 5y = 10 \qquad\qquad 2x - 5 \cdot 0 = 10$$
$$-5y = 10 \qquad\qquad 2x = 10$$
$$y = -2 \qquad\qquad x = 5$$

Step 2 Draw a dashed boundary line through $(0, -2)$ and $(5, 0)$.

Step 3 Choose a test point to determine which half-plane to shade.

$$2x - 5y \overset{?}{>} 10$$
$$2 \cdot 0 - 5 \cdot 0 \overset{?}{>} 10$$
$$0 \not> 10$$

The point $(0, 0)$ is not in the solution set, so the half-plane that does not contain the origin is shaded.

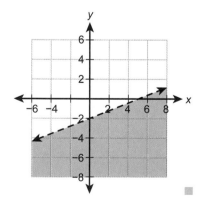

Writing Linear Inequalities from Graphs

EXAMPLE 4

Write an inequality for the graph.

A

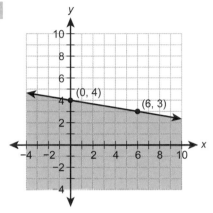

SOLUTION

Step 1 Determine the equation of the boundary line. The y-intercept is 4 and the slope is $-\frac{1}{6}$. The equation of the boundary line is $y - -\frac{1}{6}x + 4$.

Step 2 Determine the inequality sign. Because the boundary line is solid, the inequality will be a nonstrict inequality, using either $\leq$ or $\geq$. Because the shading is below the line, use $\leq$.

Step 3 Write the inequality.

$$y \leq -\frac{1}{6}x + 4$$

▶ **Think About It** The point $(0, 0)$ satisfies $y \leq -\frac{1}{6}x + 4$ because $0 \leq 4$.

B

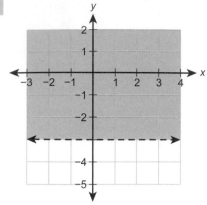

SOLUTION

Step 1 Determine the equation of the boundary line. The y-value of every ordered pair is -3, so the equation is $y = -3$.

Step 2 Determine the inequality sign. Because the boundary line is dashed, the inequality will be a strict inequality, using either $<$ or $>$. Because the shading is above the line, use $>$.

Step 3 Write the inequality.

$$y > -3 \ \blacksquare$$

▶ **Remember** The slope of a horizontal line is 0. The equation of the boundary line can be written as $y = 0x - 3$.

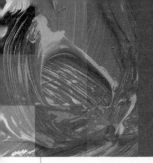

Systems of Linear Inequalities

A solution of a system of linear inequalities is any ordered pair that satisfies all the inequalities in the system.

Definition

A **system of linear inequalities** is a set of two or more linear inequalities using the same variables.

Recall that you can solve a system of linear equations by graphing. Similarly, you can also solve a system of linear incqualities by graphing. When two or more linear inequalities are graphed on the same coordinate plane, the solutions of the system are the ordered pairs in the intersection of the shaded regions.

Solving Systems of Two Linear Inequalities

To solve a system of linear inequalities, graph each inequality in the system and then identify the overlapping region.

EXAMPLE 1

Graph the system of linear inequalities. Then give one ordered pair that is a solution of the system and check your answer.

A $\begin{cases} y > 2x \\ y \geq -\frac{1}{3}x - 1 \end{cases}$

SOLUTION

Graph $y = 2x$ with a dashed line and shade above the line.
Graph $y = -\frac{1}{3}x - 1$ with a solid line and shade below it.

The intersection of the half-planes is the green shaded region. The solutions are the ordered pairs in the green region. One solution is the ordered pair $(-3, -3)$. You can verify that $(-3, -3)$ satisfies both inequalities.

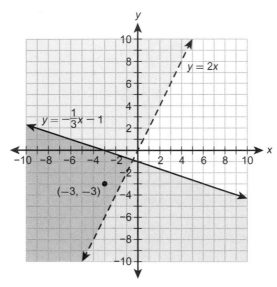

CHECK

Substitute $(-3, -3)$ in $y > 2x$.

$$y > 2x$$

$$-3 \overset{?}{>} 2(-3)$$

$$-3 > -6 \checkmark$$

Substitute $(-3, -3)$ in $y \leq -\frac{1}{3}x - 1$.

$$y \leq -\frac{1}{3}x - 1$$

$$-3 \overset{?}{\leq} -\frac{1}{3}(-3) - 1$$

$$-3 \leq 0 \checkmark$$

The ordered pair $(-3, -3)$ satisfies both inequalities, so it is a solution of the system.

▶ **Think About It** The ordered pair tested is just one of infinitely many solutions.

B $\begin{cases} y \geq -3x + 5 \\ y \leq -3x - 1 \end{cases}$

SOLUTION

The boundary lines are parallel, and both are graphed with solid lines. One is shaded above the line, and the other is shaded below. The shaded areas do not overlap; therefore, this system of linear inequalities has no solution.

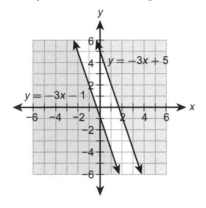

C $\begin{cases} y < 4 \\ y \geq -2 \end{cases}$

SOLUTION

The boundary lines are parallel, but the shading is in opposite directions, creating an overlapping region. This region contains the solutions of the system. One solution is $(0, 0)$.

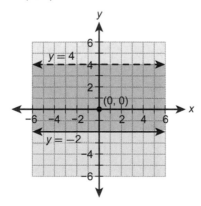

Solving Systems of More Than Two Linear Inequalities

When a system has three or more inequalities, graph each inequality on the same coordinate plane. Be careful to identify the overlapping regions correctly.

EXAMPLE 2

Graph the system of linear inequalities. Identify the overlapping shaded regions representing the solution of the system.

A
$$\begin{cases} y < 2x - 4 \\ y \leq 2 \\ y > \dfrac{4}{5}x - 4 \end{cases}$$

SOLUTION

Graph $y = 2x - 4$ with a dashed line and use small arrows below the line to show which half-plane should be shaded. Graph $y = 2$ with a solid line and draw small arrows below the line. Graph $y = \dfrac{4}{5}x - 4$ with a dashed line and draw small arrows above the line. The solution is the shaded triangular region.

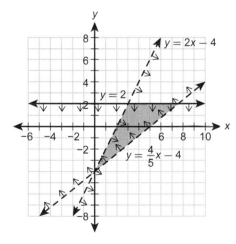

B $\begin{cases} x \geq 0 \\ y \geq 0 \\ y \leq x + 3 \\ y < -2x + 12 \end{cases}$

SOLUTION

The first two inequalities, $x \geq 0$ and $y \geq 0$, describe Quadrant I of a coordinate graph and the adjoining sections of the x- and y-axes.

Graph the line $y = x + 3$ with a solid line and draw small arrows below the line. Graph the line $y = -2x + 12$ with a dashed line and draw small arrows below the line.

The solutions of the system are found in the region bounded by the x- and y-axes and the lines $y = x + 3$ and $y = -2x + 12$. Note that $(0, 0)$ and $(0, 3)$ are solutions of the system because they represent the intersections of solid lines. However, $(6, 0)$ and $(3, 6)$ are not solutions of the system because they represent the intersections of solid lines and dashed lines.

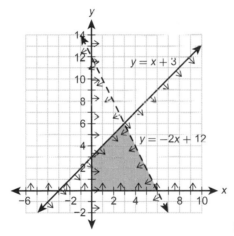

Writing Systems of Linear Inequalities from Graphs

You can write a system of linear inequalities from a graph by determining the equation for each boundary line.

EXAMPLE 3

Write the system of inequalities shown by the graph.

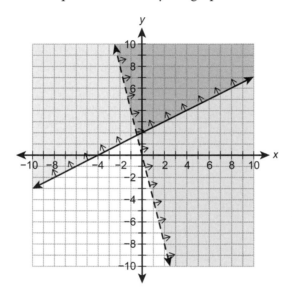

SOLUTION

Step 1 Determine the equations of the boundary lines.

The y-intercept of the solid line is 2 and its slope is $\frac{1}{2}$. The equation of the boundary line is $y = \frac{1}{2}x + 2$.

The y-intercept of the dashed line is -1 and its slope is -4. The equation of the boundary line is $y = -4x - 1$.

Step 2 Determine the inequality signs.

Because the boundary line of $y = \frac{1}{2}x + 2$ is solid, the inequality will be a nonstrict inequality, using either $\leq$ or $\geq$. The shading is above the line, so use $\geq$.

Because the boundary line of $y = -4x - 1$ is dashed, the inequality will be a strict inequality, using $<$ or $>$. The shading is above the line, so use $>$.

Step 3 Write the system of linear inequalities.

$$\begin{cases} y \geq \frac{1}{2}x + 2 \\ y > -4x - 1 \end{cases}$$

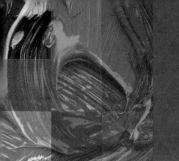

Linear Programming

Systems of linear inequalities are used in linear programming.

Definitions

Linear programming is the process of maximizing or minimizing a linear function subject to a set of conditions, called **constraints**, that are linear inequalities.

Each constraint in a linear programming problem is a linear inequality. The set of constraints that must be satisfied forms a system of linear inequalities. The graph of the solutions forms the **feasible region**, which is the set of all the ordered pairs that satisfy the constraints and are possible solutions to the problem.

▸ **Think About It** The word *feasible* means "possible to achieve." Ordered pairs outside the feasible region do not satisfy all of the constraints, so they are not possible solutions to the problem.

Determining a Feasible Region

EXAMPLE 1

Graph the feasible region.

A
$$\begin{cases} c \geq 30 \\ t \geq 8 \\ 2c + 6t \leq 170 \end{cases}$$

SOLUTION

Graph each inequality.

Shade the region where all three inequalities intersect. The feasible region is bounded because the boundary lines form a closed figure.

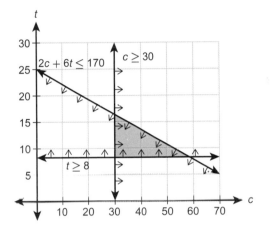

B
$$\begin{cases} v \geq 60 \\ c \geq 200 \\ c \leq 10v \end{cases}$$

SOLUTION

Graph each inequality.

Shade the region where all three inequalities intersect. The feasible region is unbounded, and there is an infinite number of solutions. ■

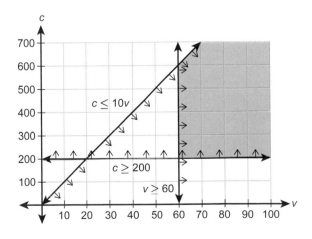

Finding an Optimal Solution

Once you know a feasible region, you can find the optimal, or best, solution for the problem. An **optimal solution** is a solution that maximizes or minimizes the objective.

An optimal solution to a linear programming problem will always occur at one of the corner points, called vertex points, of the feasible region. The maximum and minimum values of the objective function will always occur at vertex points.

EXAMPLE 2

Consider the constraints.

$$\begin{cases} c \geq 0 \\ a \geq 0 \\ c + a \leq 80 \end{cases}$$

A Graph the feasible region.

SOLUTION

Determine the coordinates of the vertices of the feasible region. The vertices are at the intersections of the graphs of the constraints. The vertices are $(0, 0)$, $(80, 0)$, and $(0, 80)$.

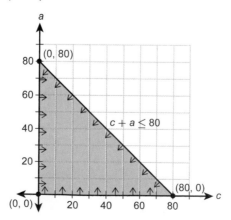

B Find the maximum value of the objective function $P = 6c + 10a$.

SOLUTION

Evaluate the objective function at the vertices of the feasible region.

Vertex	$6c + 10a$	P
$(0, 0)$	$6 \cdot 0 + 10 \cdot 0$	0
$(80, 0)$	$6 \cdot 80 + 10 \cdot 0$	480
$(0, 80)$	$6 \cdot 0 + 10 \cdot 80$	800

The maximum value for P occurs at $c = 0$ and $a = 80$. The maximum is \$800. ▪

Finding an Optimal Solution by Using a System of Equations

EXAMPLE 3

Find the maximum value of the objective function given the constraints.

$$\begin{cases} s \geq 0 \\ u > 0 \\ s \leq 24 \\ u \leq 30 \\ s + u \leq 40 \end{cases}$$

The objective function is $P = 12s + 8u$.

SOLUTION

Step 1 Graph the feasible region and determine the coordinates of the vertices. To find the coordinates of some intersections, you may need to solve a system of two equations.

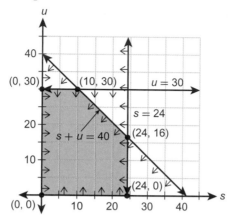

Step 2 Evaluate the objective function at each vertex.

Vertex	$12s + 8u$	P
$(0, 0)$	$12 \cdot 0 + 8 \cdot 0$	0
$(0, 30)$	$12 \cdot 0 + 8 \cdot 30$	240
$(10, 30)$	$12 \cdot 10 + 8 \cdot 30$	360
$(24, 16)$	$12 \cdot 24 + 8 \cdot 16$	416
$(24, 0)$	$12 \cdot 24 + 8 \cdot 0$	288

Step 3 The value of P is greatest at $(24, 16)$, where the maximum value is 416. ■

More Linear Programming

Linear programming can be used to solve minimization problems.

EXAMPLE

Minimize $C = 7.50x + 5.50y$ subject to the following constraints:

$$\begin{cases} 3x + 2y \geq 500 \\ x + 2y \geq 300 \\ x \geq 50 \\ y \geq 50 \end{cases}$$

SOLUTION

Graph the constraints to construct the feasible region. Then find the vertex points.

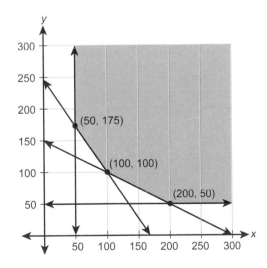

The vertex points are $(50, 175)$, $(100, 100)$, and $(200, 50)$.

Evaluate the objective function at each vertex point.

Vertex point	$7.50x + 5.50y$	C
$(50, 175)$	$7.50 \cdot 50 + 5.50 \cdot 175$	1337.50
$(100, 100)$	$7.50 \cdot 100 + 5.50 \cdot 100$	1300
$(200, 50)$	$7.50 \cdot 200 + 5.50 \cdot 50$	1775

Since the value of C is least at $(100, 100)$, the minimum of the objective function is 1300. ∎

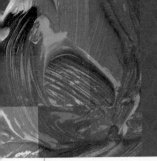

Applications of Linear Programming

Many real-world problems can be solved using linear programming.

How to Solve a Linear Programming Problem

Step 1 Define the variables.

Step 2 Determine the objective function and whether it needs to be maximized or minimized.

Step 3 Determine the constraints (linear inequalities).

Step 4 Graph the constraints to construct the feasible region.

Step 5 Find the vertex points of the feasible region.

Step 6 Substitute the coordinates of each vertex point into the objective function to determine the maximum or minimum value of the objective function.

EXAMPLE

That's How We Roll (THWR) manufactures two models of inline skates: Zoom and Whoosh. The number of hours required for assembling, finishing, and packaging, as well as the maximum time available for each process, are listed in the table.

Process	Zoom	Whoosh	Maximum
assembling (h)	2.5	3.5	1800
finishing (h)	0.5	1	450
packaging (h)	2	2	1300

THWR makes $20 in profit from each Zoom model sold and $30 from each Whoosh model sold.

A How many of each model should THWR make to produce the maximum profit?

SOLUTION

Step 1 Let x = number of Zoom models, and let y = number of Whoosh models.

Step 2 Since the company makes $20 in profit from each Zoom model sold and $30 from each Whoosh model sold, the profit function is $P = 20x + 30y$. The company wants to maximize profit, P.

Step 3 Determine the constraints.

$$\begin{cases} 2.5x + 3.5y \leq 1800 \\ 0.5x + y \leq 450 \\ 2x + 2y \leq 1300 \\ x \geq 0 \\ y \geq 0 \end{cases}$$

no more than 1800 h assembling
no more than 450 h finishing
no more than 1300 h packaging
number of Zoom models cannot be negative
number of Whoosh models cannot be negative

Step 4

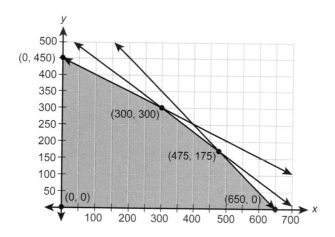

Step 5 The vertex points of the feasible region are $(0, 0)$, $(0, 450)$, $(300, 300)$, $(475, 175)$, and $(650, 0)$.

Step 6 Evaluate the objective function at each vertex point.

Vertex point	20x + 30y	P
$(0, 0)$	$20 \cdot 0 + 30 \cdot 0$	$0
$(0, 450)$	$20 \cdot 0 + 30 \cdot 450$	$13,500
$(300, 300)$	$20 \cdot 300 + 30 \cdot 300$	$15,000
$(475, 175)$	$20 \cdot 475 + 30 \cdot 175$	$14,750
$(650, 0)$	$20 \cdot 650 + 30 \cdot 0$	$13,000

Since the value of P is greatest at $(300, 300)$, the maximum profit occurs when the company sells 300 of each skate model.

B What is the maximum profit?

SOLUTION
The maximum profit is $15,000.

C THWR decides to discount the price of the Whoosh by $2 (resulting in $28 profit from each sale). How many of each model should the company now make to maximize profits?

SOLUTION
Since only the objective function will change, the same feasible region and vertex points can be used in the new objective function. Since THWR now makes $28 for each Whoosh (y) model sold, the new objective function is $P = 20x + 28y$.

Vertex point	20x + 28y	P
$(0, 0)$	$20 \cdot 0 + 28 \cdot 0$	$0
$(0, 450)$	$20 \cdot 0 + 28 \cdot 450$	$12,600
$(300, 300)$	$20 \cdot 300 + 28 \cdot 300$	$14,400
$(475, 175)$	$20 \cdot 475 + 28 \cdot 175$	$14,400
$(650, 0)$	$20 \cdot 650 + 28 \cdot 0$	$13,000

D What is the adjusted maximum profit?

SOLUTION
The adjusted maximum profit is $14,400. ■

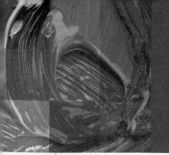

Domain in Linear Programming

Linear programming problems typically have whole number solutions.

If the vertex point that optimizes the objective function has coordinates that are not both integers, check integer values that are closest to the vertex point and that are still in the feasible region.

EXAMPLE

Brew Ha Ha Coffee & Tea Co. makes two types of handmade coffee mugs: matte and glazed. It takes 14 min on the pottery wheel and 20 min of kiln time to make each matte mug, and 15 min of wheel time and 30 min of kiln time to make each glazed mug. The company has reserved 300 min of time on the pottery wheel and 500 min of kiln time from a local potter. Brew Ha Ha charges $12 for matte mugs and $14 for glazed mugs.

A How many of each type of mug should Brew Ha Ha make to produce the maximum revenue?

SOLUTION

Step 1 Let $x =$ number of matte mugs and $y =$ number of glazed mugs.

Step 2 Since the company charges $12 for each matte mug and $14 for each glazed mug, the objective function is $R = 12x + 14y$. The company wants to maximize revenue, R.

Step 3 Write inequalities for the constraints.

$$\begin{cases} 14x + 15y \le 300 \\ 20x + 30y \le 500 \\ x \ge 0 \\ y \ge 0 \end{cases}$$

no more than 300 min wheel time
no more than 500 min kiln time
number of matte mugs cannot be negative
number of glazed mugs cannot be negative

Step 4

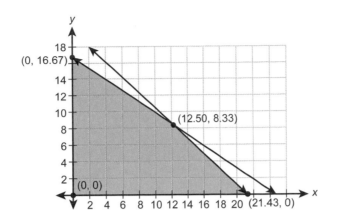

Step 5 The vertex points of the feasible region are $(0, 0)$, $(0, 16.67)$, $(12.50, 8.33)$, and $(21.43, 0)$.

Step 6 Evaluate the objective function at each vertex point.

Vertex point	$12x + 14y$	R
$(0, 0)$	$12 \cdot 0 + 14 \cdot 0$	$0
$(0, 16.67)$	$12 \cdot 0 + 14 \cdot 16.67$	$233.38
$(12.50, 8.33)$	$12 \cdot 12.50 + 14 \cdot 8.33$	$266.62
$(21.43, 0)$	$12 \cdot 21.43 + 14 \cdot 0$	$257.16

Since the maximum revenue occurs at a point $(12.50, 8.33)$ that contains nonintegers, try whole-number values near that point that are still within the constraints. Substituting $(12, 8)$ into the constraints shows that the company would use 288 h on the wheel and 480 h of kiln time, which is within the constraints. This vertex point yields revenue of $256. However, this value is below $257.16, which is the revenue created by vertex point $(21.43, 0)$. So round the x-value down to a whole number and determine the revenue there. Substituting $(21, 0)$ into the objective function yields $252, which is below the $256 revenue provided by $(12, 8)$. Thus, the company should make 12 matte mugs and 8 glazed mugs to maximize revenue.

B What is the maximum revenue?

SOLUTION
The maximum revenue is $256.

C If the company decides to sell both types of mugs for $13, how many of each should the company now make to maximize revenue?

SOLUTION
The feasible region and the vertex points are the same, but the objective function becomes $R = 13x + 13y$.

Vertex point	$13x + 13y$	R
$(0, 0)$	$13 \cdot 0 + 13 \cdot 0$	$0
$(0, 16.67)$	$13 \cdot 0 + 13 \cdot 16.67$	$216.71
$(12.50, 8.33)$	$13 \cdot 12.50 + 13 \cdot 8.33$	$270.79
$(21.43, 0)$	$13 \cdot 21.43 + 13 \cdot 0$	$278.59

The maximum revenue now occurs at $(21.43, 0)$, so check $(21, 0)$. This yields revenue of $273, which is still the maximum revenue, so at the new prices the company should make 21 matte mugs and no glazed mugs.

D What is the adjusted maximum revenue?

SOLUTION
The adjusted maximum revenue is $273. ■

Radicals and Complex Numbers

Some mathematicians, such as Benoit Mandelbrot, have found that complex numbers can be used to create beautiful images.

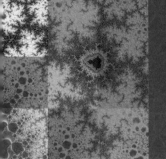

Radical Expressions

An expression that contains a radical sign, $\sqrt{}$, is a **radical expression**.

Examples of radical expressions are $\sqrt{3x}$, $\sqrt[4]{x^2y^3}$, and $\sqrt[5]{32}$.

Definitions

If a and b are real numbers, n is a positive integer, and $a^n = b$, then a is an **nth root** of b.

The nth root of b is written $\sqrt[n]{b}$, where n is the **index** of the radical and b is the **radicand**. The index is always an integer greater than 1, and the radicand can be a real number or an algebraic expression.

▶ **Think About It** If a and b are real numbers and $a^2 = b$, then a is the square root of b. This also applies to roots other than square roots.

▶ **Think About It**
NOTATION $\sqrt[n]{b}$ indicates the nth root of b when n is a positive integer.

Finding Real *n*th Roots

Real *n*th Roots of *b*

	n is even	*n* is odd
$b > 0$	two real roots (one positive and one negative)	one real root
$b < 0$	no real roots	one real root
$b = 0$	one real root, $\sqrt[n]{0} = 0$	one real root, $\sqrt[n]{0} = 0$

EXAMPLE 1

A Find the cube roots of -64.

SOLUTION

The cube root means that n is 3. Since n is odd and $b < 0$, there is one real root: $(-4)^3 = -64$. The cube root of -64 is -4.

B Find the fourth roots of -625.

SOLUTION

Since n is even and $b < 0$, there are no real roots.

C Find the fourth roots of 81.

SOLUTION

Since n is even and $b > 0$, there are two real roots: $(-3)^4 = 81$ and $3^4 = 81$. The fourth roots of 81 are ± 3. ∎

Simplified Radical Form

You can use properties of radicals to simplify expressions. A square root expression is in simplified radical form if the radicand is not a fraction, there are no radicals in the denominator, and none of the factors is a perfect square other than 1.

Product Property of Radicals

For real numbers $a \geq 0$ and $b \geq 0$,

$$\sqrt{ab} = \sqrt{a} \cdot \sqrt{b}.$$

Quotient Property of Radicals

For real numbers $a \geq 0$ and $b > 0$,

$$\sqrt{\frac{a}{b}} = \frac{\sqrt{a}}{\sqrt{b}}.$$

▶ **Think About It**

NOTATION Assume that the index of a radical expression is 2 whenever no index is written.

EXAMPLE 2

Write the expression in simplified radical form.

A $\sqrt{80}$

SOLUTION

$$\sqrt{80} = \sqrt{16 \cdot 5} \qquad \text{Use a perfect square to factor the radicand.}$$
$$= \sqrt{16} \cdot \sqrt{5} \qquad \text{Product Property of Radicals}$$
$$= 4\sqrt{5} \qquad \text{Simplify.}$$

B $\sqrt{\dfrac{2}{9}}$

SOLUTION

$\sqrt{\dfrac{2}{9}} = \dfrac{\sqrt{2}}{\sqrt{9}}$ Quotient Property of Radicals

$\phantom{\sqrt{\dfrac{2}{9}}} = \dfrac{\sqrt{2}}{3}$ Simplify.

C $\sqrt{15}$

SOLUTION

$\sqrt{15}$ is in simplified radical form because the radicand is not a fraction, there are no radicals in the denominator, and none of the factors (1, 3, 5, or 15) is a perfect square other than 1. ■

Rationalizing a Denominator

When a radical is in the denominator of a fraction, you can simplify it by multiplying both the numerator and denominator by the radical. This process is called rationalizing the denominator.

EXAMPLE 3

Write $\dfrac{3}{\sqrt{5}}$ in simplified radical form.

SOLUTION

$\dfrac{3}{\sqrt{5}} = \dfrac{3}{\sqrt{5}} \cdot \dfrac{\sqrt{5}}{\sqrt{5}}$ Multiply the numerator and denominator by $\sqrt{5}$.

$\phantom{\dfrac{3}{\sqrt{5}}} = \dfrac{3\sqrt{5}}{\sqrt{5 \cdot 5}}$ Product Property of Radicals

$\phantom{\dfrac{3}{\sqrt{5}}} = \dfrac{3\sqrt{5}}{\sqrt{25}}$ Simplify.

$\phantom{\dfrac{3}{\sqrt{5}}} = \dfrac{3\sqrt{5}}{5}$ Simplify. ■

Simplifying Algebraic Expressions

Here are examples of how you can use the product property of radicals to simplify the square root of a power of a variable.

Let $x \geq 0$.

$$\sqrt{x^2} = x$$
$$\sqrt{x^3} = \sqrt{x^2 \cdot x} = \sqrt{x^2} \cdot \sqrt{x} = x\sqrt{x}$$
$$\sqrt{x^4} = \sqrt{\left(x^2\right)^2} = x^2$$
$$\sqrt{x^5} = \sqrt{x^4 \cdot x} = \sqrt{x^4} \cdot \sqrt{x} = x^2\sqrt{x}$$

EXAMPLE 4

Write the expression in simplified radical form. Assume all variables are positive.

A $\sqrt{27x^2y^3}$

SOLUTION

$$
\begin{aligned}
\sqrt{27x^2y^3} &= \sqrt{9 \cdot 3 \cdot x^2 \cdot y^2 \cdot y} && \text{Factor the radicand.} \\
&= \sqrt{9} \cdot \sqrt{3} \cdot \sqrt{x^2} \cdot \sqrt{y^2} \cdot \sqrt{y} && \text{Product Property of Radicals} \\
&= 3\sqrt{3} \cdot xy\sqrt{y} && \text{Simplify.} \\
&= 3xy\sqrt{3y} && \text{Simplify.}
\end{aligned}
$$

B $\dfrac{a}{\sqrt{a^3}}$

SOLUTION

$\dfrac{a}{\sqrt{a^3}} = \dfrac{a}{\sqrt{a^2 \cdot a}}$ Factor the denominator.

$\qquad = \dfrac{a}{\sqrt{a^2} \cdot \sqrt{a}}$ Product Property of Radicals

$\qquad = \dfrac{a}{a\sqrt{a}}$ Simplify.

$\qquad = \dfrac{1}{\sqrt{a}} \cdot \dfrac{\sqrt{a}}{\sqrt{a}}$ Multiply the numerator and denominator by $\sqrt{a}$.

$\qquad = \dfrac{\sqrt{a}}{a}$ Simplify.

C $\sqrt{7hg}$

SOLUTION

$\sqrt{7hg}$ is in simplified radical form because the radicand is not a fraction, there are no radicals in the denominator, and none of the factors is a perfect square other than 1. ■

Multiplying Radical Expressions

To multiply radical expressions, use the product property of radicals.

EXAMPLE 5

Multiply. Assume all variables are positive.

A $\sqrt{8} \cdot \sqrt{32}$

SOLUTION

$\sqrt{8} \cdot \sqrt{32} = \sqrt{8 \cdot 32}$ Product Property of Radicals

$\qquad = \sqrt{256}$ Multiply.

$\qquad = \sqrt{16^2}$ Identify that $256 = 16^2$.

$\qquad = 16$ Simplify.

B $\sqrt{2r^3 s^9} \cdot 4\sqrt{8r^5 s^2}$

SOLUTION

$$\sqrt{2r^3 s^9} \cdot 4\sqrt{8r^5 s^2} = 4\sqrt{2r^3 s^9 \cdot 8r^5 s^2} \qquad \text{Product Property of Radicals}$$

$$= 4\sqrt{16r^8 s^{11}} \qquad \text{Product of Powers Property}$$

$$= 4\sqrt{16r^8 s^{10} s} \qquad \text{Product of Powers Property}$$

$$= 4\sqrt{4^2 \cdot \left(r^4\right)^2 \cdot \left(s^5\right)^2 \cdot s}$$

$$= 4 \cdot 4 \cdot r^4 \cdot s^5 \cdot \sqrt{s} \qquad \text{Simplify.}$$

$$= 16r^4 s^5 \sqrt{s} \qquad \text{Simplify.} \ \blacksquare$$

Adding and Subtracting Radical Expressions

Like radicals have the same index and radicand. You can use the distributive property to add or subtract like radicals.

EXAMPLE 6

Add or subtract. Assume all variables are positive.

A $8\sqrt{6} + \sqrt{5} + \sqrt{6}$

SOLUTION

$$8\sqrt{6} + \sqrt{5} + \sqrt{6} = 8\sqrt{6} + \sqrt{6} + \sqrt{5}$$

$$= (8 + 1)\sqrt{6} + \sqrt{5}$$

$$= 9\sqrt{6} + \sqrt{5}$$

B $5\sqrt{12} - 3\sqrt{48}$

SOLUTION

$$
\begin{aligned}
5\sqrt{12} - 3\sqrt{48} &= 5\sqrt{4 \cdot 3} - 3\sqrt{16 \cdot 3} \\
&= 5\sqrt{4} \cdot \sqrt{3} - 3\sqrt{16} \cdot \sqrt{3} \\
&= 10\sqrt{3} - 12\sqrt{3} \\
&= (10 - 12)\sqrt{3} \\
&= -2\sqrt{3}
\end{aligned}
$$

C Simplify.

$$
\sqrt{48t^5} - \sqrt{3t^5} - \sqrt{3t}
$$

SOLUTION

$$
\begin{aligned}
\sqrt{48t^5} - \sqrt{3t^5} - \sqrt{3t} &= \sqrt{16t^4} \cdot \sqrt{3t} - \sqrt{t^4} \cdot \sqrt{3t} - \sqrt{3t} \\
&= 4t^2\sqrt{3t} - t^2\sqrt{3t} - \sqrt{3t} \\
&= \left(4t^2 - t^2\right)\sqrt{3t} - \sqrt{3t} \\
&= 3t^2\sqrt{3t} - \sqrt{3t} \text{ or } \left(3t^2 - 1\right)\sqrt{3t} \ \blacksquare
\end{aligned}
$$

▶ **Think About It** $\left(3t^2 - 1\right)\sqrt{3t}$ is an alternate simplified form of $3t^2\sqrt{3t} - \sqrt{3t}$.

Fractional Exponents

Some radical expressions can be rewritten using fractional exponents, also known as rational exponent form.

Radicals and Rational Exponent Form

Property

For any positive integer n and any real number b,

$$\sqrt[n]{b} = b^{\frac{1}{n}}$$

except when $b < 0$ and n is even.

Properties of Radicals and Rational Exponents

For any positive integers m and n and any real number b,

$$\sqrt[n]{b^m} = \left(\sqrt[n]{b}\right)^m = b^{\frac{m}{n}}$$

except when $b < 0$ and n is even.

EXAMPLE 1

Write the expression in rational exponent form. Assume all variables are positive.

A $\sqrt[3]{5}$

SOLUTION

$$\sqrt[3]{5} = 5^{\frac{1}{3}}$$

B $\left(\sqrt{x+1}\right)^3$

SOLUTION

$$\left(\sqrt{x+1}\right)^3 = \sqrt[2]{(x+1)^3} = (x+1)^{\frac{3}{2}} \quad \blacksquare$$

EXAMPLE 2

Write the expression in radical form.

A $2^{\frac{3}{4}}$

SOLUTION

$$2^{\frac{3}{4}} = \sqrt[4]{2^3} = \sqrt[4]{8}$$

B $(4m)^{\frac{2}{3}}$

SOLUTION

$$(4m)^{\frac{2}{3}} = \sqrt[3]{(4m)^2} = \sqrt[3]{16m^2} \quad \blacksquare$$

▶ **Remember** Properties of Exponents If a and b are nonzero real numbers and m and n are integers, then

$$a^m \bullet a^n = a^{(m+n)} \qquad \text{Product of Powers}$$

$$\frac{a^m}{a^n} = a^{(m-n)} \qquad \text{Quotient of Powers}$$

$$(ab)^n = a^n b^n \qquad \text{Power of a Product}$$

$$\left(\frac{a}{b}\right)^n = \frac{a^n}{b^n} \qquad \text{Power of a Quotient}$$

$$\left(a^m\right)^n = a^{mn} \qquad \text{Power of a Power}$$

Simplifying a Radical Expression

The properties of exponents given for integer exponents may also be applied to fractional exponents, but be careful with even roots.

Properties of nth Roots of nth Powers

For any real number b and positive integer n,

$$\text{If } n \text{ is even, then } \sqrt[n]{b^n} = |b|.$$

$$\text{If } n \text{ is odd, then } \sqrt[n]{b^n} = b.$$

Product and Quotient Properties of Radicals

For any real numbers a and b, where the following roots are represented by real numbers, the following properties hold true.

Product Property of Radicals

$$\sqrt[n]{ab} = \sqrt[n]{a}\,\sqrt[n]{b}$$

Quotient Property of Radicals

$$\sqrt[n]{\frac{a}{b}} = \frac{\sqrt[n]{a}}{\sqrt[n]{b}}, \ (b \neq 0)$$

EXAMPLE 3

Simplify the expression.

A $\sqrt[4]{(-16)^4}$

SOLUTION

$$\sqrt[4]{(-16)^4} = |-16| \qquad \text{Simplify.}$$
$$\qquad\qquad = 16 \qquad\qquad \text{Simplify.}$$

B $\sqrt[3]{128}$

SOLUTION

$$\sqrt[3]{128} = \sqrt[3]{64 \cdot 2} \qquad \text{Factor 128.}$$

$$= \sqrt[3]{64} \cdot \sqrt[3]{2} \qquad \text{Product Property of Radicals}$$

$$= 4\sqrt[3]{2} \qquad \text{Simplify.}$$

C $\sqrt[3]{2^6}$

SOLUTION

$$\sqrt[3]{2^6} = \sqrt[3]{\left(2^2\right)^3} \qquad \text{Power of a Power Property}$$

$$= 2^2 \qquad \text{Simplify.}$$

$$= 4 \qquad \text{Simplify.}$$

D $\sqrt[3]{\dfrac{27}{125}}$

SOLUTION

$$\sqrt[3]{\frac{27}{125}} = \frac{\sqrt[3]{27}}{\sqrt[3]{125}} \qquad \text{Quotient Property of Radicals}$$

$$= \frac{3}{5} \qquad \text{Simplify.} \ \blacksquare$$

You can use properties of radicals or fractional exponents to simplify expressions.

EXAMPLE 4

Simplify the expression. Assume all variables are positive.

A $(-32)^{\frac{3}{5}}$

SOLUTION

$$(-32)^{\frac{3}{5}} = \left(\sqrt[5]{-32}\right)^3 = (-2)^3 = -8$$

B $\left(x^5\right)^{\frac{1}{4}} \cdot x^{\frac{3}{4}}$

SOLUTION

$$\left(x^5\right)^{\frac{1}{4}} \cdot x^{\frac{3}{4}} = x^{\frac{5}{4}} \cdot x^{\frac{3}{4}} = x^{\frac{8}{4}} = x^2 \ \blacksquare$$

EXAMPLE 5

Write the expression in simplified radical form. Assume all variables are positive.

A $\sqrt[4]{32x^{10}y^4}$

SOLUTION

$$\sqrt[4]{32x^{10}y^4} = \sqrt[4]{2^5 x^{10} y^4} \qquad \text{Write 32 as a power of 2.}$$

$$= \sqrt[4]{2^4 x^8 y^4} \cdot \sqrt[4]{2x^2} \qquad \text{Product Property of Radicals}$$

$$= 2x^2 y \sqrt[4]{2x^2} \qquad \text{Simplify.}$$

B $\sqrt[8]{a^6 b^2}$

SOLUTION

$$\sqrt[8]{a^6 b^2} = \left(a^6 b^2\right)^{\frac{1}{8}} \qquad \text{Property of Radicals}$$

$$= a^{\frac{6}{8}} b^{\frac{2}{8}} \qquad \text{Power of a Product}$$

$$= a^{\frac{3}{4}} b^{\frac{1}{4}} \qquad \text{Simplify.}$$

$$= \sqrt[4]{a^3 b} \qquad \text{Property of Radicals} \; \blacksquare$$

Applying Roots and Powers

You can apply roots and powers to many real-world situations.

Measurements may involve roots and powers.

Applications with Square Roots

EXAMPLE 1

What is the perimeter of a rectangle with a length of $6 + \sqrt{2}$ units and a width of $2 + \sqrt{6}$ units?

SOLUTION

perimeter $=$ length $+$ length $+$ width $+$ width

$$= \left(6 + \sqrt{2}\right) + \left(6 + \sqrt{2}\right) + \left(2 + \sqrt{6}\right) + \left(2 + \sqrt{6}\right)$$

$$= 6 + 6 + 2 + 2 + \sqrt{2} + \sqrt{2} + \sqrt{6} + \sqrt{6}$$

$$= 16 + 2\sqrt{2} + 2\sqrt{6}$$

The perimeter is $16 + 2\sqrt{2} + 2\sqrt{6}$ units. ▪

EXAMPLE 2

What is the area of a rectangle with a length of $4\sqrt{2}$ units and a width of $5 + \sqrt{6}$ units?

SOLUTION

$$\text{area} = \text{length} \cdot \text{width}$$
$$= \left(4\sqrt{2}\right)\left(5 + \sqrt{6}\right)$$
$$= \left(4\sqrt{2}\right)(5) + \left(4\sqrt{2}\right)\left(\sqrt{6}\right)$$
$$= 20\sqrt{2} + \left(4\sqrt{2 \cdot 6}\right)$$
$$= 20\sqrt{2} + \left(4\sqrt{12}\right)$$
$$= 20\sqrt{2} + \left(4 \cdot 2\sqrt{3}\right)$$
$$= 20\sqrt{2} + 8\sqrt{3}$$

The area is $20\sqrt{2} + 8\sqrt{3}$ units^2. ∎

Many formulas also include roots or powers. For example, the formula for electrical power is $P = \dfrac{V^2}{R}$, where P represents power (watts), R represents resistance (ohms), and V represents voltage.

EXAMPLE 3

What is the voltage used by a radio rated at 100 watts with a resistance of 8 ohms?

SOLUTION

Let $P = 100$ watts and $R = 8$ ohms.

$$P = \frac{V^2}{R}$$
$$100 = \frac{V^2}{8}$$
$$V^2 = (100)(8) = 800 \longrightarrow V = \sqrt{800} = \sqrt{2 \cdot 400} = 20\sqrt{2}$$

The voltage used by the radio is $20\sqrt{2}$ volts. ∎

The properties of exponents can be used to transform exponential functions, such as those involving future value of money.

The future-value formula, $F = P(1 + r)^t$, shows how much an investment will be worth after compounding for a given number of years. In the formula, F represents the future value of the investment, P represents the present value of the investment, r represents the rate of growth (the annual percent of interest the investment will earn), and t represents the time in years.

EXAMPLE 4

What is the approximate monthly rate of growth for an investment that has an annual interest rate of 15%?

▶ **Think About It** Many real-world problems can be modeled by exponential functions that describe how things grow or decay as time passes. Examples include studies of populations, bacteria, radioactive substances, electricity, temperatures, and credit payments.

SOLUTION

The exponential growth portion of the future-value formula is represented by the expression $(1 + r)^t$.

$(1 + r)^t$

$(1 + 0.15)^t$ Substitute 15% for r.

$(1.15)^t$ Simplify.

The expression for the annual growth is 1.15^t, but you need to model monthly growth. If t is in months, you'd need the base of the monthly growth expression (call the base m) to satisfy the equation $m^{12t} = 1.15^t$. But how do you find that value of m? The power of a power property can help.

$m^{12t} = 1.15^t$

$m^{12t} = 1.15^{\left(\frac{1}{12} \cdot 12t\right)}$ Replace t with $\frac{1}{12} \cdot 12t$.

$m^{12t} = \left(1.15^{\frac{1}{12}}\right)^{12t}$ Power of Powers Property

So $m = 1.15^{\frac{1}{12}}$, which equals 1.01171491692. To check that this solution works, look at the value of the monthly and annual rate of growth after 24 months and 2 years.

Monthly growth after 24 months	Annual growth after 2 years
$1.01171491692^{24} = 1.3225$	$1.15^2 = 1.3225$

The approximate monthly rate of growth when the annual rate is 15% would be about 1.17%. ∎

Operations with Complex Numbers

Complex numbers can be added, subtracted, multiplied, and divided.

Adding and Subtracting Complex Numbers

The commutative and associative properties of addition and multiplication, as well as the distributive property, hold for complex numbers.

Adding and Subtracting Complex Numbers

Let a, b, c, and d be real numbers.

Addition To add complex numbers, add the real parts and then add the imaginary parts.

$$(a + bi) + (c + di) = (a + c) + (b + d)i$$

Subtraction To subtract complex numbers, subtract the real parts and then subtract the imaginary parts.

$$(a + bi) - (c + di) = (a - c) + (b - d)i$$

Closure Properties for the Complex Numbers

The set of complex numbers is closed under addition, subtraction, multiplication, and division.

EXAMPLE 1

Add or subtract, and then simplify.

A $(3 + 7i) + (-9 - 4i)$

SOLUTION

$$(3 + 7i) + (-9 - 4i) = (3 + (-9)) + (7 + (-4))i$$
$$= -6 + 3i$$

B $(-5 - 2i) - (8 + 11i)$

SOLUTION

$$(-5 - 2i) - (8 + 11i) = (-5 - 8) + (-2 - 11)i$$
$$= -13 - 13i \ ■$$

Multiplying Complex Numbers

Use the distributive property to multiply complex numbers.

▶ **Remember** $i^2 = \left(\sqrt{-1}\right)^2 = -1$

EXAMPLE 2

Multiply.

$$7i(3 + 2i)$$

SOLUTION
Use the distributive property.

$$7i(3 + 2i) = 7i \bullet 3 + 7i \bullet 2i$$
$$= 21i + 14i^2$$
$$= 21i + 14(-1)$$
$$= 21i - 14$$
$$= -14 + 21i \ ■$$

Solving Radical Equations

A **radical equation** has at least one radical expression with a variable in the radicand.

Exponential Property of Equality

If $a = b$ and n is a positive integer, then $a^n = b^n$.

Solving Radical Equations

Step 1 Isolate the radical on one side of the equation.

Step 2 Raise both sides of the equation to the same power to eliminate the radical.

Step 3 Solve the equivalent equation.

Step 4 Check each solution by substituting into the original equation.

The power of a power property, $\left(a^m\right)^n = a^{mn}$, makes it possible to use the exponential property of equality to solve radical equations.

▶ **Think About It** Raising to the nth power is the inverse operation of taking the nth root.

EXAMPLE 1

Solve and check.

A $\sqrt{x + 12} = 8$

SOLUTION

$$\sqrt{x + 12} = 8$$

$$\left(\sqrt{x + 12}\right)^2 = 8^2 \qquad \text{Square both sides of the equation.}$$

$$x + 12 = 64 \qquad \text{Simplify.}$$

$$x = 52 \qquad \text{Subtract 12 from both sides.}$$

CHECK

Substitute 52 for x.

$$\sqrt{52 + 12} \overset{?}{=} 8$$
$$\sqrt{64} \overset{?}{=} 8$$
$$8 = 8 \checkmark$$

The solution is $x = 52$.

B $-5\sqrt[3]{a - 1} = 25$

SOLUTION

$$-5\sqrt[3]{a - 1} = 25$$

$$\sqrt[3]{a - 1} = -5 \qquad \text{Isolate the radical.}$$

$$\left(\sqrt[3]{a - 1}\right)^3 = (-5)^3 \qquad \text{Cube both sides of the equation.}$$

$$a - 1 = -125 \qquad \text{Simplify.}$$

$$a = -124 \qquad \text{Add 1 to both sides.}$$

CHECK

Substitute -124 for a.

$$-5\sqrt[3]{-124 - 1} \overset{?}{=} 25$$

$$-5\sqrt[3]{-125} \overset{?}{=} 25$$

$$-5(-5) \overset{?}{=} 25$$

$$25 = 25 \checkmark$$

The solution is $a = -124$. ∎

▶ **Remember** The third root of a negative number is always negative.

Identifying an Extraneous Solution

Raising each side of an equation to a power can create extraneous solutions. Always check your solutions to be certain each one satisfies the original equation.

EXAMPLE 2

Solve $x + 1 = \sqrt{5x + 11}$.

SOLUTION

$$x + 1 = \sqrt{5x + 11}$$

$$(x + 1)^2 = \left(\sqrt{5x + 11}\right)^2 \qquad \text{Square both sides of the equation.}$$

$$x^2 + 2x + 1 = 5x + 11 \qquad \text{Simplify.}$$

$$x^2 - 3x - 10 = 0 \qquad \text{Set equal to 0.}$$

$$(x - 5)(x + 2) = 0 \qquad \text{Factor.}$$

$$x = 5 \quad \text{or} \quad x = -2 \qquad \text{Zero Product Property}$$

CHECK

Substitute 5 for x.

$$5 + 1 \overset{?}{=} \sqrt{5 \cdot 5 + 11}$$

$$6 \overset{?}{=} \sqrt{36}$$

$$6 = 6 \checkmark$$

Substitute -2 for x.

$$-2 + 1 \overset{?}{=} \sqrt{5\,(-2) + 11}$$

$$-1 \neq \sqrt{1}$$

The solution $x = -2$ is extraneous. The only solution is $x = 5$. ∎

▶ **Remember** An extraneous solution is an apparent solution that does not satisfy the original equation.

Solving a Radical Equation with Two Radicals

EXAMPLE 3

Solve $\sqrt{3m - 2} = \sqrt{m + 10}$.

SOLUTION

$$\sqrt{3m - 2} = \sqrt{m + 10}$$

$$\left(\sqrt{3m - 2}\right)^2 = \left(\sqrt{m + 10}\right)^2 \qquad \text{Square both sides of the equation.}$$

$$3m - 2 = m + 10 \qquad \text{Simplify.}$$

$$2m = 12 \qquad \text{Subtraction and Addition Properties of Equality}$$

$$m = 6 \qquad \text{Division Property of Equality} \; \blacksquare$$

When squaring an equation with radicals on both sides, clear all variables from radical expressions, isolate the radical, square both sides again, and simplify.

EXAMPLE 4

Solve $\sqrt{x + 13} = \sqrt{12 - x} - 1$.

SOLUTION

$$\sqrt{x + 13} = \sqrt{12 - x} - 1$$

$$\left(\sqrt{x + 13}\right)^2 = \left(\sqrt{12 - x} - 1\right)^2 \qquad \text{Square both sides of the equation.}$$

$$x + 13 = 12 - x - 2\sqrt{12 - x} + 1 \qquad \text{Use the binomial square pattern on the right side.}$$

$$2x = -2\sqrt{12 - x} \qquad \text{Simplify.}$$

$$-x = \sqrt{12 - x} \qquad \text{Isolate the radical.}$$

$$(-x)^2 = \left(\sqrt{12 - x}\right)^2 \qquad \text{Square both sides of the equation.}$$

$$x^2 = 12 - x \qquad \text{Simplify.}$$

$$x^2 + x - 12 = 0 \qquad \text{Set equal to 0.}$$

$$(x + 4)(x - 3) = 0 \qquad \text{Factor.}$$

$$x = -4 \quad \text{or} \quad x = 3 \qquad \text{Zero Product Property}$$

CHECK

Substitute -4 for x.

$$\sqrt{-4 + 13} \overset{?}{=} \sqrt{12 - (-4)} - 1$$
$$\sqrt{9} \overset{?}{=} \sqrt{16} - 1$$
$$3 = 3 \checkmark$$

Substitute 3 for x.

$$\sqrt{3 + 13} \overset{?}{=} \sqrt{12 - 3} - 1$$
$$\sqrt{16} \overset{?}{=} \sqrt{9} - 1$$
$$4 \neq 2$$

The solution $x = 3$ is extraneous. The only solution is $x = -4$. ■

Rearranging Formulas

You can rearrange a mathematical formula to solve for a particular value. Determine which variable you want to isolate and then solve the equation for that quantity.

EXAMPLE 5

Isaac Newton derived a formula to describe the speed a rocket must travel to escape the gravitational pull of a planet. This speed is called the escape velocity, or v_{esc}.

$v_{esc} = \sqrt{\dfrac{2GM}{r}}$, where G is the gravitational constant, M is the mass of the planet, and r is the radius of the planet. Solve the formula for r.

> ▶ **Remember** When solving a radical equation, square both sides of the equation to clear the radical.

SOLUTION

$$v_{esc} = \sqrt{\frac{2GM}{r}}$$

$$\left(v_{esc}\right)^2 = \left(\sqrt{\frac{2GM}{r}}\right)^2 \qquad \text{Square both sides of the equation.}$$

$$\left(v_{esc}\right)^2 = \frac{2GM}{r} \qquad \text{Simplify.}$$

$$r \bullet \left(v_{esc}\right)^2 = \frac{2GM}{r} \bullet r \qquad \text{Multiply both sides by } r.$$

$$\frac{r \bullet \left(v_{esc}\right)^2}{\left(v_{esc}\right)^2} = \frac{2GM}{\left(v_{esc}\right)^2} \qquad \text{Divide both sides of the equation by } \left(v_{esc}\right)^2.$$

$$r = \frac{2GM}{\left(v_{esc}\right)^2} \qquad \text{Simplify.} \ \blacksquare$$

Polynomials

Topic List

Successful spaceflight relies on many, many fast calculations. Computer scientists use polynomials to enable spacecraft to perform every calculation as quickly as possible.

Working with Polynomials

> A polynomial is a monomial or sum of monomials.

The prefix *poly–* means "many." A polynomial can be a sum of many monomials.

Definitions

A **monomial** is a number, a variable, or the product of a number and one or more variables. All variables in a monomial must have whole-number exponents. A monomial cannot have a variable in a denominator or under a radical symbol. Monomials are sometimes called terms.

The **coefficient** of a monomial with multiple factors is the numerical factor.

A monomial with no variable factors is called a **constant**.

A **polynomial** is a monomial or sum of monomials.

Determining Whether an Expression Is a Polynomial

EXAMPLE 1

Determine whether the expression is a polynomial. If it is not, explain.

A $3\sqrt{x} + 17x + 1$

SOLUTION
This expression is not a polynomial. It has a variable under a radical symbol.

B $2x^3 - x^2 - 5$

SOLUTION

This expression is a polynomial. It is a sum of monomials because

$$2x^3 - x^2 - 5 = 2x^3 + \left(-x^2\right) + (-5).$$

C $x^{-5} + 4x^4 - 1$

SOLUTION

This expression is not a polynomial. It has a variable with a negative exponent.

▶ **Think About It** In Example 1A, $\sqrt{x} = x^{\frac{1}{2}}$, so a variable has an exponent that is not a whole number.

In Example 1C, $x^{-5} = \dfrac{1}{x^5}$, so there is a variable in a denominator.

D $\dfrac{2}{3}x^3 - x^0$

SOLUTION

This expression is a polynomial. Note that 0 is a whole number.

$$\dfrac{2}{3}x^3 - x^0 = \dfrac{2}{3}x^3 - 1 \ \blacksquare$$

▶ **Remember** The whole numbers are $\{0, 1, 2, 3, \ldots\}$.

Monomials and Like Terms

EXAMPLE 2

Which of the following are like terms?

$$6x^2 \quad x^2y \quad -2xy \quad -2x^2y \quad 10x^2 \quad -x^2$$

SOLUTION

$6x^2$, $10x^2$, and $-x^2$ are like terms.

x^2y and $-2x^2y$ are like terms.

$-2xy$ is not like any of the other terms. ■

EXAMPLE 3

Determine the degree of the monomial.

$$-21x^2y^5z^3$$

SOLUTION

Add the exponents of the variables.

$$-21x^2y^5z^3$$

$$\mathbf{2 + 5 + 3} = 10$$

The degree of the monomial is 10. ∎

Simplifying and Classifying Polynomials

EXAMPLE 4

Simplify $8x + 2x^3 + 9x + 2 - 6x^2 - 5x^3$. Then identify the leading coefficient.

SOLUTION

Combine like terms.

$$\mathbf{8x + 2x^3 + 9x + 2 - 6x^2 - 5x^3}$$

$$\mathbf{17x - 3x^3 + 2 - 6x^2}$$

Then write the terms in order of decreasing degree. The simplified form is $-3x^3 - 6x^2 + 17x + 2$ and the leading coefficient is -3. ∎

▶ **Think About It** Combining like terms uses the distributive property.

$$8x + 9x = (8 + 9)x = 17x$$

A polynomial can be classified by its number of terms or by its degree.

Classifying Polynomials by Number of Terms

Type	Number of terms	Example
monomial	1	12
		$-\dfrac{2}{5}xy^3$
binomial	2	$a + b$
		$1 - 3c^5$
trinomial	3	$x^2 + 3x - 10$
		$a^2 + 4ab + 4b^2$

▶ **Think About It** Prefixes can help you remember the number of terms in monomials, binomials, and trinomials.

Mono– means "one," as in **mono**cle or **mono**poly.

Bi– means "two," as in **bi**cycle or **bi**lingual.

Tri– means "three," as in **tri**cycle or **tri**athlon.

Many of the polynomials in the study of algebra are polynomials in one variable.

Definition

A **polynomial in x** is a polynomial of the form

$$a_n x^n + a_{n-1} x^{n-1} + \ldots + a_2 x^2 + a_1 x + a_0$$

where the exponents are all whole numbers, the coefficients are all real numbers, and $a_n \neq 0$.

Note that the polynomial in the definition can be written as

$$a_n x^n + a_{n-1} x^{n-1} + \ldots + a_2 x^2 + a_1 x^1 + a_0 x^0.$$

The exponents are $n, n-1, n-2, \ldots, 2, 1,$ and 0. The coefficients are $a_n, a_{n-1}, a_{n-2}, \ldots, a_2, a_1,$ and a_0.

Classifying Polynomials by Degree

Type	Degree	Example
constant	0	-7
linear	1	$9x - 12$
quadratic	2	$x^2 + 8x + 16$
cubic	3	$6x^3 - 2x^2 - 5$
quartic	4	$5x^4 - 3x + 1$
quintic	5	$-x^5 + 2x^4 - 3x^3 + 7x^2 - 10x + 1$
nth degree	n	$a_n x^n + a_{n-1} x^{n-1} + \ldots + a_1 x + a_0$

EXAMPLE 5

Classify $5a^4 + a^2 - 3$ by its number of terms and by its degree.

SOLUTION
The expression $5a^4 + a^2 - 3$ has three terms, so it is a trinomial. The term with the greatest degree is $5a^4$, and its degree is 4, so the degree of the polynomial is 4. It is a quartic trinomial. ■

EXAMPLE 6

A Add horizontally.

$$(7x + 14) + \left(2x^2 - 3x + 2\right)$$

SOLUTION

$$(7x + 14) + \left(2x^2 - 3x + 2\right) = 7x + 14 + 2x^2 - 3x + 2 \qquad \text{Eliminate parentheses.}$$

$$= 2x^2 + 7x - 3x + 14 + 2 \qquad \text{Write in order of decreasing degree.}$$

$$= 2x^2 + 4x + 16 \qquad \text{Combine like terms.}$$

B Add vertically.

$$(-4x^3 + 2x^2 + 9) + (7x^3 + 10x^2 - 3x - 4).$$

SOLUTION

$$
\begin{array}{l}
-4x^3 + 2x^2 \phantom{{}-3x} + 9 \\
+7x^3 + 10x^2 - 3x - 4 \\
\hline
3x^3 + 12x^2 - 3x + 5
\end{array}
$$

Write one polynomial under the other so that like terms appear in the same columns.

Add and combine like terms. ■

EXAMPLE 7

A Subtract horizontally.

$$(a^2 + 3a) - (2a^2 - 5a + 1)$$

SOLUTION

To subtract polynomials, add the opposite of every term in the subtrahend. The rest of the work is the same as adding polynomials.

$$
\begin{aligned}
(a^2 + 3a) - (2a^2 - 5a + 1) &= a^2 + 3a - 2a^2 + 5a - 1 \\
&= a^2 - 2a^2 + 3a + 5a - 1 \\
&= -a^2 + 8a - 1
\end{aligned}
$$

▶ **Remember** minuend − subtrahend = difference

B Subtract vertically.

$$(2x^4 - 10x^2 - 6x + 1) - (2x^4 + 7x^3 + 6x + 1)$$

SOLUTION

$$
\begin{array}{l}
2x^4 -10x^2 - 6x + 1 \\
-\ (2x^4 + 7x^3 + 6x + 1) \\
\hline
\end{array}
$$

Write the second polynomial under the first polynomial so that like terms appear in the same columns.

$$
\begin{array}{l}
2x^4 -10x^2 - 6x + 1 \\
+(-2x^4 - 7x^3 - 6x - 1) \\
\hline
{} -7x^3 -10x^2 - 12x
\end{array}
$$

To subtract, add the opposite of every term in the second polynomial. ■

▶ **Think About It** Subtraction is not commutative. You must subtract the second polynomial from the first polynomial.

Polynomials and Arithmetic

Polynomials can be added, subtracted, multiplied, and divided just like real numbers can. When you add, subtract, or multiply polynomials, you always end up with a polynomial result, which is not always true when dividing polynomials.

Closure

Definition

A set is **closed under an operation** if the result of the operation on any two elements of the set is also an element of the set.

For instance, the set of even numbers is closed under addition. If you add any two even numbers, the sum is also an even number.

EXAMPLE 1

Determine whether the set is closed under subtraction. If so, explain why; if it is not closed, give a counterexample.

A the set of positive integers

SOLUTION
The set of positive integers is not closed under subtraction. For instance, $6 - 9 = -3$ and -3 is not a positive integer.

B the set of even integers

SOLUTION

The set of even integers is closed under subtraction. An even integer can be written as $2x$, where x is an integer. Subtract two even integers $2p$ and $2q$: $2p - 2q = 2(p - q)$. The value $(p - q)$ is an integer, so $2 \cdot (p - q)$ is an integer as well. The set of even integers is closed under subtraction. ▪

▶ **Think About It** A **counterexample** is an example that shows that a statement is false. You need only a single counterexample to show that a statement is false.

Operations Under Which Polynomials Are Closed

The set of polynomials is closed under addition, subtraction, and multiplication.

▶ **Remember** A polynomial is a monomial or the sum of monomials. The variables in polynomials must have whole-number exponents. Also, a constant without a variable, such as -4, is considered a polynomial because it is a monomial.

EXAMPLE 2

Explain why the set of polynomials is closed under addition.

SOLUTION

Start with a simple case—the addition of two binomials of degree one. $(ax + b) + (cx + d)$ where a, b, c, and d are all integers

$$(ax + b) + (cx + d) = (ax + cx) + (b + d)$$
$$= (a + c)x + (b + d)$$

The values $(a + c)$ and $(b + d)$ are integers, so the result of adding two binomials, $(ax + b) + (cx + d)$, is also a polynomial.

Expanding this argument, you can use like terms to simplify the sum of any polynomials. Consider the sum of the polynomials.

$$\left(ax^3 + bx^2 + cx + d\right) + \left(px^3 + qx^2 + rx + s\right)$$

The result of this sum is a polynomial.

$$(a + p)x^3 + (b + q)x^2 + (c + r)x + (d + s) \ \blacksquare$$

> **Remember** The degree of a monomial is the sum of the exponents of its variable factors. The degree of a polynomial is the degree of the monomial with the greatest degree.

Operations Under Which Polynomials Are Not Closed

EXAMPLE 3

Give a counterexample to show that polynomials are not closed under division.

SOLUTION
There are many instances in which polynomials are not closed under division. For instance, consider $(x - 4) \div \left(x^2 - 4x\right)$.

$$\frac{x - 4}{x^2 - 4x} = \frac{x - 4}{x(x - 4)} = \frac{1}{x}$$

A monomial cannot have a variable in a denominator, so $\frac{1}{x}$ is not a polynomial. $\blacksquare$

Multiplying Polynomials

To multiply polynomials, use various properties, including
the distributive property.

Multiplying Two Monomials

To multiply monomials, rearrange the factors so that the constants are
grouped together and variable factors with the same base are grouped
together. In other words, just put the constants together, the x's together,
the y's together, and so on.

EXAMPLE 1

Multiply $-3x^3y^2z^6 \cdot 2x^4y$.

SOLUTION

$-3x^3y^2z^6 \cdot 2x^4y = -3 \cdot 2 \cdot x^3x^4 \cdot y^2y \cdot z^6$ Commutative and Associative Properties

$\qquad\qquad\qquad = -6x^7y^3z^6$ Product of Powers ■

Multiplying a Polynomial by a Monomial

The distributive property states that for any real numbers a, b, and c,
$a(b + c) = ab + ac$. The distributive property also applies when the
order is changed or when there are more than two terms in the group.
For example,

$$(b + c)a = ba + ca \text{ and } a(b + c + d) = ab + ac + ad.$$

EXAMPLE 2

Multiply.

$$5a\left(2a^2 - 7a - 4\right)$$

SOLUTION

$$5a\left(2a^2 - 7a - 4\right) = 5a \cdot 2a^2 + 5a \cdot (-7a) + 5a \cdot (-4) \qquad \text{Distributive Property}$$

$$= 10a^3 - 35a^2 - 20a \qquad \text{Multiply the monomials.} \ \blacksquare$$

Multiplying a Polynomial by a Polynomial

EXAMPLE 3

Multiply and simplify.

A $(3x + 2)(x - 1)$

SOLUTION

$$(3x + 2)(x - 1) = 3x(x - 1) + 2(x - 1) \qquad$$ Think of $(x - 1)$ as a single quantity. Apply the distributive property. Multiply $(x - 1)$ by $3x$ and then by 2.

$$= 3x \cdot x + 3x \cdot (-1) + 2 \cdot x + 2 \cdot (-1) \qquad$$ Apply the distributive property to multiply $3x(x - 1)$. Apply the distributive property to multiply $2(x - 1)$.

$$= 3x^2 - 3x + 2x - 2 \qquad$$ Multiply the monomials.

$$= 3x^2 - x - 2 \qquad$$ Combine like terms.

B $(x+3)(x^2-2x-1)$

SOLUTION

$$(x+3)(x^2-2x-1) = x(x^2-2x-1) + 3(x^2-2x-1)$$
$$= x \cdot x^2 + x \cdot (-2x) + x \cdot (-1) + 3 \cdot x^2 + 3 \cdot (-2x) + 3 \cdot (-1)$$
$$= x^3 - 2x^2 - x + 3x^2 - 6x - 3$$
$$= x^3 + x^2 - 7x - 3$$

C $(x^3+2x^2-x)(x^2-4x-3)$

SOLUTION

Use the distributive property to multiply.

$$(x^3+2x^2-x)(x^2-4x-3) = x^3(x^2-4x-3) + 2x^2(x^2-4x-3) - x(x^2-4x-3)$$
$$= x^3 \cdot x^2 + x^3 \cdot (-4x) + x^3 \cdot (-3) + 2x^2 \cdot x^2 + 2x^2 \cdot (-4x)$$
$$+ 2x^2 \cdot (-3) - x \cdot x^2 - x \cdot (-4x) - x \cdot (-3)$$
$$= x^5 - 4x^4 - 3x^3 + 2x^4 - 8x^3 - 6x^2 - x^3 + 4x^2 + 3x$$
$$= x^5 - 2x^4 - 12x^3 - 2x^2 + 3x \blacksquare$$

Multiplying Two Binomials Using the FOIL Method

When you apply the distributive property to multiply two polynomials, each term in one polynomial is multiplied by each term in the other polynomial. When both polynomials are binomials, you can use the FOIL method as a way to organize your steps. The letters of the word **FOIL** stand for **First, Outer, Inner,** and **Last.**

▶ **Think About It** The FOIL method combines the distributive property and the commutative property.

EXAMPLE 4

Multiply $(x + 5)(3x - 2)$.

SOLUTION

$$\overset{\text{First} \quad \text{Outer} \quad \text{Inner} \quad \text{Last}}{(x + 5)(3x - 2) = 3x^2 \ - \ 2x \ + \ 15x \ - \ 10}$$

$$= 3x^2 - 2x + 15x - 10 \qquad \text{Identify like terms.}$$

$$= 3x^2 + 13x - 10 \qquad \text{Combine like terms.} \ \blacksquare$$

Writing Polynomial Models for Areas of Polygons

Polynomials can be used to represent areas of plane figures.

EXAMPLE 5

A Write a simplified polynomial to represent the area of the rectangle.

SOLUTION

Use the formula for the area of a rectangle.

$3x + 1$

$x + 4$

$\text{area} = \text{length} \times \text{width}$

$$A = (3x + 1)(x + 4)$$

$$= 3x^2 + 12x + x + 4 \qquad \text{FOIL method}$$

$$= 3x^2 + 13x + 4 \qquad \text{Combine like terms.}$$

B Use two different methods to write a simplified polynomial that represents the area of the large square.

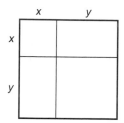

SOLUTION

Method 1 The area of the large square is the sum of the four areas.

$$x^2 + xy + xy + y^2, \text{ or } x^2 + 2xy + y^2$$

Method 2 The length of each side of the large square is $x + y$. Use the formula for the area of a square.

area = side length $\times$ side length

$$A = (x + y)(x + y)$$
$$= x^2 + xy + xy + y^2 \qquad \text{FOIL method}$$
$$= x^2 + 2xy + y^2 \qquad \text{Combine like terms.} \blacksquare$$

Factoring Patterns

Polynomials are written in many different forms, some of which have recognizable factoring patterns.

Factoring the Greatest Common Monomial Factor

When all the terms of a polynomial have a common factor, you can use the distributive property to factor it out, so it is usually a good first thing to look for when factoring a polynomial.

EXAMPLE 1

Factor the greatest common monomial factor from $16x^3 - 12x^2 + 24x$.

SOLUTION

Step 1 Find the greatest common factor (GCF) of the polynomial. The GCF of the coefficients 16, 12, and 24 is 4, while the GCF of the variable expressions x^3, x^2, and x is x. So the GCF of the polynomial is $4x$.

Step 2 Factor out the GCF.

$$16x^3 - 12x^2 + 24x = 4x\left(4x^2 - 3x + 6\right)$$ ■

▶ **Think About It** Finding the GCF of a polynomial is really finding the GCF of the terms of the polynomial.

Factoring Special Patterns

You can use factoring patterns of special products to factor some polynomials.

<table>
<tr><td colspan="2" align="center">**Factoring Patterns**</td></tr>
<tr><td>Pattern</td><td>Example</td></tr>
<tr><td>Difference of Squares
$a^2 - b^2 = (a - b)(a + b)$</td><td>$x^2 - 16 = (x - 4)(x + 4)$</td></tr>
<tr><td>Perfect Square Trinomial
$a^2 + 2ab + b^2 = (a + b)^2$
$a^2 - 2ab + b^2 = (a - b)^2$</td><td>$x^2 + 10x + 25 = (x + 5)^2$
$x^2 - 10x + 25 = (x - 5)^2$</td></tr>
<tr><td>Difference of Cubes
$a^3 - b^3 = (a - b)(a^2 + ab + b^2)$</td><td>$x^3 - 8 = (x - 2)(x^2 + 2x + 4)$</td></tr>
<tr><td>Sum of Cubes
$a^3 + b^3 = (a + b)(a^2 - ab + b^2)$</td><td>$x^3 + 8 = (x + 2)(x^2 - 2x + 4)$</td></tr>
</table>

EXAMPLE 2

Factor.

A $9x^2 - 121$

SOLUTION

The binomial $9x^2 - 121$ can be written as $(3x)^2 - 11^2$ and can be factored with the difference of squares pattern.

$$9x^2 - 121 = (3x - 11)(3x + 11)$$

▶ **Think About It** The difference of two squares is a binomial that factors into the product of two binomials.

B $x^3 - 64$

SOLUTION

The binomial $x^3 - 64$ can be written as $x^3 - 4^3$ and can be factored with the difference of cubes pattern.

$$x^3 - 64 = (x - 4)(x^2 + 4x + 16)$$

C $x^2 - 14x + 49$

SOLUTION

The trinomial $x^2 - 14x + 49$ can be written as $x^2 - 2 \cdot 7x + 7^2$ and can be factored with the perfect square pattern.

$$x^2 - 14x + 49 = (x - 7)^2$$

D $2x^3 + 64x^2$

SOLUTION

The binomial $2x^3 + 64x^2$ has a common monomial $2x^2$ that can be factored out.

$$2x^3 + 64x^2 = 2x^2(x + 32)$$

E $x^2 + 36$

SOLUTION

The binomial $x^2 + 36$ is a sum of two squares that cannot be factored.

> **Think About It** The sum of two squares cannot be factored with real numbers.

F $x^3 + 125$

SOLUTION

The binomial $x^3 + 125$ can be written as $x^3 + 5^3$ and can be factored with the sum of cubes pattern.

$$x^3 + 125 = (x + 5)(x^2 - 5x + 25) \blacksquare$$

Factoring Trinomials of the Form $x^2 + bx + c$

When you use the FOIL method to multiply two binomials $(x + s)(x + t)$, you can write the product as follows:

$$x^2 + tx + sx + st = x^2 + (t + s)x + st$$

Some trinomials of the form $x^2 + bx + c$ can be factored as

$$x^2 + bx + c = x^2 + (t + s)x + st$$
$$= (x + s)(x + t)$$

where $t + s = b$ and $st = c$.

You can use this pattern to help you with a guess-and-check strategy to factor trinomials of the form $x^2 + bx + c$.

▶ **Think About It** If there are no values for *s* and *t* with product *c* and sum *b*, then the polynomial can't be factored. Any polynomial that can't be factored is a **prime polynomial**.

EXAMPLE 3

Factor.

A $x^2 + 15x + 36$

SOLUTION

In this trinomial, *b* and *c* are both positive, so *s* and *t* are both positive. Find the solution by "guessing" the factors of 36 and checking to determine which factor pair has a sum of 15.

$$x^2 + 15x + 36 = (x + 3)(x + 12)$$

Positive factors of 36	Sum of the factors
1, 36	37
2, 18	20
3, 12	**15**
4, 9	13
6, 6	12

B $x^2 + 5x - 14$

SOLUTION

In this trinomial, c is negative, so s and t have opposite signs. Find the solution by "guessing" the factors of -14 and checking to determine which factor pair has a sum of 5.

$$x^2 + 5x - 14 = (x - 2)(x + 7)$$

Opposite-sign factors of -14	Sum of the factors
1, -14	-13
-1, 14	13
-2, 7	**5**
2, -7	-5

C $x^2 - 6x - 7$

SOLUTION

In this trinomial, c is negative, so s and t have opposite signs. Find the solution by "guessing" the factors of -7 and checking to determine which factor pair has a sum of -6.

$$x^2 - 6x - 7 = (x + 1)(x - 7)$$

Opposite-sign factors of -7	Sum of the factors
1, -7	**-6**
-1, 7	6

D $x^2 - 13x + 22$

SOLUTION

In this trinomial, b is negative and c is positive, so s and t are both negative. Find the solution by guessing the factors of 22 and checking to determine which factor pair has a sum of -13.

$$x^2 - 13x + 22 = (x - 2)(x - 11)$$

Negative factors of 22	Sum of the factors
$-1, -22$	-23
$-2, -11$	**-13**

E $x^2 - 7x + 9$

SOLUTION

In this trinomial, b is negative and c is positive, so s and t are both negative. Write the negative factors of 9 and check to determine which pair has a sum of -7.

None of the factor pairs have a sum of -7, so this trinomial cannot be factored and is prime.

Negative factors of 9	Sum of the factors
$-1, -9$	-10
$-3, -3$	-6

More Factoring Patterns

Polynomials are written in many different forms, some of which are recognizable factoring patterns.

Factoring and Checking the Sum and Difference of Cube Patterns

You can check whether your factors are correct by multiplying them together.

EXAMPLE 1

Factor and use multiplication to check the answer.

A $27x^3 - 64$

SOLUTION

The binomial $27x^3 - 64$ can be written as $(3x)^3 - 4^3$ and can be factored with the difference of cubes pattern.

$$27x^3 - 64 = (3x - 4)\left(9x^2 + 12x + 16\right)$$

CHECK

$$
\begin{array}{r}
9x^2 + 12x + 16 \\
\times \qquad\qquad 3x - 4 \\
\hline
-36x^2 - 48x - 64 \\
27x^3 + 36x^2 + 48x \\
\hline
27x^3 - 64 \ \checkmark
\end{array}
$$

B $8x^3 + 125$

SOLUTION

The binomial $8x^3 + 125$ can be written as $(2x)^3 + 5^3$ and can be factored with the sum of cubes pattern.

$$8x^3 + 125 = (2x + 5)(4x^2 - 10x + 25)$$

CHECK

$$
\begin{array}{r}
4x^2 - 10x + 25 \\
\times \qquad\quad 2x + \ \ 5 \\
\hline
20x^2 - 50x + 125 \\
8x^3 - 20x^2 + \ 50x \qquad\qquad \\
\hline
8x^3 \qquad\qquad\qquad + 125 \ \checkmark \ \blacksquare
\end{array}
$$

Factoring by Grouping

Some polynomials can be factored by grouping. With this method, a common polynomial term is factored from pairs of terms.

EXAMPLE 2

Factor.

A $x^3 + 2x^2 - 25x - 50$

SOLUTION

Group the polynomial by terms and factor out a common binomial from each group.

$$
\begin{aligned}
x^3 + 2x^2 - 25x - 50 &= \left(x^3 + 2x^2\right) - (25x + 50) && \text{Group into pairs of terms.} \\
&= x^2(x + 2) - 25(x + 2) && \text{Factor the common binomial.} \\
&= \left(x^2 - 25\right)(x + 2) && \text{Distributive Property} \\
&= (x - 5)(x + 5)(x + 2) && \text{Factor the difference of squares.}
\end{aligned}
$$

B $2y^2 + 5y - 7$

SOLUTION

It doesn't look like you can group this polynomial, but if you can find a way to split the middle term, you will be able to group the polynomial by its terms.

$$2 \cdot (-7) = -14 \qquad \text{Find the product } ac.$$

$$-2, 7 \qquad \text{Find two factors of } -14 \text{ whose sum is 5.}$$

$$2y^2 - 2y + 7y - 7 \qquad \text{Rewrite } 5y \text{ as the sum of } -2y \text{ and } 7y.$$

$$= \left(2y^2 - 2y\right) + \left(7y - 7\right) \qquad \text{Group pairs of terms.}$$

$$= 2y\left(y - 1\right) + 7\left(y - 1\right) \qquad \text{Find a common binomial factor for each group.}$$

$$= \left(2y + 7\right)\left(y - 1\right) \qquad \text{Distributive Property} \ \blacksquare$$

Factoring Completely

To factor a polynomial completely, first look for a greatest common factor. If you find one, factor it out of the polynomial. Examine what remains. Look for special factors (difference of squares, difference of cubes, sum of cubes, perfect square trinomial) and try to factor by grouping. You can use the guess-and-check strategy to factor trinomials of the form $x^2 + bx + c$.

▶ **Remember** If a polynomial cannot be factored, it is called prime.

EXAMPLE 3

Factor completely.

A $4x^4 - 4$

SOLUTION

$$4x^4 - 4 = 4\left(x^4 - 1\right) \qquad \text{Factor out the greatest common monomial factor.}$$

$$= 4\left(x^2 + 1\right)\left(x^2 - 1\right) \qquad \text{Factor the difference of squares.}$$

$$= 4\left(x^2 + 1\right)(x + 1)(x - 1) \qquad \text{Factor another difference of squares.}$$

B $-32z^2 - 48z - 18$

SOLUTION

$-32z^2 - 48z - 18 = -2(16z^2 + 24z + 9)$ Factor out the greatest common monomial factor.

$\qquad\qquad\qquad = -2(4z + 3)^2$ Factor the perfect square trinomial. ■

EXAMPLE 4

Factor completely. If the polynomial is not factorable, write *prime*.

A $20x^4 + 80x^3 - 5x^2 - 20x$

SOLUTION

$20x^4 + 80x^3 - 5x^2 - 20x$

$\qquad = 5x\left(4x^3 + 16x^2 - x - 4\right)$ Factor the greatest common monomial factor.

$\qquad = 5x\left[\left(4x^3 + 16x^2\right) - (x + 4)\right]$ Group into pairs of terms.

$\qquad = 5x\left[4x^2(x + 4) - (x + 4)\right]$ Find a common binomial factor for each group.

$\qquad = 5x\left(4x^2 - 1\right)(x + 4)$ Distributive Property

$\qquad = 5x(2x + 1)(2x - 1)(x + 4)$ Factor the difference of squares.

B $25x^4 + 16y^6$

SOLUTION

The binomial $25x^4 + 16y^6$ is prime because it has no common monomial factors and is the sum of two squares, $\left(5x^2\right)^2$ and $\left(4y^3\right)^2$.

C $40a^3 + 135b^6$

SOLUTION

$40a^3 + 135b^6 = 5\left(8a^3 + 27b^6\right)$ Factor the greatest common monomial factor.

$\qquad = 5\left[(2a)^3 + \left(3b^2\right)^3\right]$ Rewrite the factor as the sum of cubes.

$\qquad = 5\left[\left(2a + 3b^2\right)\left((2a)^2 - 2a \cdot 3b^2 + \left(3b^2\right)^2\right)\right]$ Factor the sum of cubes.

$\qquad = 5\left(2a + 3b^2\right)\left(4a^2 - 6ab^2 + 9b^4\right)$ Simplify.

D $300 - 3(x - 1)^2$

SOLUTION

$300 - 3(x - 1)^2 = 3\left[100 - (x - 1)^2\right]$ Factor the greatest common monomial factor.

$= 3\left[\mathbf{10} - (\mathbf{x} - \mathbf{1})\right]\left[\mathbf{10} + (\mathbf{x} - \mathbf{1})\right]$ Factor the difference of two squares.

$= 3(10 - x + 1)(10 + x - 1)$ Simplify.

$= 3(-x + 11)(x + 9)$ Simplify.

E $1 - t^6$

SOLUTION

$1 - t^6 = \left(1 + t^3\right)\left(1 - t^3\right)$ Factor the difference of squares.

$= (1 + t)\left(1 - 2t + t^2\right)(1 - t)\left(1 + 2t + t^2\right)$ Factor the sum of cubes and the difference of cubes. ■

Solving Polynomial Equations

To solve a polynomial equation, set the equation equal to zero and factor completely. Then apply the zero product property to find the solutions of the equation.

Zero Product Property

The zero product property states that if the product of two or more expressions is zero, then one or more of the expressions are equal to zero.

Solving a Polynomial Equation in Factored Form

Set each factor equal to zero to find all the solutions of the polynomial equation.

EXAMPLE 1

Solve the equation.

A $(x + 1)(5x - 4) = 0$

SOLUTION

Set each factor equal to zero and solve.

$$x + 1 = 0 \qquad\qquad 5x - 4 = 0$$
$$x = -1 \qquad\qquad 5x = 4$$
$$x = \frac{4}{5}$$

The solution set is $\left\{ -1, \dfrac{4}{5} \right\}$.

> ► **Think About It** Always be certain that the original equation is set equal to zero before solving.

B $3(2x + 1)(x - 2) = 0$

SOLUTION

For each factor containing a variable, set the factor equal to zero and solve.

$$2x + 1 = 0 \qquad x - 2 = 0$$
$$2x = -1 \qquad\quad x = 2$$
$$x = -\frac{1}{2}$$

The solution set is $\left\{ -\frac{1}{2}, 2 \right\}$. ■

Using Factoring Patterns to Solve a Polynomial Equation

You can use factoring patterns to help solve some polynomial equations, but do not try to factor and use the zero product property unless the equation has zero alone on one side.

EXAMPLE 2

Use factoring and the zero product property to solve the equation.

A $4x^2 - 16 = 9$

SOLUTION

Set the equation equal to zero first and then factor the polynomial.

$$4x^2 - 16 = 9$$

$$4x^2 - 25 = 0 \qquad \text{Transform the equation so it has zero alone on one side of the equals sign.}$$

$$(2x - 5)(2x + 5) = 0 \qquad \text{Factor the difference of squares.}$$

Apply the zero product property.

$$2x - 5 = 0 \qquad 2x + 5 = 0$$
$$2x = 5 \qquad\quad 2x = -5$$
$$x = \frac{5}{2} \qquad\quad x = -\frac{5}{2}$$

The solution set is $\left\{ -\frac{5}{2}, \frac{5}{2} \right\}$.

B $2x^3 + 4x^2 + 2x = 0$

SOLUTION

Factor the polynomial completely and then solve the equation.

$$2x^3 + 4x^2 + 2x = 0$$
$$2x\left(x^2 + 2x + 1\right) = 0 \qquad \text{Factor out the greatest common monomial.}$$
$$2x(x + 1)(x + 1) = 0 \qquad \text{Factor the perfect square trinomial.}$$

Apply the zero product property.

$$2x - 0 \qquad x + 1 - 0 \qquad x + 1 - 0$$
$$x - 0 \qquad\quad x - -1 \qquad\quad x - -1$$

The solution set is $\{-1, 0\}$.

> **Think About It** Because the factor $(x + 1)$ appears two times in the factored form of the equation, -1 is a solution with multiplicity 2.

C $x^3 + 3x^2 - 4x - 12 = 0$

SOLUTION

Factor by grouping and then solve the equation.

$$x^3 + 3x^2 - 4x - 12 = 0$$
$$\left(x^3 + 3x^2\right) + (-4x - 12) = 0 \qquad \text{Group monomials with a common factor.}$$
$$x^2(x + 3) + (-4)(x + 3) = 0 \qquad \text{Factor out the greatest common monomial for each group.}$$
$$\left(x^2 - 4\right)(x + 3) = 0 \qquad \text{Distributive Property}$$
$$(x + 2)(x - 2)(x + 3) = 0 \qquad \text{Factor the difference of squares.}$$

Apply the zero product property.

$$x + 2 = 0 \qquad x - 2 = 0 \qquad x + 3 = 0$$
$$x = -2 \qquad x = 2 \qquad x = -3$$

The solution set is $\{-3, -2, 2\}$.

D $8x^4 - 15x^3 = 2x^2$

> ▶ **Remember** To solve a polynomial equation, set the equation equal to zero first and then factor the polynomial.

SOLUTION

Factor out any common factors. Factor the remaining trinomial. Then solve the equation.

$$8x^4 - 15x^3 - 2x^2 = 0$$
$$x^2\left(8x^2 - 15x - 2\right) = 0 \qquad \text{Factor out the GCF.}$$
$$x^2(8x + 1)(x - 2) = 0 \qquad \text{Distributive Property}$$

Apply the zero product property.

$$x^2 = 0 \qquad\qquad 8x + 1 = 0 \qquad\qquad x - 2 = 0$$
$$x = 0 \qquad\qquad 8x = -1 \qquad\qquad x = 2$$
$$x = -\frac{1}{8}$$

The solution set is $\left\{-\dfrac{1}{8}, 0, 2\right\}$. ■

Checking the Solutions of a Polynomial Equation

To verify that the solutions found are correct, substitute each one in the original equation. All correct solutions will make the original equation true.

EXAMPLE 3

Use factoring to solve the equation and check the solutions.

$$(2x + 1)^3 - (2x + 1) = 0$$

SOLUTION

Factor the polynomial completely.

$$(2x + 1)^3 - (2x + 1) = 0$$

$$\mathbf{(2x + 1)}\left[(2x + 1)^2 - 1\right] = 0 \qquad \text{Factor out the common binomial.}$$

$$(2x + 1)\left[(2x + 1) - 1\right]\left[(2x + 1) + 1\right] = 0 \qquad \text{Factor the difference of squares inside the brackets.}$$

$$(2x + 1)(2x)(2x + 2) = 0 \qquad \text{Simplify inside the brackets.}$$

Apply the zero product property.

$$
\begin{array}{ccc}
2x + 1 - 0 & 2x = 0 & 2x + 2 = 0 \\
2x = -1 & x = 0 & 2x = -2 \\
x = -\dfrac{1}{2} & & x = -1
\end{array}
$$

Check each solution by substituting into the original equation.

Let $x = -\dfrac{1}{2}$.

$$(2x + 1)^3 - (2x + 1) = \left(2 \cdot \left(-\frac{1}{2}\right) + 1\right)^3 - \left(2 \cdot \left(-\frac{1}{2}\right) + 1\right)$$

$$= (-1 + 1)^3 - (-1 + 1)$$

$$= 0 - 0$$

$$= 0 \checkmark$$

Let $x = 0$.

$$(2x + 1)^3 - (2x + 1) = (2 \cdot 0 + 1)^3 - (2 \cdot 0 + 1)$$
$$= 1^3 - 1$$
$$= 1 - 1$$
$$= 0 \checkmark$$

Let $x = -1$.

$$(2x + 1)^3 - (2x + 1) = (2 \cdot (-1) + 1)^3 - (2 \cdot (-1) + 1)$$
$$= (-2 + 1)^3 - (-2 + 1)$$
$$= (-1)^3 - (-1)$$
$$= -1 + 1$$
$$= 0 \checkmark$$

Each solution checks out correctly. The solution set is $\left\{ -1, -\frac{1}{2}, 0 \right\}$. ■

Solving Equations with Complex Solutions

Some quadratic equations can be solved by finding the square root of each side of the equation.

Solving a Quadratic Equation with Real Solutions

The square root property says that if $x^2 = a$, then $x = \pm\sqrt{a}$. If $a > 0$, then the solutions for x are real numbers.

EXAMPLE 1

Solve $4x^2 = 80$ and check the solution.

SOLUTION

$4x^2 = 80$

$x^2 = 20$ Divide both sides of the equation by 4.

$x = \pm\sqrt{20}$ Take the square root of both sides.

$x = \pm\sqrt{4} \cdot \sqrt{5}$ Product Property of Square Roots

$x = \pm 2\sqrt{5}$ Simplify.

▶ **Remember** The product property of square roots states that
$$\sqrt{ab} = \sqrt{a} \cdot \sqrt{b}$$
for real numbers $a > 0$ and $b > 0$.

CHECK

Substitute $2\sqrt{5}$ for x.   Substitute $-2\sqrt{5}$ for x.

$$4\left(2\sqrt{5}\right)^2 \overset{?}{=} 80 \qquad\quad 4\left(-2\sqrt{5}\right)^2 \overset{?}{=} 80$$
$$4 \cdot 20 \overset{?}{=} 80 \qquad\qquad\quad 4 \cdot 20 \overset{?}{=} 80$$
$$80 = 80 \checkmark \qquad\qquad\qquad 80 = 80 \checkmark$$

The solution is correct. ■

Solving a Quadratic Equation with Complex Solutions

Quadratic equations such as $x^2 = -2$ have no real-number solutions because there is no square of a real number that equals -2. Quadratic equations of this form have complex-number solutions.

Square Root Property for Imaginary Numbers

If $d > 0$, then $x^2 = -d$ has two imaginary solutions, $x = i\sqrt{d}$ and $x = -i\sqrt{d}$.

▶ **Think About It** When using the square root property, you can say you are "taking the square root of both sides."

EXAMPLE 2

Solve $3x^2 + 21 = 0$ and check the solution.

SOLUTION

$3x^2 + 21 = 0$

$\quad\quad 3x^2 = -21$ Subtract 21 from both sides.

$\quad\quad\quad x^2 = -7$ Divide both sides by 3.

$\quad\quad \sqrt{x^2} = \pm\sqrt{-7}$ Take the square root of both sides.

$\quad\quad\quad\; x = \pm i\sqrt{7}$ Simplify.

CHECK

Substitute $i\sqrt{7}$ for x.   Substitute $-i\sqrt{7}$ for x.

$3\left(i\sqrt{7}\right)^2 + 21 \overset{?}{=} 0 \quad\quad\quad 3\left(-i\sqrt{7}\right)^2 + 21 \overset{?}{=} 0$

$3\left(7i^2\right) + 21 \overset{?}{=} 0 \quad\quad\quad\quad 3\left(7i^2\right) + 21 \overset{?}{=} 0$

$\;\;3(-7) + 21 \overset{?}{=} 0 \quad\quad\quad\quad\;\; 3(-7) + 21 \overset{?}{=} 0$

$\;\;-21 \mid 21 \overset{?}{=} 0 \quad\quad\quad\quad\quad\;\; -21 + 21 \overset{?}{=} 0$

$\quad\quad\quad\quad 0 = 0\;\checkmark \quad\quad\quad\quad\quad\quad\quad\quad 0 = 0\;\checkmark$

The solution is correct. ▪

EXAMPLE 3

Solve $(x + 3)^2 = -5$ and check the solution.

SOLUTION

$\quad (x + 3)^2 = -5$

$\sqrt{(x + 3)^2} = \pm\sqrt{-5}$ Take the square root of both sides.

$\quad\quad x + 3 = \pm i\sqrt{5}$ Simplify.

$\quad\quad\quad\;\; x = -3 \pm i\sqrt{5}$ Subtract 3 from both sides.

CHECK

Substitute $-3 + i\sqrt{5}$ for x.   Substitute $-3 - i\sqrt{5}$ for x.

$\left[\left(-3 + i\sqrt{5}\right) + 3\right]^2 \overset{?}{=} -5 \quad \left[\left(-3 - i\sqrt{5}\right) + 3\right]^2 \overset{?}{=} -5$

$\quad\quad\quad\quad\left(i\sqrt{5}\right)^2 \overset{?}{=} -5 \quad\quad\quad\quad\quad\quad \left(-i\sqrt{5}\right)^2 \overset{?}{=} -5$

$\quad\quad\quad\quad\quad\;\; 5i^2 \overset{?}{=} -5 \quad\quad\quad\quad\quad\quad\quad\quad\;\; 5i^2 \overset{?}{=} 5$

$\quad\quad\quad\quad\;\; 5(-1) \overset{?}{=} -5 \quad\quad\quad\quad\quad\quad\; 5(-1) \overset{?}{=} -5$

$\quad\quad\quad\quad\quad\quad -5 = -5\;\checkmark \quad\quad\quad\quad\quad\quad\quad -5 = -5\;\checkmark$

The solution is correct. ▪

Finding an Equation, Given the Solutions

EXAMPLE 4

Find a polynomial equation in the form $p(z) = 0$ that has the given solutions.

A $z = \pm 8i$

SOLUTION

$$z = \pm 8i$$
$$z^2 = (\pm 8i)^2 \qquad \text{Square both sides.}$$
$$z^2 = 64 \cdot i^2 \qquad \text{Simplify.}$$
$$z^2 = -64$$
$$z^2 + 64 = 0 \qquad \text{Put the equation into the right form.}$$

B $z = 3 \pm i\sqrt{7}$

SOLUTION

$$z = 3 \pm i\sqrt{7}$$
$$z - 3 = \pm i\sqrt{7} \qquad \text{Subtract 3 from both sides.}$$
$$(z - 3)^2 = \left(\pm i\sqrt{7}\right)^2 \qquad \text{Square both sides.}$$
$$(z - 3)^2 = 7 \cdot i^2 \qquad \text{Simplify.}$$
$$(z - 3)^2 = -7$$
$$z^2 - 6z + 16 = 0 \qquad \text{Put the equation into the right form.} \blacksquare$$

Completing the Square

You can write any quadratic equation as a perfect square equation.

In a perfect square trinomial, the constant term is always equal to the square of half the coefficient of the x term, as shown in the examples.

$$(x + 5)^2 = x^2 + 10x + 25 = x^2 + 10x + \left(\frac{10}{2}\right)^2$$

$$(x - 4)^2 = x^2 - 8x + 16 = x^2 - 8x + \left(\frac{-8}{2}\right)^2$$

You can use this fact to turn a quadratic expression into a perfect square trinomial.

Complete the square by finding the number that should be added to each expression to change it into a perfect square trinomial.

Definition

Completing the square is the process of transforming an expression of the form $x^2 + bx$ into a perfect square trinomial by adding the term $\left(\frac{b}{2}\right)^2$ to it.

EXAMPLE 1

Find the number that should be added to the expression $x^2 + 14x$ to change it into a perfect square trinomial.

> **Think About It** The last term in a perfect square trinomial is always positive.

SOLUTION

Take half of 14 and square the result.

$$\left(\frac{14}{2}\right)^2 = 7^2 = 49$$

The number is 49.

CHECK

Determine whether $x^2 + 14x + 49$ is a perfect square trinomial.

$$x^2 + 14x + 49 = (x+7)(x+7) = (x+7)^2 \checkmark$$

The number 49 makes the expression a perfect square trinomial. ∎

Solving a Quadratic Equation by Completing the Square

Completing the square makes it possible to write any quadratic equation as a perfect square equation. Use the following steps to solve any quadratic equation by completing the square.

How to Use Completing the Square to Solve a Quadratic Equation

Step 1 Write the equation in the form $x^2 + bx = c$.

Step 2 Add $\left(\frac{b}{2}\right)^2$ to each side of the equation and simplify.

Step 3 Factor the perfect square trinomial and solve for x.

EXAMPLE 2

Transform the equation into a perfect square equation and solve.

> ▶ **Remember** Before you complete the square, the coefficient of the squared term must be 1.

A $4x^2 = 3 + 4x$

SOLUTION

Step 1 Write the equation in the form $x^2 + bx = c$ by subtracting $4x$ from each side of the equation and then dividing each side by 4.

$$4x^2 = 3 + 4x$$

$$4x^2 - 4x = 3 \qquad \text{Subtract } 4x \text{ from each side.}$$

$$x^2 - x = \frac{3}{4} \qquad \text{Divide each side by 4.}$$

> ▶ **Think About It** Do not multiply out the $\left(\dfrac{b}{2}\right)^2$ term on the left side. That way, the trinomial is easier to factor and you are less likely to make a mistake.

Step 2 Add $\left(-\dfrac{1}{2}\right)^2$ to each side.

$$x^2 - x = \frac{3}{4}$$

$$x^2 - x + \left(-\frac{1}{2}\right)^2 = \frac{3}{4} + \frac{1}{4} \qquad \text{Add } \left(-\frac{1}{2}\right)^2 = \frac{1}{4} \text{ to each side.}$$

$$x^2 - x + \left(-\frac{1}{2}\right)^2 = 1 \qquad \text{Simplify.}$$

Step 3 Factor the perfect square trinomial and solve for x.

$$x^2 - x + \left(-\frac{1}{2}\right)^2 = 1$$

$$\left(x - \frac{1}{2}\right)^2 = 1 \qquad \text{Factor the perfect square trinomial.}$$

$$\left(x - \frac{1}{2}\right) = \pm\sqrt{1} \qquad \text{Take the square root of each side.}$$

$$x = \frac{1}{2} \pm 1 \qquad \text{Add } \frac{1}{2} \text{ to each side and simplify.}$$

The solution set is $\left\{\frac{3}{2}, -\frac{1}{2}\right\}$.

▶ **Think About It** Sometimes quadratic equations have solutions that are irrational numbers.

B $x^2 + 20x + 8 = 0$

SOLUTION

Step 1 $x^2 + 20x + 8 = 0$

$$x^2 + 20x = -8 \qquad \text{Subtract 8 from each side.}$$

Step 2 $x^2 + 20x + 10^2 = -8 + 100 \qquad \text{Add } \left(\frac{20}{2}\right)^2 = 100 \text{ to each side.}$

$$x^2 + 20x + 10^2 = 92 \qquad \text{Simplify.}$$

Step 3 $(x + 10)^2 = 92 \qquad \text{Factor the perfect square trinomial.}$

$$x + 10 = \pm\sqrt{92} \qquad \text{Take the square root of each side.}$$

$$x + 10 = \pm 2\sqrt{23} \qquad \text{Simplify.}$$

$$x = -10 \pm 2\sqrt{23} \qquad \text{Subtract 10 from each side.}$$

The solution set is $\{-10 + 2\sqrt{23}, -10 - 2\sqrt{23}\}$. ■

Application: Art

EXAMPLE 3

An 8 in. by 10 in. painting is framed so that the total area of the painting with the frame is 100 in^2. Find the width of the frame to the nearest hundredth of an inch.

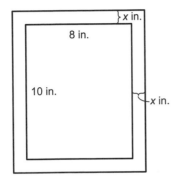

SOLUTION

Use the problem-solving plan.

Step 1 *Identify* Find the width of the frame.

Step 2 *Strategize* The length and width of the frame is x inches. Write the length and width of the painting, with the frame, in terms of x.

The total width in inches is $8 + x + x = 8 + 2x$.

The total length in inches is $10 + x + x = 10 + 2x$.

Step 3 *Set Up* Use the length and width to write and solve an equation for the area.

$(8 + 2x)(10 + 2x) = 100$ Area is length times width.

Step 4 *Solve*

$$(8 + 2x)(10 + 2x) = 100$$

$$80 + 36x + 4x^2 = 100 \qquad \text{Multiply the binomials.}$$

$$20 + 9x + x^2 = 25 \qquad \text{Divide each side by 4.}$$

$$9x + x^2 = 5 \qquad \text{Subtract 20 from each side.}$$

$$x^2 + 9x = 5 \qquad \text{Rearrange the terms.}$$

$$x^2 + 9x + \left(\frac{9}{2}\right)^2 = 5 + \frac{81}{4} \qquad \text{Add } \left(\frac{9}{2}\right)^2 = \frac{81}{4} \text{ to each side.}$$

$$\left(x + \frac{9}{2}\right)^2 = \frac{101}{4} \qquad \text{Factor the perfect square trinomial and simplify.}$$

$$\left(x + \frac{9}{2}\right) = \pm\sqrt{\frac{101}{4}} \qquad \text{Take the square root of each side.}$$

$$x = -\frac{9}{2} \pm \frac{\sqrt{101}}{2} \qquad \text{Subtract } \frac{9}{2} \text{ from each side.}$$

$$x = -\frac{9}{2} + \frac{\sqrt{101}}{2} \quad \text{or} \quad x = -\frac{9}{2} - \frac{\sqrt{101}}{2} \quad \text{Simplify.}$$

$$x \approx 0.5249 \qquad\qquad\quad x \approx -9.5249$$

The width of the frame must be positive, so you can disregard the negative solution. The width is about 0.52 in.

Step 5 *Check*

$$(8 + 2x)(10 + 2x) = 100$$

$$(8 + 2 \cdot \textbf{0.52})(10 + 2 \cdot \textbf{0.52}) \stackrel{?}{=} 100$$

$$9.04 \cdot 11.04 \stackrel{?}{=} 100$$

$$99.80 \approx 100 \checkmark$$

The approximate solution is accurate. ■

The Quadratic Formula

You can solve any quadratic equation in standard form using the quadratic formula.

Use completing the square on the standard form of a quadratic equation, $ax^2 + bx + c = 0$, to derive the **quadratic formula**.

$$ax^2 + bx + c = 0$$

$$ax^2 + bx = -c \qquad \text{Subtract } c \text{ from each side.}$$

$$x^2 + \frac{b}{a}x = -\frac{c}{a} \qquad \text{Divide each side by } a.$$

$$x^2 + \frac{b}{a}x + \left(\frac{b}{2a}\right)^2 = -\frac{c}{a} + \frac{b^2}{4a^2} \qquad \text{Add } \left(\frac{b}{2a}\right)^2 = \frac{b^2}{4a^2} \text{ to each side.}$$

$$x^2 + \frac{b}{a}x + \left(\frac{b}{2a}\right)^2 = -\frac{4ac}{4a^2} + \frac{b^2}{4a^2} \qquad \text{Multiply } \frac{c}{a} \text{ by } \frac{4a}{4a} \text{ to get a common denominator.}$$

$$x^2 + \frac{b}{a}x + \left(\frac{b}{2a}\right)^2 = \frac{b^2 - 4ac}{4a^2} \qquad \text{Simplify.}$$

$$\left(x + \frac{b}{2a}\right)^2 = \frac{b^2 - 4ac}{4a^2} \qquad \text{Factor the perfect square trinomial.}$$

$$\left(x + \frac{b}{2a}\right) = \pm\sqrt{\frac{b^2 - 4ac}{4a^2}} \qquad \text{Take the square root of each side.}$$

$$x + \frac{b}{2a} = \pm\frac{\sqrt{b^2 - 4ac}}{2a} \qquad \text{Simplify.}$$

$$x = -\frac{b}{2a} \pm \frac{\sqrt{b^2 - 4ac}}{2a} \qquad \text{Subtract } \frac{b}{2a} \text{ from each side.}$$

$$x = \frac{-b \pm \sqrt{b^2 - 4ac}}{2a} \qquad \text{Simplify.}$$

Using the Quadratic Formula

Quadratic Formula

For a quadratic equation written in standard form, $ax^2 + bx + c = 0$, where $a \neq 0$, the solutions of the equation can be found using the quadratic formula.

$$x = \frac{-b \pm \sqrt{b^2 - 4ac}}{2a}$$

To use the quadratic formula, write the quadratic equation you are trying to solve in standard form, and then identify the values of a, b, and c.

EXAMPLE 1

Solve the equation. Estimate irrational solutions to the nearest tenth.

A $x^2 + 9x - 22 = 0$

SOLUTION

Since the equation is in standard form, identify a, b, and c: $a = 1$, $b = 9$, and $c = -22$.

$$x = \frac{-b \pm \sqrt{b^2 - 4ac}}{2a}$$

$$x = \frac{-9 \pm \sqrt{9^2 - 4 \cdot 1 \cdot (-22)}}{2 \cdot 1} \qquad \text{Substitute values for } a, b, \text{ and } c.$$

$$x = \frac{-9 \pm \sqrt{81 - (-88)}}{2} \qquad \text{Simplify the radicand.}$$

$$x = \frac{-9 \pm \sqrt{169}}{2} \qquad \text{Simplify.}$$

$$x = \frac{-9 \pm 13}{2} \qquad \text{Evaluate the square root.}$$

$$x = \frac{-9 + 13}{2} \text{ or } x = \frac{-9 - 13}{2} \qquad \text{Write } x = \frac{-9 \pm 13}{2} \text{ as two equations.}$$

$$x = \frac{4}{2} \qquad\qquad x = \frac{-22}{2} \qquad \text{Simplify each numerator.}$$

$$x = 2 \qquad\qquad x = -11 \qquad \text{Divide.}$$

The solution set is $\{2, -11\}$.

B $x^2 + 3x = 5$

SOLUTION

Write the equation in standard form by subtracting 5 from each side.

$$x^2 + 3x = 5$$

$$x^2 + 3x - 5 = 0 \qquad \text{Subtract 5 from each side.}$$

Identify a, b, and c: $a = 1$, $b = 3$, and $c = -5$.

$$x = \frac{-b \pm \sqrt{b^2 - 4ac}}{2a}$$

$$x = \frac{-3 \pm \sqrt{3^2 - 4 \cdot 1 \cdot (-5)}}{2 \cdot 1} \qquad \text{Substitute values for } a, b, \text{ and } c.$$

$$x = \frac{-3 \pm \sqrt{9 - (-20)}}{2} \qquad \text{Simplify the radicand.}$$

$$x = \frac{-3 \pm \sqrt{29}}{2} \qquad \text{Simplify.}$$

$$x = \frac{-3 + \sqrt{29}}{2} \approx 1.2 \text{ or } x = \frac{-3 - \sqrt{29}}{2} \approx -4.2 \qquad \text{Write } x = \frac{-3 \pm \sqrt{29}}{2} \text{ as two equations.}$$

The solution set is $\{1.2, -4.2\}$. ∎

Using the Discriminant

The **discriminant** is the radicand $b^2 - 4ac$ in the quadratic formula. If you know the value of the discriminant, you can determine how many solutions the equation has and whether the solutions are rational, irrational, or nonreal.

Property

The equation, $ax^2 + bx + c = 0$, where $a \neq 0$, has

- Two rational solutions if $b^2 - 4ac > 0$ and $b^2 - 4ac$ is a perfect square.
- Two irrational solutions if $b^2 - 4ac > 0$ and $b^2 - 4ac$ is not a perfect square.
- One rational solution if $b^2 - 4ac = 0$.
- No real solutions if $b^2 - 4ac < 0$.

EXAMPLE 2

Use the discriminant to determine the number and type of solutions the equation has.

> ▶ **Remember** A number is a perfect square if it can be written as the square of a rational number.

A $2x^2 + 13x + 15 = 0$

SOLUTION

Identify a, b, and c: $a = 2$, $b = 13$, and $c = 15$.

$$b^2 - 4ac = 13^2 - 4 \cdot 2 \cdot 15 = 169 - 120 = 49$$

The discriminant, 49, is positive and is a perfect square, so the equation has two rational solutions.

B $x^2 - \dfrac{1}{2}x + \dfrac{1}{16} = 0$

SOLUTION

Identify a, b, and c: $a = 1$, $b = -\dfrac{1}{2}$, and $c = \dfrac{1}{16}$.

$$b^2 - 4ac = \left(-\frac{1}{2}\right)^2 - 4 \cdot 1 \cdot \frac{1}{16} = \frac{1}{4} - \frac{1}{4} = 0$$

The discriminant is zero, so the equation has one rational solution.

C $x^2 + 5 = 0$

SOLUTION

Identify a, b, and c: $a = 1$, $b = 0$, and $c = 5$.

$$b^2 - 4ac = 0^2 - 4 \cdot 1 \cdot 5 = 0 - 20 = -20$$

The discriminant, -20, is negative, so the equation has no real solutions. ▪

Application: Determining Whether a Polynomial Is Factorable

The expression $ax^2 + bx + c$ is factorable if the solutions to the equation $ax^2 + bx + c = 0$ are rational. The expression $ax^2 + bx + c$ is factorable if the discriminant is either a perfect square or zero.

EXAMPLE 3

Determine whether the polynomial is factorable.

A $30x^2 - 31x - 44$

SOLUTION

Find the discriminant.

$$a = 30, b = -31, \text{ and } c = -44$$

$$\begin{aligned} b^2 - 4ac &= (-31)^2 - 4 \cdot 30 \cdot (-44) \\ &= 961 + 5280 \\ &= 6241 \end{aligned}$$

Because $6241 = 69^2$, it is a perfect square, so $30x^2 - 31x - 44$ is factorable.

B $27x^2 + 14x - 15$

SOLUTION

Find the discriminant.

$$a = 27, b = 14, \text{ and } c = -15$$

$$\begin{aligned} b^2 - 4ac &= 14^2 - 4 \cdot 27 \cdot (-15) \\ &= 196 + 1620 \\ &= 1816 \end{aligned}$$

Because 1816 is not a perfect square, $27x^2 + 14x - 15$ is not factorable. ▪

Formulas with Quadratics

Many formulas include squared variables. To solve for a squared variable in a formula, you can use the same techniques you use to solve quadratic equations with a single variable.

EXAMPLE 1

Solve the formula $F = \dfrac{GmM}{r^2}$ for r.

SOLUTION

$$F = \frac{GmM}{r^2}$$

$$r^2 F = GmM \qquad\qquad \text{Multiply each side by } r^2.$$

$$r^2 = \frac{GmM}{F} \qquad\qquad \text{Divide each side by } F.$$

$$r = \pm\sqrt{\frac{GmM}{F}} \qquad\qquad \text{Take the square root of each side.}$$

$$r = \pm\frac{\sqrt{GmM}}{\sqrt{F}} \cdot \frac{\sqrt{F}}{\sqrt{F}} \qquad\qquad \text{Rationalize the denominator.}$$

$$r = \pm\frac{\sqrt{GmMF}}{F} \qquad\qquad \text{Simplify.}$$

The solutions are $r = \dfrac{\sqrt{GmMF}}{F}$ and $r = -\dfrac{\sqrt{GmMF}}{F}$. ◼

▶ **Think About It** In the formula for Example 1, F is the force of gravity between two bodies with masses m and M having centers that are separated by a distance r. G is a proportionality constant.

EXAMPLE 2

Solve $d = -16t^2 + 64t$ for t.

SOLUTION

The equation has terms of t^2 and t. You can rewrite the equation in standard form $ax^2 + bx + c = 0$, using t instead of x as the variable.

$$d = -16t^2 + 64t$$

$$0 = -16t^2 + 64t - d \qquad \text{Subtract } d \text{ from each side.}$$

$$-16t^2 + 64t - d = 0 \qquad \text{Standard form}$$

You can now use the quadratic formula to solve $-16t^2 + 64t - d = 0$ for t.

$$x = \frac{-b \pm \sqrt{b^2 - 4ac}}{2a} \qquad \text{Quadratic formula}$$

$$t = \frac{-64 \pm \sqrt{64^2 - 4(-16)(-d)}}{2(-16)} \qquad \text{Let } x = t, a = -16, b = 64, \text{ and } c = -d.$$

$$t = \frac{-64 \pm \sqrt{4096 - 64d}}{-32} \qquad \text{Simplify.}$$

$$t = \frac{-64 \pm \sqrt{64(64 - d)}}{-32} \qquad \text{Factor 64 out of both terms in the radicand.}$$

$$t = \frac{-64 \pm 8\sqrt{64 - d}}{-32} \qquad \text{Simplify.}$$

$$t = \frac{8 \pm \sqrt{64 - d}}{4} \qquad \text{Simplify.}$$

The solutions are $t = \dfrac{8 + \sqrt{64 - d}}{4}$ and $t = \dfrac{8 - \sqrt{64 - d}}{4}$. ■

▶ **Think About It** In the formula for Example 2, *d* is the distance (in feet) above the ground for an object *t* seconds after it is released with an upward velocity of 64 ft/s.

Factoring with Complex Numbers

By understanding the sum of squares pattern, you can factor certain polynomials and write equations given imaginary and complex roots.

Sum of Squares

You can use complex numbers to factor a binomial that is the sum of squares.

Sum of Squares
The sum of squares pattern is $$a^2 + b^2 = (a + bi)(a - bi).$$

Use FOIL to prove that this pattern works.

$$(a + bi)(a - bi) = a^2 - a(bi) + (bi)a - b^2 i^2$$
$$= a^2 - b^2(-1)$$
$$= a^2 + b^2$$

Recall that **complex conjugates** are two complex numbers of the form $a + bi$ and $a - bi$. Together, the expressions $a + bi$ and $a - bi$ form a **conjugate pair**. In the sum of squares pattern, the factors are a conjugate pair.

EXAMPLE 1

Factor $x^2 + 121$ over the complex numbers.

SOLUTION

Use the sum of squares pattern. Notice that $121 = 11^2$, so
$x^2 + 121 = (x + 11i)(x - 11i)$. ∎

EXAMPLE 2

Factor $4m^2 + 10$ over the complex numbers.

SOLUTION

Use the sum of squares pattern by rewriting $4m^2$ as $(2m)^2$ and $10 = \left(\sqrt{10}\right)^2$.

$$4m^2 + 10 = \left(2m + i\sqrt{10}\right)\left(2m - i\sqrt{10}\right)\ \blacksquare$$

Creating Equations from Imaginary Roots

When the roots of a quadratic equation are opposite imaginary numbers, you can use the sum of squares pattern to write the equation that has those roots.

> ▶ **Think About It** Roots of the quadratic equation $P(x) = 0$ are solutions of the equation, which are roots of the quadratic polynomial $P(x)$. Saying that these are roots of the equation is a common shorthand.

EXAMPLE 3

The roots of a quadratic equation are $i\sqrt{8}$ and $-i\sqrt{8}$. What is the equation?

SOLUTION

If the roots of an equation are $i\sqrt{8}$ and $-i\sqrt{8}$, then the factors of the equation are $\left(x + i\sqrt{8}\right)$ and $\left(x - i\sqrt{8}\right)$.

By the difference of squares pattern, these factors multiply to $x^2 + \left(\sqrt{8}\right)^2$ or $x^2 + 8$.

The desired equation is $x^2 + 8 = 0$, which could be written as $x^2 = -8$. ■

Creating Equations from Complex Conjugate Roots

When the roots of a quadratic equation are complex conjugates, you can use the sum of squares pattern to write the equation that has those roots.

How to Create a Quadratic Equation from Complex Conjugate Roots

Use these steps to create a quadratic equation from complex conjugate roots $a + bi$ and $a - bi$.

Step 1 Let the variable be x. Write the factors as $\left(x - \left(a + bi\right)\right)$ and $\left(x - \left(a - bi\right)\right)$ and set their product to zero.

Step 2 Rewrite the factors as $\left(\left(x - a\right) - bi\right)$ and $\left(\left(x - a\right) + bi\right)$.

Step 3 Multiply using the difference of squares pattern.

EXAMPLE 4

Write a quadratic equation that has roots $7 + 3i$ and $7 - 3i$.

SOLUTION

Step 1 Let the variable be x. Write the equation.

$$\left(x - \left(7 + 3i\right)\right)\left(x - \left(7 - 3i\right)\right) = 0$$

Step 2 Use the associative property to rewrite the factors.

$$\left(\left(x - 7\right) - 3i\right)\left(\left(x - 7\right) + 3i\right) - 0$$

Step 3 Multiply the factors.

$$\left[\left(x - 7\right) - 3i\right]\left[\left(x - 7\right) + 3i\right] = 0$$
$$\left[\left(x - 7\right)^2 - 9i^2\right] = 0$$
$$\left[\left(x^2 - 14x + 49\right) + 9\right] = 0$$
$$x^2 - 14x + 58 = 0$$

CHECK

Use the quadratic formula to solve the equation.

$$x = \frac{14 \pm \sqrt{(14)^2 - 4 \cdot 1 \cdot 58}}{2 \cdot 1}$$

$$= \frac{14 \pm \sqrt{196 - 232}}{2}$$

$$= \frac{14 \pm \sqrt{-36}}{2}$$

$$= \frac{14 \pm 6i}{2} = 7 \pm 3i \checkmark$$

The roots found using the quadratic formula are the given roots. ■

Polynomial Functions

When water comes out of a pipe, it usually looks very smooth. This characteristic is called laminar flow. Over time, the water becomes less smooth as its flow becomes more turbulent. Engineers use polynomials to model both types of flow.

Power Functions

Graphs of power functions differ in shape, depending on the degree of the polynomial.

You can predict how the graph of a function will look and behave if you know its degree and leading coefficient.

Identifying Graphs of Power Functions

Definition
A **power function** is any function that can be written in the form $$f(x) = ax^n + b$$ where n is a positive integer, a is any nonzero real number, and b is any real number.

Graphs of linear, quadratic, and cubic functions differ greatly in their appearance.

Linear
Degree 1

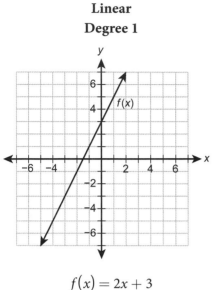

$$f(x) = 2x + 3$$

The graph of a linear function is a line.

Quadratic
Degree 2

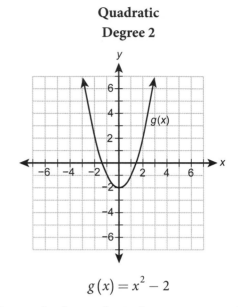

$$g(x) = x^2 - 2$$

The graph of a quadratic function is a parabola.

Cubic
Degree 3

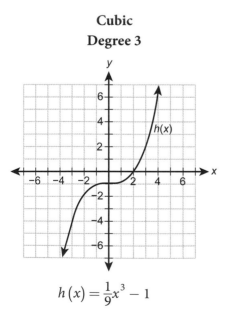

$$h(x) = \frac{1}{9}x^3 - 1$$

The graph of a cubic function is shaped like a sideways S.

EXAMPLE 1

Determine whether the graph is a linear, quadratic, or cubic function.

A

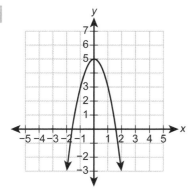

B

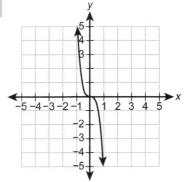

SOLUTION

The function is a parabola, so it is quadratic.

SOLUTION

The function is S-shaped, so it is cubic.

Graphing Power Functions

EXAMPLE 2

A Graph $f(x) = -x^3 + 3$.

SOLUTION

Step 1 Make a table of values.

x	−3	−2	−1	0	1	2	3
$f(x)$	30	11	4	3	2	−5	−24

Step 2 Graph the function. Plot each point and join the points with a smooth curve.

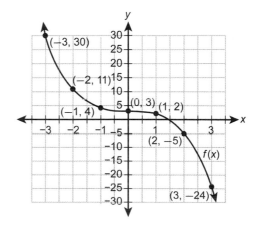

B Graph $g(x) = 4x^2 - 2$.

SOLUTION

Step 1 Make a table of values.

x	−3	−2	−1	0	1	2	3
g(x)	34	14	2	−2	2	14	34

Step 2 Graph the function. Plot each point and join the points with a smooth curve.

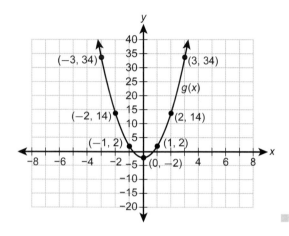

Describing the End Behavior of a Polynomial Function

Knowing what to expect for the end behavior of a graph can help you visualize a polynomial function.

Definition
The **end behavior** of a function is how the function behaves when the domain values increase or decrease without bound.

The end behavior of a polynomial function depends on the degree of the function and on the sign of the leading coefficient.

End Behavior of Power Functions

End Behavior of Power Functions: $f(x) = ax^n + b$

n is even, $a > 0$

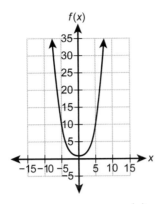

As x increases without bound, $f(x)$ eventually increases without bound. As x decreases without bound, $f(x)$ eventually increases without bound.

n is even, $a < 0$

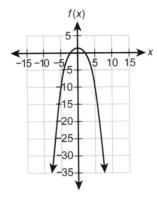

As x increases without bound, $f(x)$ eventually decreases without bound. As x decreases without bound, $f(x)$ eventually decreases without bound.

n is odd, $a > 0$

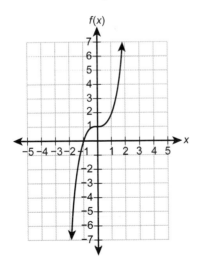

As x increases without bound, $f(x)$ eventually increases without bound. As x decreases without bound, $f(x)$ eventually decreases without bound.

n is odd, $a < 0$

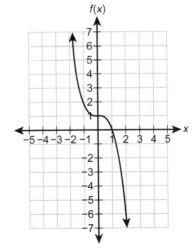

As x increases without bound, $f(x)$ eventually decreases without bound. As x decreases without bound, $f(x)$ eventually increases without bound.

EXAMPLE 3

Describe the end behavior of the function.

A $f(x) = -2x^4 + 7$

SOLUTION

The function has degree 4 and the leading coefficient is negative, so as x increases without bound, $f(x)$ eventually decreases without bound, and as x decreases without bound, $f(x)$ eventually decreases without bound.

B $f(x) = x^3 - 1$

SOLUTION

The function is cubic and the leading coefficient is positive, so as x increases without bound, $f(x)$ eventually increases without bound, and as x decreases without bound, $f(x)$ eventually decreases without bound. ▪

Relating Power Functions Within a Family of Graphs

Power Functions

Power Function Graph Family: $f(x) = ax^n + b$

Each change in the value of a or b results in a different transformation of the parent graph, $f(x) = x^n$.

Continued

Power Functions (Continued)

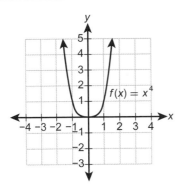

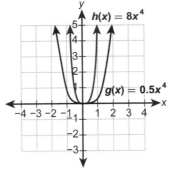

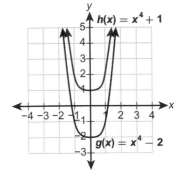

All equations of the form $f(x) = x^n$ go through the origin.

If you change only the parameter a, the graphs expand or contract while passing through the origin.

If you change only the parameter b, the graphs shift up or down on the y-axis, resulting in different y-intercepts.

Writing a Power Function When Given a Point

EXAMPLE 4

Find the equation for the power function of the form $p(x) = ax^2$ that contains the point $(-2, 12)$.

SOLUTION

$p(x) = ax^2$

$12 = a \cdot (-2)^2$ Substitute 12 for $p(x)$ and -2 for x.

$\dfrac{12}{4} = a$ Solve for a.

$3 = a$

Substitute the value found for a into $p(x) = ax^2$. The function is $p(x) = 3x^2$. ∎

Identifying Odd and Even Functions

You can also determine whether a function is even or odd.

Definitions

A function g is even if $g(-x) = g(x)$ for all values of x. The graph of an even function is symmetric about the y-axis.

A function h is odd if $h(-x) = -h(x)$ for all values of x. The graph of an odd function is symmetric about the origin.

EXAMPLE 5

Identify the function as even, odd, or neither.

A $f(x) = -2x^2 + 1$

SOLUTION
geometrically

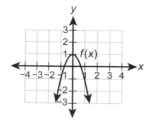

The function is symmetric about the y-axis.

algebraically
$$f(-x) = -2(-x)^2 + 1$$
$$= -2x^2 + 1$$
$$= f(x)$$

The function $f(x) = -2x^2 + 1$ is an even function.

B $g(x) = 7x^3 + 2$

SOLUTION
geometrically

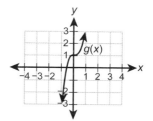

The function is not symmetric about the y-axis or the origin.

algebraically
$$g(-x) = 7(-x)^3 + 2$$
$$= -7x^3 + 2$$

The function $g(x) = 7x^3 + 2$ is neither even nor odd.

C $h(x) = 5x$

SOLUTION

geometrically

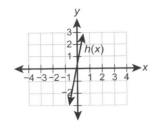

The function is symmetric about the origin.

algebraically

$$h(-x) = 5(-x)$$
$$= -5x$$
$$= -h(x)$$

The function $h(x) = 5x$ is an odd function. ▪

Using a Table of Values to Classify a Polynomial

By finding the successive differences when given a table of values, you can determine what degree the power function has. First differences are the differences of the function values. Second differences are the differences of the first differences. Third differences are the differences of the second differences, and so on.

linear $f(x) = 3x + 2 = 3x^1 + 2$ has **1**st successive differences equal.

quadratic $f(x) = x^2 - 4x - 5$ has **2**nd successive differences equal.

cubic $f(x) = 2x^3 + 9$ has **3**rd successive differences equal.

quartic $f(x) = 5x^4 - 3x^2 + 1$ has **4**th successive differences equal.

Successive Differences of Power Functions
An nth-degree power function has a constant nth successive difference.

EXAMPLE 6

Determine whether the table of values represents a linear, quadratic, or cubic function.

A

x	-2	-1	0	1	2
$f(x)$	-8	-6	-4	-2	0

$$-2 \quad -2 \quad -2 \quad -2$$

SOLUTION

The differences of successive $f(x)$ values are equal, so this table of values represents a linear function.

B

x	-2	-1	0	1	2
$g(x)$	7	4	3	4	7

$$3 \quad 1 \quad -1 \quad -3$$
$$2 \quad 2 \quad 2$$

SOLUTION

The successive differences of $g(x)$ values are not equal, so find the differences of the first differences. Because these second differences are equal, the table of values represents a quadratic function.

C

x	−4	−3	−2	−1	0	1	2	3	4
h(x)	−64	−27	−8	−1	0	1	8	27	64

−37   −19   −7   −1   −1   −7   −19   −37

−18   −12   −6   0   6   12   18

−6   **−6**   **−6**   **−6**   **−6**   **−6**

SOLUTION

The successive differences of $h(x)$ are not equal and the second differences are not equal, so find the third differences. The third differences are equal, so the table of values represents a cubic function. ■

Polynomial Long Division

If you know how to use long division with numbers, then you can use the same strategy to divide polynomials.

You can set up a division problem with polynomials the same way you do with numbers. Place the dividend inside the division symbol and the divisor to the left of it. The quotient goes on top of the division symbol.

	Numbers	Polynomials
Vertically	$$\begin{array}{r} 5 \\ 15\overline{)75} \\ -75 \\ \hline 0 \end{array}$$	$$\begin{array}{r} x^2 \\ 3\overline{)3x^2} \\ -3x^2 \\ \hline 0 \end{array}$$
Horizontally	$75 \div 15 = 5$	$3x^2 \div 3 = x^2$

Dividing a Second-Degree Polynomial by a First-Degree Binomial

As you do when you divide numbers, repeat the process of divide, multiply, and subtract until no more divisions can be made.

EXAMPLE 1

Divide.

A $\left(x^2 - 6x - 27\right) \div (x + 3)$

SOLUTION

Step 1

$$\begin{array}{r} x \phantom{{}- 6x - 27} \\ x + 3 \overline{)\, x^2 - 6x - 27} \\ -\left(x^2 + 3x\right) \phantom{{}27} \\ \hline -9x - 27 \end{array}$$

Divide: $\dfrac{x^2}{x} = x$.

Multiply: $x \bullet (x + 3) = x^2 + 3x$.

Subtract: $\left(x^2 - 6x\right) - \left(x^2 + 3x\right) = -9x$.

Bring down -27.

Step 2

$$\begin{array}{r} x - 9 \\ x + 3 \overline{)\, x^2 - 6x - 27} \\ -\left(x^2 + 3x\right) \phantom{{}27} \\ \hline -9x - 27 \\ -\left(-9x - 27\right) \\ \hline 0 \end{array}$$

Divide: $\dfrac{-9x}{x} = -9$.

Multiply: $-9 \bullet (x + 3) = -9x - 27$.

Subtract: $\left(-9x - 27\right) - \left(-9x - 27\right) = 0$.

So $x^2 - 6x - 27$ divided by $x + 3$ is $x - 9$.

B $2x^2 + 13x - 4$ by $2x - 1$

SOLUTION

Step 1

$$\begin{array}{r} x \phantom{{}+ 13x - 4} \\ 2x - 1 \overline{)\, 2x^2 + 13x - 4} \\ -\left(2x^2 - x\right) \\ \hline 14x - 4 \end{array}$$

Divide: $\dfrac{2x^2}{2x} = x$.

Multiply: $x \bullet (2x - 1) = 2x^2 - x$.

Subtract: $\left(2x^2 + 13x\right) - \left(2x^2 - x\right) = 14x$.

Bring down -4.

Step 2

$$\begin{array}{r} x + 7 \\ 2x - 1 \overline{)\, 2x^2 + 13x \phantom{{}-} 4} \\ -\left(2x^2 - x\right) \\ \hline 14x - 4 \\ -\left(14x - 7\right) \\ \hline 3 \end{array}$$

Divide: $\dfrac{14x}{2x} = 7$.

Multiply: $7 \bullet (2x - 1) = 14x - 7$.

Subtract: $\left(14x - 4\right) - \left(14x - 7\right) = 3$.

So $2x^2 + 13x - 4$ divided by $2x - 1$ is $x + 7$ with remainder 3. ■

Representing and Checking a Quotient

Names of Expressions in a Polynomial Division

$$
\begin{array}{r}
x+1 \\
2x-1 \overline{)\, 2x^2 + 13x - 4} \\
-\left(2x^2 - x\right) \\
\hline
14x - 4 \\
-\left(14x - 7\right) \\
\hline
3
\end{array}
$$

divisor $\longrightarrow$ $2x - 1$

dividend $\longleftarrow$ $2x^2 + 13x - 4$

quotient $\longleftarrow$ $x + 1$

remainder $\longleftarrow$ 3

Different Ways to Express Related Multiplication and Division Facts

With numbers	With polynomials
$13 \div 5 = 2\text{ R}3$	$\left(2x^2 + 13x - 4\right) \div \left(2x - 1\right) = x + 7\text{ R}3$
$\dfrac{13}{5} = 2 + \dfrac{3}{5}$	$\dfrac{2x^2 + 13x - 4}{2x - 1} = x + 7 + \dfrac{3}{2x - 1}$

Because multiplication and division are inverse operations, you can check your answer to a division problem by multiplying.

Using Multiplication to Check a Quotient

quotient • divisor + remainder = dividend

EXAMPLE 2

A Determine whether $2x + 4 + \dfrac{2}{x-5}$ is the quotient of $\left(2x^2 - 6x - 18\right) \div (x - 5)$.

SOLUTION

$$(2x + 4)(x - 5) + 2 \overset{?}{=} 2x^2 - 6x - 18 \qquad \textbf{quotient} \cdot \textbf{divisor} + \textbf{remainder} = \text{dividend}$$

$$2x^2 - 10x + 4x - 20 + 2 \overset{?}{=} 2x^2 - 6x - 18 \qquad \text{Multiply.}$$

$$2x^2 - 6x - 18 = 2x^2 - 6x - 18 \qquad \text{Simplify.}$$

So $2x + 4 + \dfrac{2}{x-5}$ is the quotient of $\left(2x^2 - 6x - 18\right) \div (x - 5)$.

B Determine whether $3x - 5$ is the quotient of $\left(6x^2 - 2x - 15\right) \div (2x + 3)$.

SOLUTION

$$(3x - 5)(2x + 3) \overset{?}{=} 6x^2 - 2x - 15 \qquad \textbf{quotient} \cdot \textbf{divisor} = \text{dividend}$$

$$6x^2 + 9x - 10x - 15 \overset{?}{=} 6x^2 - 2x - 15 \qquad \text{Multiply.}$$

$$6x^2 - x - 15 \neq 6x^2 - 2x - 15 \qquad \text{Simplify.}$$

So $3x - 5$ is not the quotient of $\left(6x^2 - 2x - 15\right) \div (2x + 3)$. ∎

Dividing a Fourth-Degree Polynomial by a First-Degree Binomial

EXAMPLE 3

Divide $2x^4 - 4x + 7x^2 + 1$ by $x + 1$.

SOLUTION

Rewrite the dividend so that its terms are in order of decreasing degree, and write $0x^3$ for the missing x^3 term.

$$2x^4 - 4x + 7x^2 + 1 = 2x^4 + 0x^3 + 7x^2 - 4x + 1$$

Divide.

$$
\require{enclose}
\begin{array}{r}
2x^3 - 2x^2 + 9x - 13 \\[2pt]
x+1 \enclose{longdiv}{2x^4 + 0x^3 + 7x^2 - 4x + 1} \\
\end{array}
$$

$$-\left(2x^4 + 2x^3\right)$$
$$-2x^3 + 7x^2$$
$$-\left(-2x^3 - 2x^2\right)$$
$$9x^2 - 4x$$
$$-\left(9x^2 + 9x\right)$$
$$-13x + 1$$
$$-(-13x - 13)$$
$$14$$

The quotient is $2x^3 - 2x^2 + 9x - 13$. The remainder is 14.

$$\left(2x^4 - 4x + 7x^2 + 1\right) \div (x + 1) = 2x^3 - 2x^2 + 9x - 13 + \frac{14}{x+1}$$

▶ **Think About It** When you multiply a term in the quotient by the divisor, align the terms of the product with their like terms in the dividend. Notice that in Example 3, the product $-\left(2x^4 + 2x^3\right)$ is written so that $2x^4$ is directly below $2x^4$ and $2x^3$ is directly below $0x^3$.

Determining Whether One Polynomial Is a Factor of Another Polynomial

EXAMPLE 4

Determine whether $a - 2$ is a factor of $a^3 - 7a + 6$.

SOLUTION

$$
\begin{array}{r}
a^2 + 2a - 3 \\
a - 2\overline{\smash{)}a^3 + 0a^2 - 7a + 6} \\
-\left(a^3 - 2a^2\right) \\
\overline{2a^2 - 7a} \\
-\left(2a^2 - 4a\right) \\
\overline{-3a + 6} \\
-\left(3a + 6\right) \\
\overline{0}
\end{array}
$$

The remainder is 0, so $a - 2$ is a factor of $a^3 - 7a + 6$. ▪

▶ **Think About It** When the remainder is 0, both the divisor and the quotient are factors of the dividend.

To check your answer, multiply $(a - 2)\left(a^2 + 2a - 3\right)$. Verify that the product is $a^3 - 7a + 6$.

Synthetic Division

As long as you're careful, long division always works, but it takes time. Another method you can use to divide polynomials is synthetic division.

For synthetic division to work, the divisor must be a binomial in the form $x - k$, where k is a constant.

Using Synthetic Division to Divide Polynomials

Suppose you want to divide $2x^2 + 3x + 7$ by $x - 2$. The process of finding the quotient using both long division and synthetic division is shown.

Long Division

$$\begin{array}{r} 2x + 7 \\ x - 2 \overline{)\,2x^2 + 3x + 7\,} \\ -\left(2x^2 - 4x\right) \\ \hline 7x + 7 \\ -\left(7x - 14\right) \\ \hline 21 \end{array}$$

Synthetic Division

$$\begin{array}{r|rrr} 2 & 2 & 3 & 7 \\ & & 4 & 14 \\ \hline & 2 & 7 & 21 \end{array}$$

Synthetic division is considered a shorthand method for long division, but remember that it only works when the divisor is in the form $x - k$.

▶ **Think About It** When you use synthetic division, notice that the coefficients of the dividend appear in the top row and the coefficients of the quotient appear with the remainder in the bottom row.

EXAMPLE 1

Divide $3x^3 + 11x^2 - 2x - 24$ by $x + 3$.

SOLUTION

The divisor is $x + 3$. To get the form $x - k$, write $x + 3$ as $x - (-3)$, so $k = -3$.

Step 1

$$\underline{-3} \bigm| \quad 3 \quad 11 \quad -2 \quad -24$$

Put the value for k in the box and put the coefficients to the right of it.

Step 2

$$
\begin{array}{r|rrrr}
-3 & 3 & 11 & -2 & -24 \\
   &   & -9 &   &   \\
\hline
   & 3 &   &   &
\end{array}
$$

Bring down the first coefficient, 3, and then multiply by -3. Put the result in the next column.

Step 3

$$
\begin{array}{r|rrrr}
-3 & 3 & \mathbf{11} & -2 & -24 \\
   &   & \mathbf{-9} & -6 &   \\
\hline
   & 3 & \mathbf{2} &   &
\end{array}
$$

Add 11 and -9 and then multiply the sum, 2, by -3. Put the result in the next column.

Step 4

$$
\begin{array}{r|rrrr}
-3 & 3 & 11 & \mathbf{-2} & -24 \\
   &   & -9 & \mathbf{-6} & 24 \\
\hline
   & 3 & 2 & \mathbf{-8} &
\end{array}
$$

Add -2 and -6 and then multiply the sum, -8, by -3. Put the product in the next column.

Step 5

$$
\begin{array}{r|rrrr}
-3 & 3 & 11 & -2 & \mathbf{-24} \\
   &   & -9 & -6 & \mathbf{24} \\
\hline
   & 3 & 2 & -8 & \mathbf{0}
\end{array}
$$

Add -24 and 24. The sum, 0, is the remainder.

Step 6

$$\begin{array}{r|rrrr} -3 & 3 & 11 & -2 & -24 \\ & & -9 & -6 & 24 \\ \hline & 3 & 2 & -8 & 0 \end{array}$$

$$3x^2 + 2x - 8 \qquad R0$$

Write the quotient. Begin writing the quotient with a power of x that is one less than the greatest power of x in the dividend.

The quotient has no remainder, so

$$\left(3x^3 + 11x^2 - 2x - 24\right) \div (x + 3) = 3x^2 + 2x - 8.$$

EXAMPLE 2

Divide $x^3 - 6x^2 - x + 32$ by $x - 5$.

SOLUTION

The divisor is $x - 5$, so $k = 5$.

Step 1

$$\begin{array}{r|rrrr} 5 & 1 & -6 & -1 & 32 \\ & & & & \\ \hline \end{array}$$

Put the value for k in the box and put the coefficients to the right of it.

Step 2

$$\begin{array}{r|rrrr} 5 & 1 & -6 & -1 & 32 \\ & & 5 & & \\ \hline & 1 & & & \end{array}$$

Bring down the first coefficient, 1, and then multiply by 5. Put the result in the next column.

Step 3

$$\begin{array}{r|rrrr} 5 & 1 & -6 & -1 & 32 \\ & & 5 & -5 & \\ \hline & 1 & -1 & & \end{array}$$

Add -6 and 5 and then multiply the sum, -1, by 5. Put the result in the next column.

Step 4

5	1	−6	−1	32
		5	−5	−30
	1	−1	−6	

Add −1 and −5 and then multiply the sum, −6, by 5. Put the product in the next column.

Step 5

5	1	−6	−1	32
		5	−5	−30
	1	−1	−6	2

Add 32 and −30. The sum, 2, is the remainder.

Step 6

5	1	−6	−1	32
		5	−5	−30
	1	−1	−6	2

$$x^2 - x \ - \ 6 \qquad R2$$

Write the quotient. Begin writing the quotient with a power of x that is one less than the greatest power of x in the dividend.

The quotient has remainder 2, so

$$\left(x^3 - 6x^2 - x + 32\right) \div \left(x - 5\right) = x^2 - x - 6 + \frac{2}{x - 5}.\ \blacksquare$$

EXAMPLE 3

Divide $2x^4 + 9x^3 - 7x + 36$ by $x + 4$.

SOLUTION

The divisor is $x + 4$. To get the form $x - k$, write $x + 4 = x - \left(-4\right)$ so $k = -4$.
The dividend is missing an x^2 term, so use 0 for that coefficient.

Step 1

−4	2	9	0	−7	36

Put the value for k in the box and put the coefficients to the right of it.

Step 2

$$\begin{array}{r|rrrrr} -4 & 2 & 9 & 0 & -7 & 36 \\ & & -8 & & & \\ \hline & 2 & & & & \end{array}$$

Bring down the first coefficient, 2, and then multiply by −4. Put the result in the next column.

Step 3

$$\begin{array}{r|rrrrr} -4 & 2 & 9 & 0 & -7 & 36 \\ & & -8 & -4 & & \\ \hline & 2 & 1 & & & \end{array}$$

Add 9 and −8 and then multiply the sum, 1, by −4. Put the result in the next column.

Step 4

$$\begin{array}{r|rrrrr} -4 & 2 & 9 & 0 & -7 & 36 \\ & & -8 & -4 & 16 & \\ \hline & 2 & 1 & -4 & & \end{array}$$

Add 0 and −4 and then multiply the sum, −4, by −4. Put the product in the next column.

Step 5

$$\begin{array}{r|rrrrr} -4 & 2 & 9 & 0 & -7 & 36 \\ & & -8 & -4 & 16 & -36 \\ \hline & 2 & 1 & -4 & 9 & \end{array}$$

Add −7 and 16 and then multiply the sum, 9, by −4. Put the product in the next column.

Step 6

$$\begin{array}{r|rrrrr} -4 & 2 & 9 & 0 & -7 & 36 \\ & & -8 & -4 & 16 & -36 \\ \hline & 2 & 1 & -4 & 9 & 0 \end{array}$$

Add 36 and −36. The sum, 0, is the remainder.

Step 7

$$\begin{array}{r|rrrrr} -4 & 2 & 9 & 0 & -7 & 36 \\ & & -8 & -4 & 16 & -36 \\ \hline & 2 & 1 & -4 & 9 & 0 \\ & \downarrow & \downarrow & \downarrow & \downarrow & \downarrow \\ & 2x^3 & + x^2 & - 4x & + 9 & \text{R0} \end{array}$$

Write the quotient. Begin writing the quotient with a power of x that is one less than the greatest power of x in the dividend.

The quotient has no remainder, so

$$\left(2x^4 + 9x^3 - 7x + 36\right) \div \left(x + 4\right) = 2x^3 + x^2 - 4x + 9. \; \blacksquare$$

Dividing Polynomials Using Synthetic Division When the Divisor Is Not in the Form $x - k$

EXAMPLE 4

Divide $4y^3 - 5y - 10$ by $2y - 3$.

SOLUTION

To use synthetic division, you must have a divisor in the form $x - k$. Rewrite the division problem by factoring 2 from the divisor and the dividend.

$$\frac{4y^3 - 5y - 10}{2y - 3} - \frac{2\left(2y^3 - \frac{5}{2}y - 5\right)}{2\left(y - \frac{3}{2}\right)} = \frac{2y^3 - \frac{5}{2}y - 5}{y - \frac{3}{2}}$$

The dividend is now $2y^3 - \frac{5}{2}y - 5$ and the divisor is $y - \frac{3}{2}$, so $k = \frac{3}{2}$.

The dividend is missing a y^2 term, so use 0 for that coefficient.

Step 1

$$\frac{3}{2} \, \bigg| \quad 2 \quad 0 \quad -\frac{5}{2} \quad -5$$

Put the value for k in the box and put the coefficients to the right of it.

Step 2

$$\frac{3}{2} \, \bigg| \quad 2 \quad 0 \quad -\frac{5}{2} \quad -5$$
$$\qquad\qquad\quad 3$$
$$\qquad\;\; 2$$

Bring down the first coefficient, 2, and then multiply by $\frac{3}{2}$. Put the result in the next column.

Step 3

$$\frac{3}{2} \, \bigg| \quad 2 \quad \mathbf{0} \quad -\frac{5}{2} \quad -5$$
$$\qquad\qquad\quad 3 \quad \frac{9}{2}$$
$$\qquad\;\; 2 \quad 3$$

Add 0 and 3 and then multiply the sum, 3, by $\frac{3}{2}$. Put the result in the next column.

Step 4

$$\begin{array}{r|rrrr} \dfrac{3}{2} & 2 & 0 & -\dfrac{5}{2} & -5 \\ & & 3 & \dfrac{9}{2} & 3 \\ \hline & 2 & 3 & \mathbf{2} & \end{array}$$

Add $-\dfrac{5}{2}$ and $\dfrac{9}{2}$ and then multiply the sum, 2, by $\dfrac{3}{2}$. Put the product in the next column.

Step 5

$$\begin{array}{r|rrrr} \dfrac{3}{2} & 2 & 0 & -\dfrac{5}{2} & \mathbf{-5} \\ & & 3 & \dfrac{9}{2} & \mathbf{3} \\ \hline & 2 & 3 & 2 & \mathbf{-2} \end{array}$$

Add -5 and 3. The sum, -2, is the remainder.

Step 6

$$\begin{array}{r|rrrr} \dfrac{3}{2} & 2 & 0 & -\dfrac{5}{2} & -5 \\ & & 3 & \dfrac{9}{2} & 3 \\ \hline & 2 & 3 & 2 & -2 \\ & \downarrow & \downarrow & \downarrow & \downarrow \\ & 2y^2 + & 3y\ + & 2 & R-2 \end{array}$$

Write the quotient. Begin writing the quotient with a power of x that is one less than the greatest power of x in the dividend.

The quotient has a remainder of -2, so

$$\left(4y^3 - 5y - 10\right) \div (2y - 3) = 2y^2 + 3y + 2 - \dfrac{2}{y - \dfrac{3}{2}}$$

$$= 2y^2 \mid 3y \mid 2 \quad \dfrac{4}{2y - 3}. \ \blacksquare$$

▶ **Remember** To simplify a compound fraction, multiply the numerator and denominator by their least common denominator.

$$\dfrac{2}{y - \dfrac{3}{2}} = \dfrac{\mathbf{2} \cdot 2}{\mathbf{2} \cdot \left(y - \dfrac{3}{2}\right)} = \dfrac{4}{2y - 3}$$

The Polynomial Remainder Theorem

You can use the polynomial remainder theorem to evaluate a polynomial function.

Polynomial Remainder Theorem

If a polynomial $p(x)$ is divided by $x - a$, then the remainder is $p(a)$.

$$\underset{\uparrow}{p(x)} = \underset{\uparrow}{q(x)} \cdot \underset{\uparrow}{(x-a)} + \underset{\uparrow}{p(a)}$$

$$\text{dividend} = \text{quotient} \cdot \text{divisor} + \text{remainder}$$

To prove this theorem, recall that you can use multiplication to check a quotient.

Let $p(x)$ represent the dividend, $q(x)$ represent the quotient, and $r(x)$ represent the remainder. If $x - a$ is the divisor, then the formula can be written as follows:

$$p(x) = q(x) \cdot (x - a) + r(x)$$

Now substitute a for x.

$p(a) = q(a) \cdot (a - a) + r(a)$ Substitute a for x.

$p(a) = q(a) \cdot 0 + r(a)$ $a - a = 0$

$p(a) = r(a)$ Zero Property of Multiplication

Therefore, the remainder is the value of the polynomial evaluated for a.

Evaluating a Polynomial

Sometimes synthetic division is an easier and quicker method to evaluate a polynomial, especially when a calculator is not readily available.

Given $f(x) = x^4 - 3x^3 + x^2 - 1$, find $f(-2)$.

SOLUTION

Use synthetic division and the remainder theorem.

$$
\begin{array}{r|rrrrr}
-2 & 1 & -3 & 1 & 0 & -1 \\
   &   & -2 & 10 & -22 & 44 \\
\hline
   & 1 & -5 & 11 & -22 & 43
\end{array}
$$

The remainder is 43, so $f(-2) = 43$.

Substitute -2 for x in $f(x)$ to check.

$$f(-2) = (-2)^4 - 3 \cdot (-2)^3 + (-2)^2 - 1 = 16 + 24 + 4 - 1 = 43 \ \blacksquare$$

Using the Remainder Theorem to Graph a Polynomial

Graph the function by using the remainder theorem.

A $f(x) = x^2 - 4x - 1$

SOLUTION

Use synthetic division repeatedly to find and plot ordered pairs.

Organize your work in a table. List the coefficients of the dividend at the top. Perform the steps mentally and write only the numbers that appear in the bottom row. Plot each pair $(a, f(a))$.

	1	−4	−1
−1	1	−5	4
0	1	−4	−1
1	1	−3	−4
2	1	−2	−5
3	1	−1	−4
4	1	0	−1
5	1	1	4

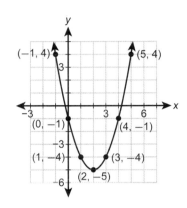

B $g(x) = x^3 - 5x^2 + 6x + 4$

SOLUTION

Use synthetic division repeatedly to find and plot ordered pairs.

	1	−5	6	4
−1	1	−6	12	−8
0	1	−5	6	4
1	1	−4	2	6
2	1	−3	0	4
3	1	−2	0	4
4	1	−1	2	12

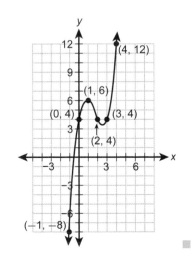

Application: Projectile Motion

EXAMPLE 3

A baseball is hit into the air with an initial vertical velocity of 20 m/s. The height of the baseball after t seconds is modeled by the polynomial function $h(t) = -9.8t^2 + 20t + 1$, where $h(t)$ is the height in meters (neglecting air resistance). What is the height of the baseball after 1.5 s?

SOLUTION

The height of the baseball in meters after t seconds is $h(t)$. To find the height of the baseball after 1.5 s, find $h(1.5)$.

Method 1 Use the remainder theorem.

Divide $-9.8t^2 + 20t + 1$ by $t - 1.5$, using synthetic division.

$$
\begin{array}{r|rrr}
1.5 & -9.8 & 20 & 1 \\
    &   & -14.7 & 7.95 \\
\hline
    & -9.8 & 5.3 & 8.95 \\
\end{array}
$$

The remainder is 8.95, so $h(1.5) = 8.95$.

▶ **Think About It** You can use one method to solve the problem and the other method to check your answer.

Method 2 Substitute 1.5 for t in $h(t)$.

$$
\begin{aligned}
h(t) &= -9.8t^2 + 20t + 1 \\
h(1.5) &= -9.8 \cdot 1.5^2 + 20 \cdot 1.5 + 1 \\
&= -9.8 \cdot 2.25 + 20 \cdot 1.5 + 1 \\
&= 8.95
\end{aligned}
$$

The height of the baseball after 1.5 s is 8.95 m. ▪

Factors and Rational Roots

Synthetic division can help you factor polynomials.

Factor Theorem

For any polynomial $p(x)$, the binomial $x - a$ is a factor of $p(x)$ if and only if $p(a) = 0$.

The remainder theorem is used to prove the factor theorem.

For the proof, use $p(x)$ for the dividend, $q(x)$ for the quotient, and $r(x)$ for the remainder. Therefore, $p(x) = q(x) \cdot (x - a) + r(x)$.

Because the theorem uses "if and only if," there are two cases.

Case 1 Assume $p(a) = 0$. Then by the remainder theorem, $r(a) = 0$. Because the quotient does not have a remainder, $x - a$ is a factor of the dividend.

Case 2 Assume $x - a$ is a factor. Then the remainder $r(a)$ equals 0. By the remainder theorem, $r(a) = p(a)$, and $0 = p(a)$ by substitution.

Using the Factor Theorem

So what does the factor theorem mean? It means that if you evaluate a polynomial for some value of x and the result is zero, then you can use that value to factor the polynomial.

EXAMPLE 1

Determine whether $x - 3$ is a factor of $f(x) = 2x^4 + 2x^3 - 11x^2 + x - 6$.

SOLUTION

Since $x + 3 = x - (-3)$, $a = -3$. So find $f(-3)$.

$$\begin{aligned} f(-3) &= 2(-3)^4 + 2(-3)^3 - 11(-3)^2 + (-3) - 6 \\ &= 2 \cdot 81 + 2 \cdot (-27) - 11 \cdot 9 - 3 - 6 \\ &= 162 - 54 - 99 - 3 - 6 \\ &= 0 \end{aligned}$$

Since $f(-3) = 0$, $x + 3$ is a factor of $f(x) = 2x^4 + 2x^3 - 11x^2 + x - 6$. ∎

For any polynomial function $p(x)$, a solution of the equation $p(x) = 0$ is called a zero or root of $p(x)$. In Example 1, you could say that -3 is a zero of $f(x)$.

EXAMPLE 2

Factor the polynomial $f(x) = x^3 - 19x - 30$, given that $x = 5$ is a zero.

SOLUTION

Step 1 If $x = 5$ is a zero, then $x - 5$ is a factor. Use synthetic division to divide $x^3 - 19x - 30$ by $x - 5$.

$$\begin{array}{r|rrrr} 5 & 1 & 0 & -19 & -30 \\ & & 5 & 25 & 30 \\ \hline & 1 & 5 & 6 & 0 \end{array}$$

Step 2 Write the polynomial as a product of $x - 5$ and the quotient from Step 1. Then factor the quotient.

$$\begin{aligned} x^3 - 19x - 30 &= (x - 5)(x^2 + 5x + 6) \\ &= (x - 5)(x + 3)(x + 2) \end{aligned}$$

So $f(x) = x^3 - 19x - 30 = (x - 5)(x + 3)(x + 2)$. ∎

EXAMPLE 3

Find all the roots of $P(x) = x^3 - 19x - 30$.

SOLUTION

By the factor theorem, if $x - a$ is a factor of $P(x)$, then $P(a) = 0$.
Example 2 shows that $x^3 - 19x - 30 = (x - 5)(x + 3)(x + 2)$.
Therefore 5, -3, and -2 are the roots of $P(x) = x^3 - 19x - 30$. ∎

▶ **Remember** A root is a value that makes a polynomial zero.

Finding Possible Rational Roots

It's easy to find all the roots if you are given a head start, but what if you aren't given any of the roots? How can you find all the roots on your own? The rational root theorem can give you a set of values to try.

Rational Root Theorem

If $\dfrac{p}{q}$ is in simplest form and is a rational root of the polynomial

$f(x) = a_n x^n + a_{n-1} x^{n-1} + \ldots + a_1 x + a_0$ with integer coefficients,
then p must be a factor of a_0 and q must be a factor of a_n.

▶ **Remember** A rational number is a real number that can be written as a quotient of two integers.

EXAMPLE 4

Find the possible rational roots of the polynomial.

A $f(x) = 2x^3 + 16x^2 + 19x + 5$

SOLUTION

If $\frac{p}{q}$ is a rational root of the polynomial $2x^3 + 16x^2 + 19x + 5$, then p is a factor of the constant term, 5, and q is a factor of the leading coefficient, 2. List the factors of 5 and the factors of 2.

The factors of 5 are ± 1 and ± 5.

The factors of 2 are ± 1 and ± 2.

The possible roots of $\frac{p}{q}$ are $\pm \frac{1}{1}, \pm \frac{1}{2}, \pm \frac{5}{1}$, and $\pm \frac{5}{2}$.

Simplifying gives the following possible rational roots of $2x^3 + 16x^2 + 19x + 5 = 0$:

$$\pm 1, \pm \frac{1}{2}, \pm 5, \text{ and } \pm \frac{5}{2}$$

B $g(x) = 3x^3 - 11x^2 + 20x - 9$

SOLUTION

If $\frac{p}{q}$ is a rational root of the polynomial $3x^3 - 11x^2 + 20x - 9$, then p is a factor of the constant term, -9, and q is a factor of the leading coefficient, 3. List the factors of -9 and the factors of 3.

The factors of -9 are $\pm 1, \pm 3$, and ± 9.

The factors of 3 are ± 1 and ± 3.

The possible roots of $\frac{p}{q}$ are $\pm \frac{1}{1}, \pm \frac{1}{3}, \pm \frac{3}{1}, \pm \frac{3}{3}, \pm \frac{9}{1}$, and $\pm \frac{9}{3}$.

Simplifying gives the following possible rational roots of $3x^3 - 11x^2 + 20x - 9 = 0$:

$$\pm 1, \pm \frac{1}{3}, \pm 3, \text{ and } \pm 9 \ \blacksquare$$

Using the Rational Root Theorem to Factor a Polynomial

EXAMPLE 5

Factor completely.

A $x^3 - x^2 - 10x - 8$

SOLUTION

Identify the possible rational roots: ± 1, ± 2, ± 4, and ± 8.

Test for possible roots.

$$
\begin{array}{r|rrrr}
-1 & 1 & -1 & -10 & -8 \\
   &   & -1 & 2 & 8 \\
\hline
   & 1 & -2 & -8 & 0
\end{array}
$$

Because -1 is a root, $(x + 1)$ is a factor. The other factor is $x^2 - 2x - 8$, which can be factored: $(x - 4)(x + 2)$.

The factored form is $(x + 1)(x - 4)(x + 2)$.

> ▶ **Think About It** You may need to test several roots before finding one that makes the remainder 0. Test easier numbers such as −1 and 1 before testing larger numbers and fractions.

B $x^3 - 3x^2 - 5x + 15$

SOLUTION

Identify the possible rational roots: ± 1, ± 3, ± 5, and ± 15.

Test for possible roots.

$$
\begin{array}{r|rrrr}
   & 1 & -3 & -5 & 15 \\
\hline
1 & 1 & -2 & -7 & 8 \\
-1 & 1 & -4 & -1 & 16 \\
3 & 1 & 0 & -5 & 0
\end{array}
$$

Think About It Organize your work in a table. List the coefficients of the polynomial at the top. Perform the steps mentally and write only the numbers that appear in the bottom row.

Because 3 is the first possible root with a remainder of 0, $(x - 3)$ is a factor. The other factor is $x^2 - 5$. Solve $x^2 - 5 = 0$ to find the other roots.

$$x^2 - 5 = 0$$
$$x^2 = 5$$
$$x = \pm\sqrt{5}$$

The factored form is $(x - 3)(x + \sqrt{5})(x - \sqrt{5})$.

C $3x^3 + x^2 - 38x + 24$

SOLUTION

The possible rational roots are $\pm\frac{1}{3}$, $\pm\frac{2}{3}$, ±1, $\pm\frac{4}{3}$, ±2, $\pm\frac{8}{3}$, ±3, ±4, ±6, ±8, ±12, and ±24.

	3	1	−38	24
1	3	4	−34	−10
−1	3	−2	−36	54
2	3	7	−24	−24
−2	3	−5	−28	80
$\frac{2}{3}$	3	3	−36	0

Testing the possible roots by synthetic division reveals that $\frac{2}{3}$ is a root.

So $\left(x - \frac{2}{3}\right)$ is a factor. The other factor is $3x^2 + 3x - 36$, which factors into $3(x + 4)(x - 3)$.

The factored form is $3\left(x - \frac{2}{3}\right)(x + 4)(x - 3)$, which can also be written as $(3x - 2)(x + 4)(x - 3)$. ■

Graphing Polynomials

Because any root of $f(x)$ is also an x-intercept of the graph of $f(x)$, you can determine the roots of a polynomial function from its graph.

Using a Graph to Determine the Roots of a Polynomial

EXAMPLE 1

A Find the roots of $f(x) = x^2 + 4x - 21$.

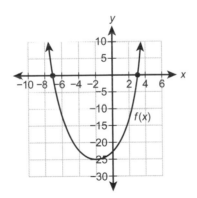

SOLUTION

The graph of $f(x) = x^2 + 4x - 21$ appears to intersect the x-axis at $(3, 0)$ and $(-7, 0)$, which means that 3 and -7 seem to be roots, both of which are consistent with the possible rational roots according to the rational root theorem.

CHECK

Find $f(3)$ and $f(-7)$ to check your answer.

$$f(3) = 3^2 + 4 \cdot 3 - 21 \qquad f(-7) = (-7)^2 + 4 \cdot (-7) - 21$$
$$= 9 + 12 - 21 \qquad\qquad = 49 - 28 - 21$$
$$= 0 \checkmark \qquad\qquad\qquad = 0 \checkmark$$

Since $f(3) = 0$ and $f(-7) = 0$, 3 and -7 are the roots of $f(x)$.

B Find the roots of $g(x) = x^3 - 4x^2 + x + 6 = 0$.

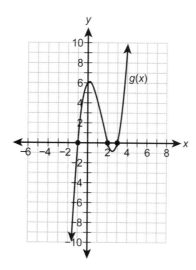

SOLUTION

The graph of $g(x) = x^3 - 4x^2 + x + 6 = 0$ appears to intersect the x-axis at $(-1, 0)$, $(2, 0)$, and $(3, 0)$, which means that -1, 2, and 3 seem to be roots, all of which are consistent with the possible rational roots according to the rational root theorem.

CHECK

You can check your answer by factoring. Use any one of the roots obtained from the graph and turn it into a factor: $x - (-1) = x + 1$. Use synthetic division to divide.

$$
\begin{array}{r|rrrr}
-1 & 1 & -4 & 1 & 6 \\
   &   & -1 & 5 & -6 \\
\hline
   & 1 & -5 & 6 & 0 \\
\end{array}
$$

Use the quotient to write the polynomial as a product of factors.

$$\begin{aligned} x^3 - 4x^2 + x + 6 &= (x+1)\left(x^2 - 5x + 6\right) \\ &= (x+1)(x-2)(x-3) \checkmark \end{aligned}$$

The factors show that the roots are -1, 2, and 3. ■

Graphing a Polynomial Function by Using Intercepts

You can draw the graph of a function by finding its x-intercepts and incorporating what you know about the end behavior of power functions.

EXAMPLE 2

Draw the graph of $f(x) = x^4 - 3x^3 - 11x^2 + 3x + 10$.

SOLUTION

Step 1 Use the rational root theorem to find the possible rational roots of $f(x)$. The leading coefficient is 1 and the constant term is 10, so the possible rational roots are ± 1, ± 2, ± 5, and ± 10.

Step 2 Use synthetic division to test the possible roots.

$$\begin{array}{r|rrrrr} 1 & 1 & -3 & -11 & 3 & 10 \\ & & 1 & -2 & -13 & -10 \\ \hline & 1 & -2 & -13 & -10 & 0 \end{array}$$

Since 1 is a root, $x - 1$ is a factor. You can write the polynomial as $(x-1)\left(x^3 - 2x^2 - 13x - 10\right)$.

Use synthetic division to find a factor of the cubic polynomial $x^3 - 2x^2 - 13x - 10$. The leading coefficient is 1 and the constant term is -10, so the possible rational roots are ± 1, ± 2, ± 5, and ± 10.

$$\begin{array}{r|rrrr} -1 & 1 & -2 & -13 & -10 \\ & & -1 & 3 & 10 \\ \hline & 1 & -3 & -10 & 0 \end{array}$$

Since -1 is a root, $x + 1$ is a factor. You can write the polynomial as $(x-1)(x+1)\left(x^2 - 3x - 10\right)$.

Step 3 You could continue to use synthetic division to find the factors of the quadratic polynomial, but factoring it into two binomials is quicker. The function in factored form is $f(x) = (x - 1)(x + 1)(x - 5)(x + 2)$. The x-intercepts, then, are $1, -1, 5,$ and -2. Plot the x-intercepts.

▶ **Think About It** Note that there are an infinite number of polynomials with these four roots. These polynomials all have the form

$$f(x) = a(x - 1)(x + 1)(x - 5)(x + 2).$$

When you find another point, you can determine a by substituting for x and $f(x)$ in the equation.

Step 4 Graph the polynomial. Because the function is a polynomial with even degree and a positive leading coefficient, the graph approaches positive infinity as x approaches both negative and positive infinity. Use synthetic division to find additional points.

	1	-3	-11	3	10
-1.5	1	-4.5	-4.25	9.375	-4.0625
0	1	-3	-11	3	10
2	1	-1	-3	-23	-36
4	1	1	-7	-25	-90

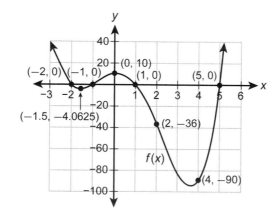

Graphing a Polynomial Function by Using Roots

EXAMPLE 3

Draw the graph of $p(x) = x^3 - x^2 - 5x + 2$.

SOLUTION

Step 1 Use the rational root theorem to find the possible rational roots of $p(x)$. The leading coefficient is 1 and the constant term is 2, so the possible rational roots are ± 1 and ± 2.

Step 2 Test the possible rational roots until you find a root of the polynomial.

$$
\begin{array}{r|rrrr}
 & 1 & -1 & -5 & 2 \\
\hline
-1 & 1 & -2 & -3 & 5 \\
1 & 1 & 0 & -5 & -3 \\
-2 & 1 & -3 & 1 & 0 \\
\end{array}
$$

Since -2 is a root, $x + 2$ is a factor. You can write the polynomial as $(x + 2)(x^2 - 3x + 1)$.

Step 3 Use the quadratic formula to solve $x^2 - 3x + 1 = 0$ and find the remaining two irrational roots.

$$x = \frac{3 \pm \sqrt{(-3)^2 - 4 \cdot 1 \cdot 1}}{2 \cdot 1}$$

$$= \frac{3 \pm \sqrt{5}}{2}$$

The roots of the polynomial are -2, $\dfrac{3 + \sqrt{5}}{2}$, and $\dfrac{3 - \sqrt{5}}{2}$.

Step 4 Graph the function. Plot the *x*-intercepts, which are -2, $\dfrac{3+\sqrt{5}}{2} \approx 2.62$, and $\dfrac{3-\sqrt{5}}{2} \approx 0.38$.

The function is cubic, so it is S-shaped. Because the function is a polynomial with odd degree and has a positive leading coefficient, the graph approaches negative infinity as *x* approaches negative infinity, and the graph approaches positive infinity as *x* approaches positive infinity.

Find and plot a few additional points.

x	-3	-1	0	1
p(*x*)	-19	5	2	-3

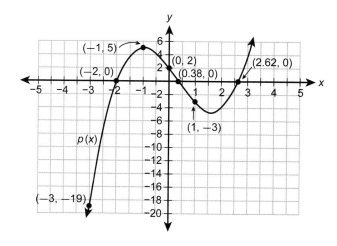

Factoring Polynomials Completely

Every polynomial of degree $n > 0$ can be written as the product of n linear factors.

Factoring a Binomial Over the Set of Complex Numbers

EXAMPLE 1

Write $x^2 + 25$ as the product of two linear factors.

SOLUTION

The equation $x^2 + 25 = 0$ is equivalent to the equation $x^2 = -25$, which has solutions $5i$ and $-5i$. Therefore, $x^2 + 25 = (x + 5i)(x - 5i)$. ▪

The polynomial in Example 1 has no real zeros, but it has two complex zeros. Some polynomials have both real zeros and complex zeros.

> ▶ **Think About It** Recall that the set of real numbers is a subset of the set of complex numbers. If a polynomial has both real zeros and complex zeros, then all of its zeros are complex. In fact, all the zeros of a polynomial can be considered complex.

Understanding Multiplicity

For a polynomial that has a linear factor appearing more than once, the idea of multiplicity is useful.

Definition
For any polynomial $p(x)$, a root a of $p(x)$ has **multiplicity** m if the factor $(x - a)$ occurs m times in the factorization of $p(x)$.

If a is a real root with odd multiplicity, the graph of the function crosses the x-axis at $x = a$. If a is a real root with even multiplicity, the graph of the function touches, but does not cross, the x-axis at $x = a$.

EXAMPLE 2

Given that $f(x) = x^4 - 5x^3 + x^2 + 21x - 18 = (x - 3)(x - 3)(x - 1)(x + 2)$:

A Find the multiplicity of each root of $f(x)$.

SOLUTION

The roots are 3, 3, 1, and -2. The root 3 occurs two times, so it has a multiplicity of 2. The roots 1 and -2 occur once, so each has a multiplicity of 1.

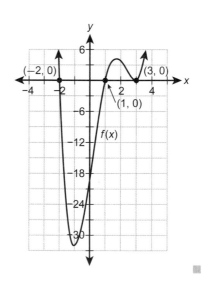

B Describe the behavior of the graph at each root.

SOLUTION

The graph of $f(x) = x^4 - 5x^3 + x^2 + 21x - 18$ shows the behavior of the function at its zeros. The graph crosses the x-axis at the zeros of odd multiplicity: $x = 1$ and $x = -2$. The graph touches, but does not cross, the x-axis at the root of even multiplicity: $x = 3$.

Finding the Number of Roots of a Polynomial

Fundamental Theorem of Algebra

Every polynomial $p(x)$ with degree n, $n > 0$, has at least one complex root.

Corollary Every polynomial $p(x)$ with degree n, $n > 0$, has n complex roots as long as any root with multiplicity m is counted m times.

EXAMPLE 3

Find the number of complex roots of the polynomial.

A $x^5 + 3x^4 + x^2 + 1$

SOLUTION

The polynomial has degree 5, so there are five complex roots.

B $x - 3$

SOLUTION

The polynomial has degree 1, so there is one complex root. ∎

Factoring a Polynomial Over the Set of Complex Numbers

How to Factor a Polynomial Completely Over the Set of Complex Numbers

Step 1 Use the degree of the polynomial to determine the total number of complex roots you need to find.

Step 2 Identify the possible rational roots.

Step 3 Find rational roots (using a graph, synthetic division, or other strategies) and use them to factor the polynomial.

Step 4 Factor the remaining polynomial.

EXAMPLE 4

Factor the polynomial completely. Then sketch the graph.

A $f(x) = x^3 - 6x^2 + 10x - 8$

SOLUTION

Step 1 The polynomial is of degree 3, so there are three complex roots.

Step 2 Use the rational root theorem to identify all possible rational roots. The leading coefficient is 1 and the constant is -8, so the possible rational roots are ± 1, ± 2, ± 4, and ± 8.

Step 3 Of the possible rational roots, only 4 is actually a root.

	1	-6	10	-8
1	1	-5	5	-3
-1	1	-7	17	-25
2	1	-4	2	-4
-2	1	-8	26	-60
4	1	-2	2	**0**

So $f(x) = (x - 4)(1x^2 - 2x + 2) = (x - 4)(x^2 - 2x + 2)$.

Step 4 Find the two remaining roots. Use the quadratic formula to solve $x^2 - 2x + 2 = 0$.

$$x = \frac{2 \pm \sqrt{(-2)^2 - 4 \cdot 1 \cdot 2}}{2 \cdot 1} = \frac{2 \pm \sqrt{-4}}{2}$$

$$= \frac{2 \pm 2i}{2}$$

$$= 1 \pm i$$

The roots $1 + i$ and $1 - i$ are complex. So the complete factorization of $f(x)$ is $f(x) = (x - 4)\left[x - (1 + i)\right]\left[x - (1 - i)\right]$.

The roots of the polynomial $f(x) = x^3 - 6x^2 + 10x - 8$ are 4, $1 + i$, and $1 - i$. In the graph of a function with both real roots and complex roots, only the real roots are x-intercepts. The graph of $f(x)$ shows that only the real root, 4, is an x-intercept.

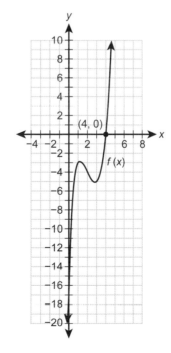

B $f(x) = x^4 - 2x^3 - 3x^2 + 2x + 2$

SOLUTION

Step 1 The polynomial is of degree 4, so there are four complex roots.

Step 2 By the rational root theorem, the possible rational roots are ± 1 and ± 2.

Step 3 Synthetic division shows -1 and 1 as roots.

$$
\begin{array}{r|rrrrr}
-1 & 1 & -2 & -3 & 2 & 2 \\
   &   & -1 & 3 & 0 & -2 \\
\hline
   & 1 & -3 & 0 & 2 & 0
\end{array}
$$

$$
\begin{array}{r|rrrr}
1 & 1 & -3 & 0 & 2 \\
  &   & 1 & -2 & -2 \\
\hline
  & 1 & -2 & -2 & 0
\end{array}
$$

So $f(x) = (x+1)(x-1)(1x^2 - 2x - 2)$.

> ▶ **Think About It** Use the quotient from the first synthetic division to set up the synthetic division for the next root. This will save you some work and give you a quotient that is a quadratic.

Step 4 Find the two remaining roots. Use the quadratic formula to solve $x^2 - 2x - 2 = 0$.

$$
x = \frac{2 \pm \sqrt{(-2)^2 - 4 \cdot 1(-2)}}{2 \cdot 1} = \frac{2 \pm \sqrt{12}}{2}
$$

$$
= \frac{2 \pm 2\sqrt{3}}{2}
$$

$$
= 1 \pm \sqrt{3}
$$

The roots $1 + \sqrt{3}$ and $1 - \sqrt{3}$ are irrational.

The factorization of $f(x)$ is

$$f(x) = (x+1)(x-1)\left[x - \left(1 + \sqrt{3}\right)\right]\left[x - \left(1 - \sqrt{3}\right)\right].$$

Because all the roots are real, all four roots are x-intercepts, as shown in the graph. The irrational roots are approximately -0.73 and 2.73.

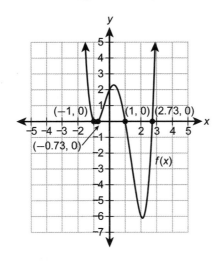

Rational Expressions

Topic List

Meteorologists use lots of math to understand, model, and predict weather. One example involves rational expressions in the Clausius-Clapeyron equation for water vapor, which helps them model precipitation such as rain, snow, and sleet.

Dividing Monomials and Polynomials

A ratio is a comparison of two quantities, often written as a fraction. If the quantities are represented by polynomials, the ratio is a rational expression.

Definition
A **rational expression** is a ratio whose numerator and denominator are polynomials, and whose denominator is nonzero.

▶ **Think About It** A rational expression has the form $\frac{p}{q}$, where p and q are polynomials and $q \neq 0$. The restriction $q \neq 0$ ensures that $\frac{p}{q}$ is defined.

Finding Restrictions on the Domain of a Rational Expression

To find the domain of a rational expression, find the values of the variables that make the denominator equal to 0. These values are excluded from the domain.

EXAMPLE 1

Find the domain restrictions for the expression.

A $\dfrac{x^4y}{3xy^5}$.

SOLUTION

$$3xy^5 = 0 \text{ when } x = 0 \text{ or } y = 0.$$

The domain restrictions are $x \neq 0$ and $y \neq 0$.

B $\dfrac{3x^3 - 7x}{4 - 3x}$

SOLUTION

$$4 - 3x = 0$$
$$4 = 3x$$
$$\frac{4}{3} = x$$

The domain restriction is $x \neq \dfrac{4}{3}$.

C $\dfrac{x^2 + 10x - 5}{x^2 + 2x - 48}$

SOLUTION

$$x^2 + 2x - 48 = 0$$
$$(x + 8)(x - 6) = 0$$
$$x + 8 = 0 \quad \text{or} \quad x - 6 = 0$$
$$x = -8 \qquad\qquad x = 6$$

The domain restrictions are $x \neq -8$ and $x \neq 6$. ■

Simplifying Rational Expressions

Simplifying a rational expression is similar to simplifying a fraction. Identify and divide out any factors you find in the numerator and the denominator. Be careful, though; both the numerator and the denominator must be written as products of factors. You can't divide out a factor in the denominator with a term that is being added in the numerator.

EXAMPLE 2

Find the domain restrictions and simplify the expression.

A $\dfrac{8x^2y^5}{24xy^7}$

SOLUTION

The domain restrictions are $x \neq 0$ and $y \neq 0$.

$\dfrac{8x^2y^5}{24xy^7} = \dfrac{8xy^5 \bullet x}{8xy^5 \bullet 3y^2}$ Factor the greatest common factor from the numerator and the denominator.

$= \dfrac{\overset{1}{\cancel{8xy^5}} \bullet x}{\underset{1}{\cancel{8xy^5}} \bullet 3y^2}$ Divide out the common factor.

$= \dfrac{x}{3y^2}$ Simplify.

B $\dfrac{8a^2 - 20a + 16}{4a}$

SOLUTION

To find the restrictions on the domain, set $4a = 0$ and solve.
The domain restriction is $a \neq 0$.

$\dfrac{8a^2 - 20a + 16}{4a} = \dfrac{8a^2}{4a} - \dfrac{20a}{4a} + \dfrac{16}{4a}$ Divide each term of the polynomial by the monomial.

$= \dfrac{\overset{2a}{\cancel{8a^2}}}{\underset{1}{\cancel{4a}}} - \dfrac{\overset{5}{\cancel{20a}}}{\underset{1}{\cancel{4a}}} + \dfrac{\overset{4}{\cancel{16}}}{\underset{a}{\cancel{4a}}}$ Divide out common factors.

$= 2a - 5 + \dfrac{4}{a}$ Simplify.

C $\dfrac{(x+1)(x+3)}{(x+1)(x+2)}$

SOLUTION

To find the restrictions on the domain, set $(x+1)(x+2) = 0$ and solve. The domain restrictions are $x \neq -1$ and $x \neq -2$.

$\dfrac{(x+1)(x+3)}{(x+1)(x+2)} = \dfrac{\overset{1}{\cancel{(x+1)}}(x+3)}{\underset{1}{\cancel{(x+1)}}(x+2)}$ Divide out the common factor.

$= \dfrac{x+3}{x+2}$ Simplify.

D $\dfrac{3x^2 + 16x - 12}{x^2 + 2x - 24}$

SOLUTION

To find the domain restrictions, set $x^2 + 2x - 24 = 0$ and solve.

$$x^2 + 2x - 24 = 0$$
$$(x - 4)(x + 6) = 0$$
$$x - 4 = 0 \quad \text{or} \quad x + 6 = 0$$
$$x = 4 \qquad\qquad x = -6$$

The domain restrictions are $x \neq 4$ and $x \neq -6$.

$$\dfrac{3x^2 + 16x - 12}{x^2 + 2x - 24} = \dfrac{(3x - 2)(x + 6)}{(x - 4)(x + 6)} \qquad \text{Factor the trinomials.}$$

$$= \dfrac{(3x - 2)\overset{1}{\cancel{(x + 6)}}}{(x - 4)\underset{1}{\cancel{(x + 6)}}} \qquad \text{Divide out the common factor.}$$

$$= \dfrac{3x - 2}{x - 4} \qquad \text{Simplify.}$$

E $\dfrac{5x^2 - 20x}{4 - x}$

SOLUTION

To find the restrictions on the domain, set $4 - x = 0$ and solve.

$$4 - x = 0$$
$$4 = x$$

The domain restriction is $x \neq 4$.

$$\dfrac{5x^2 - 20x}{4 - x} = \dfrac{5x(x - 4)}{4 - x} \qquad \text{Factor the numerator.}$$

$$= \dfrac{5x(x - 4)}{-1(x - 4)} \qquad \begin{array}{l} x - 4 \text{ and } 4 - x \text{ are opposites. Rewrite } 4 - x \\ \text{in the denominator as } -1(x - 4). \end{array}$$

$$= \dfrac{5x\overset{1}{\cancel{(x - 4)}}}{-1\underset{1}{\cancel{(x - 4)}}} \qquad \text{Divide out the common factor.}$$

$$= -5x \qquad \text{Simplify.} \;\blacksquare$$

> **Think About It** To demonstrate that $x - 4$ and $4 - x$ are opposites, choose a value for x. Let $x = 7$.
>
> Then $x - 4 = 7 - 4 = 3$ and $4 - x = 4 - 7 = -3$.
>
> In general, binomial factors of the forms $(a - b)$ and $(b - a)$ are opposites of each other, and $\dfrac{a - b}{b - a} = -1$.

Interpreting Real-World Rational Expressions

Algebraic expressions are often used to represent real-world situations. It is important to interpret the meaning of each term of the expression in the context of the problem.

EXAMPLE 3

Canoes 1 and 2 can travel at a rate of 9 mph when there is no current. Canoe 2 traveled 5 mi more than the distance (d) of Canoe 1.

The expression $\dfrac{d + 5}{9 + c}$ represents the time, in hours, it took for Canoe 2 to travel a particular distance when there is a current (c). Interpret the expressions $d + 5$ and $9 + c$ in the context of the problem.

SOLUTION

The distance formula is $d = rt$. When you divide this formula by r, you get the equation $t = \dfrac{d}{r}$.

The variable d in the expression $\dfrac{d + 5}{9 + c}$ represents the distance Canoe 1 traveled. Canoe 2 traveled 5 mi more than the distance of Canoe 1, so the distance traveled by Canoe 2 is $d + 5$.

Both canoes traveled at a rate of 9 mph with no current. The variable c represents the rate of the current in miles per hour. Canoe 2 traveled 9 mph plus the rate of the current, so the expression $9 + c$ represents Canoe 2's rate. ■

Complex Fractions

A compound event involves two or more actions. Similarly, a compound or complex fraction has two or more operations.

Definition

A **complex fraction** is a fraction that has a fraction in the numerator and/or denominator.

▶ **Think About It** A complex fraction can contain numerical fractions, rational expressions, or both.

Examples

$$\dfrac{\dfrac{1}{b}+3}{\dfrac{2}{b-5}} \qquad \dfrac{\dfrac{1}{4}-x}{\dfrac{1}{8}} \qquad \dfrac{\dfrac{1}{2}}{\dfrac{2}{5}}$$

Simplifying a Complex Fraction

To simplify a complex fraction, either multiply the numerator and the denominator of the complex fraction by a common denominator of the fractions within the fraction (the LCD method) or divide the numerator of the complex fraction by the denominator (the division method).

▶ **Remember** The LCD is the least common denominator of two or more fractions.

EXAMPLE 1

Simplify the expression.

A $\dfrac{\dfrac{2}{3}}{\dfrac{3}{5}}$

SOLUTION

LCD Method

$$\frac{\dfrac{2}{3}}{\dfrac{3}{5}} = \frac{\dfrac{2}{3} \bullet 15}{\dfrac{3}{5} \bullet 15} = \frac{\dfrac{2}{\cancel{3}} \bullet \overset{5}{\cancel{15}}}{\dfrac{3}{\cancel{5}} \bullet \overset{3}{\cancel{15}}} = \frac{10}{9} = 1\frac{1}{9}$$

Division Method

$$\frac{\dfrac{2}{3}}{\dfrac{3}{5}} = \frac{2}{3} \div \frac{3}{5} = \frac{2}{3} \bullet \frac{5}{3} = \frac{10}{9} = 1\frac{1}{9}$$

B $\dfrac{\dfrac{a}{b}}{\dfrac{c}{d}}$

SOLUTION

LCD Method

$$\frac{\dfrac{a}{b}}{\dfrac{c}{d}} = \frac{\dfrac{a}{b} \bullet bd}{\dfrac{c}{d} \bullet bd} = \frac{\dfrac{a}{\cancel{b}} \bullet \overset{d}{\cancel{bd}}}{\dfrac{c}{\cancel{d}} \bullet \overset{b}{\cancel{bd}}} = \frac{ad}{bc}$$

Division Method

$$\frac{\dfrac{a}{b}}{\dfrac{c}{d}} = \frac{a}{b} \div \frac{c}{d} = \frac{a}{b} \bullet \frac{d}{c} = \frac{ad}{bc} \ \blacksquare$$

EXAMPLE 2

Simplify the expression.

A $\dfrac{\dfrac{1}{2} + 5}{3 \ | \ \dfrac{1}{4}}$

SOLUTION

$$\frac{\frac{1}{2}+5}{3+\frac{1}{4}} = \frac{\left(\frac{1}{2}+5\right)\cdot 4}{\left(3+\frac{1}{4}\right)\cdot 4}$$ Multiply the numerator and denominator by the LCD: 4.

$$= \frac{\frac{1}{2}\cdot 4 + 5\cdot 4}{3\cdot 4 + \frac{1}{4}\cdot 4}$$ Distribute 4.

$$= \frac{2+20}{12+1}$$ Simplify.

$$= \frac{22}{13}$$ Simplify.

$$= 1\frac{9}{13}$$ Simplify.

B $$\dfrac{5+\dfrac{1}{2a}}{\dfrac{3}{2a}}$$

SOLUTION

$$\dfrac{5+\dfrac{1}{2a}}{\dfrac{3}{2a}} = \left(5+\frac{1}{2a}\right)\div\frac{3}{2a}$$ Rewrite as division.

$$= \left(\frac{5\cdot 2a}{2a}+\frac{1}{2a}\right)\div\frac{3}{2a}$$ Rewrite the first fraction of the dividend using the LCD: $2a$.

$$= \left(\frac{10a}{2a}+\frac{1}{2a}\right)\div\frac{3}{2a}$$ Simplify.

$$= \left(\frac{10a+1}{2a}\right)\div\frac{3}{2a}$$ Simplify.

$$= \frac{10a+1}{2a}\cdot\frac{2a}{3}$$ Division is the same as multiplication by the reciprocal of the divisor.

$$= \frac{10a+1}{\cancel{2a}_{1}}\cdot\frac{\cancel{2a}^{1}}{3}$$ Divide out the common factor.

$$= \frac{10a+1}{3}$$ Simplify. ■

Using an LCD to Simplify a Complex Algebraic Fraction

To simplify a complex fraction with variables, multiply the numerator and denominator by the LCD of all fractions that appear in the numerator or denominator. Then simplify. Use this method when there is addition or subtraction in a fraction of the numerator and/or denominator.

EXAMPLE 3

Simplify.

$$\frac{\dfrac{1}{x-3}+\dfrac{3}{x}}{\dfrac{2}{x-3}}$$

SOLUTION

$$\frac{\dfrac{1}{x-3}+\dfrac{3}{x}}{\dfrac{2}{x-3}} = \frac{\dfrac{1}{x-3}+\dfrac{3}{x}}{\dfrac{2}{x-3}} \cdot \frac{x(x-3)}{x(x-3)}$$

Multiply the numerator and denominator by the LCD: $x(x-3)$.

$$= \frac{\dfrac{1}{x-3}\cdot x(x-3)+\dfrac{3}{x}\cdot x(x-3)}{\dfrac{2}{(x-3)}\cdot x(x-3)}$$

Distribute $x(x-3)$.

$$= \frac{\dfrac{1}{\cancel{(x-3)}}\cdot x\cancel{(x-3)}^{1}+\dfrac{3}{\cancel{x}}\cdot \cancel{x}(x-3)}{\dfrac{2}{\cancel{(x-3)}_{1}}\cdot x\cancel{(x-3)}_{1}}$$

Divide out common factors.

$$= \frac{x+3(x-3)}{2x}$$

Simplify.

$$= \frac{4x-9}{2x}$$

Simplify. ▪

Adding and Subtracting Rational Expressions

As with numbers, rational expressions can be added and subtracted.

Adding or Subtracting Rational Expressions with Like Denominators

To add or subtract rational expressions with like denominators, add or subtract the numerators. Keep the same common denominator.

EXAMPLE 1

Add.

$$\frac{x^2 + 2x}{x - 3} + \frac{x^2 - 3x - 15}{x - 3}$$

SOLUTION

$$\frac{x^2 + 2x}{x - 3} + \frac{x^2 - 3x - 15}{x - 3} = \frac{\left(x^2 + 2x\right) + \left(x^2 - 3x - 15\right)}{x - 3}$$ Add the numerators.

$$= \frac{2x^2 - x - 15}{x - 3}$$ Combine like terms.

$$= \frac{(2x + 5)\overset{1}{\cancel{(x - 3)}}}{\underset{1}{\cancel{(x - 3)}}}$$ Factor and simplify if possible.

$$= 2x + 5$$ Simplify. ∎

Adding or Subtracting Rational Expressions with Unlike Denominators

To add or subtract rational expressions with unlike denominators, first rewrite the expressions with a common denominator, preferably the least common denominator. Then add or subtract. Just like with any fractions, the least common denominator of two rational expressions is the least common multiple of the denominators.

> ▶ **Think About It** Use these steps to find the least common denominator:
>
> **Step 1** Fully factor each denominator.
>
> **Step 2** Write each factor the greatest number of times it appears in any one denominator.
>
> **Step 3** Multiply the factors described in Step 2; the LCD is the product of those factors.

EXAMPLE 2

Subtract.

A $\dfrac{7x+3}{(x+1)(x-3)} - \dfrac{5}{x+1}$

SOLUTION

$$\dfrac{7x+3}{(x+1)(x-3)} - \dfrac{5}{x+1} \qquad \text{The denominators are in factored form.}$$

The LCD is $\quad x+1 \quad \bullet \quad x-3$.

$(x+1)$ appears once in the first and the second denominators.

$(x-3)$ appears once in the first denominator.

$$= \frac{7x+3}{(x+1)(x-3)} - \frac{5}{x+1} \cdot \frac{x-3}{x-3}$$

The first ratio has the LCD. Multiply the second ratio by 1. For the appropriate form of 1, decide what factor(s) would be needed to get the LCD.

$$= \frac{7x+3}{(x+1)(x-3)} - \frac{5x-15}{(x+1)(x-3)}$$

Expand the second numerator.

$$= \frac{(7x+3) - (5x-15)}{(x+1)(x-3)}$$

Subtract the numerators.

$$= \frac{2x+18}{(x+1)(x-3)} = \frac{2(x+9)}{(x+1)(x-3)}$$

Simplify the numerator.

B $\dfrac{8}{5a^3 + 25a^2} - \dfrac{a+2}{a^3 + 10a^2 + 25a}$

SOLUTION

$$\frac{8}{5a^3 + 25a^2} - \frac{a+2}{a^3 + 10a^2 + 25a}$$

$$= \frac{8}{5a^2(a+5)} - \frac{a+2}{a(a+5)(a+5)}$$

Factor the denominators so you can find the LCD.

The LCD is $\underbrace{5}_{} \cdot \underbrace{a^2}_{} \cdot \underbrace{(a+5)(a+5)}_{}$.

| 5 appears once in the first denominator. | a appears twice (second power) in the first denominator and once in the second. | (a + 5) appears twice in the second denominator. |

$$= \frac{8}{5a^2(a+5)} \cdot \frac{a+5}{a+5} - \frac{a+2}{a(a+5)(a+5)} \cdot \frac{5a}{5a}$$

Multiply each ratio by 1. To determine the appropriate form of 1 for each ratio, decide what factor(s) would be needed to get the LCD as the denominator.

$$= \frac{8a+40}{5a^2(a+5)(a+5)} - \frac{5a^2+10a}{5a^2(a+5)(a+5)}$$

Expand the numerators.

$$= \frac{(8a+40) - (5a^2+10a)}{5a^2(a+5)(a+5)}$$

Subtract the numerators.

$$= \frac{-5a^2 - 2a + 40}{5a^2(a+5)(a+5)}$$

Simplify the numerator to get $-5a^2 - 2a + 40$, which cannot be factored. ∎

Multiplying and Dividing Rational Expressions

As with numbers, rational expressions can be multiplied and divided.

Multiplying Rational Expressions

To multiply rational expressions, multiply the numerators and multiply the denominators. Divide out common factors to simplify.

EXAMPLE 1

Multiply.

A $\dfrac{3h}{(h-7)(h-2)} \cdot \dfrac{h-7}{h(h+8)}$

SOLUTION

$\dfrac{3h}{(h-7)(h-2)} \cdot \dfrac{h-7}{h(h+8)} = \dfrac{3h(h-7)}{(h-7)(h-2)(h)(h+8)}$

The polynomials are in factored form, so multiply the numerators and the denominators.

$= \dfrac{3\cancel{h}(\cancel{h-7})}{(\cancel{h-7})(h-2)(\cancel{h})(h+8)}$

Divide out common factors.

$= \dfrac{3}{(h-2)(h+8)}$

Simplify.

$= \dfrac{3}{h^2 \mid 6h \quad 16}$

Alternate simplified form

▶ **Think About It** Both $\dfrac{3}{(h-2)(h+8)}$ and $\dfrac{3}{h^2+6h-16}$ are in simplified form. Recognizing that they are equal can be helpful when you work with rational functions.

B $\dfrac{2x^2 - 10x}{x^2 - 2x - 8} \cdot \dfrac{x + 2}{6x^3 - 30x^2}$

SOLUTION

$$\dfrac{2x^2 - 10x}{x^2 - 2x - 8} \cdot \dfrac{x + 2}{6x^3 - 30x^2} = \dfrac{2x(x - 5)}{(x + 2)(x - 4)} \cdot \dfrac{x + 2}{6x^2(x - 5)}$$ Factor the polynomials.

$$= \dfrac{2x(x - 5)(x + 2)}{(x + 2)(x - 4)(6x^2)(x - 5)}$$ Multiply the numerators and the denominators.

$$= \dfrac{2x(x - 5)(x + 2)}{(x + 2)(x - 4)(2x \cdot 3x)(x - 5)}$$ Divide out common factors. To identify the greatest common monomial factor, write $6x^2$ as $2x \cdot 3x$.

$$= \dfrac{1}{(3x)(x - 4)}$$ Simplify.

$$= \dfrac{1}{3x^2 - 12x}$$ Alternate simplified form ▪

Dividing Rational Expressions

To divide by a rational expression, multiply by its reciprocal.

EXAMPLE 2

Divide.

A $\dfrac{5(x - 2)}{(x + 12)\,(x + 3)} \div \dfrac{15(x - 2)}{x\,(x + 12)}$

SOLUTION

Write the division problem as multiplying by a reciprocal.

$$\dfrac{5(x - 2)}{(x + 12)\,(x + 3)} \div \dfrac{15(x - 2)}{x\,(x + 12)} = \dfrac{5(x - 2)}{(x + 12)(x + 3)} \cdot \dfrac{x\,(x + 12)}{15(x - 2)}$$ Multiply by the reciprocal of the divisor.

$$= \dfrac{5(x - 2)(x)(x + 12)}{(x + 12)(x + 3)(15)(x - 2)}$$ Multiply numerators and denominators. Divide out common factors.

$$= \dfrac{x}{3(x + 3)} \text{ or } \dfrac{x}{3x + 9}$$ Simplify.

B $\dfrac{p^2 - 16}{4p^2 + 4p + 1} \div \dfrac{2p^2 - 7p - 4}{6p^2 + 3p}$

SOLUTION

Write the division problem as multiplying by a reciprocal.

$$\dfrac{p^2 - 16}{4p^2 + 4p + 1} \div \dfrac{2p^2 - 7p - 4}{6p^2 + 3p} = \dfrac{p^2 - 16}{4p^2 + 4p + 1} \cdot \dfrac{6p^2 + 3p}{2p^2 - 7p - 4}$$
Multiply by the reciprocal of the divisor.

$$= \dfrac{(p + 4)(p - 4)}{(2p + 1)(2p + 1)} \cdot \dfrac{3p(2p + 1)}{(p - 4)(2p + 1)}$$
Factor.

$$= \dfrac{(p + 4)\cancel{(p - 4)}(3p)\cancel{(2p + 1)}}{(2p + 1)(2p + 1)\cancel{(p - 4)}\cancel{(2p + 1)}}$$
Multiply numerators and denominators. Divide out common factors.

$$= \dfrac{3p(p + 4)}{(2p + 1)^2} \text{ or } \dfrac{3p^2 + 12p}{4p^2 + 4p + 1}$$
Simplify. ■

Solving Rational Equations

A rational equation is an equation that contains one or more rational expressions.

Methods of Solving Rational Equations

LCD method Multiply both sides of the equation by the least common denominator (LCD) of the rational expressions. Then solve the resulting equation. This method works for any rational equation.

Cross multiplication method If the equation is in a form that looks like $\frac{a}{b} = \frac{c}{d}$, you can cross multiply, then solve the resulting equation.
The method of cross multiplying is based on the following property:

$$\frac{a}{b} = \frac{c}{d} \text{ if and only if } ad = bc$$

Because rational equations have variables in denominators, you have to be careful with the domain. Any value of the variable that makes a denominator equal zero cannot be a solution, and therefore must be excluded. It's a good idea to start by identifying those values that must be excluded before you begin to solve the equation.

▶ **Think About It** If you forget to identify the values that must be excluded, you should discover them when you check your solutions.

EXAMPLE 1

Solve and check.

$$\frac{15}{x-6} = \frac{5}{x}$$

SOLUTION

To find the restrictions on the domain, set the denominators equal to zero and solve. The domain restrictions are $x \neq 0$ and $x \neq 6$. Now solve the equation.

$$\frac{15}{x-6} = \frac{5}{x}$$

$15x = 5(x-6)$ Cross multiply.

$15x = 5x - 30$ Distribute the 5.

$10x = -30$ Subtract $5x$.

$x = -3$ Divide by 10.

CHECK

$$\frac{15}{x-6} = \frac{5}{x}$$

$$\frac{15}{-3-6} \stackrel{?}{=} \frac{5}{-3}$$ Substitute -3 for x in the original equation.

$$\frac{15}{-9} \stackrel{?}{=} \frac{5}{-3}$$

$$-\frac{5}{3} = -\frac{5}{3} \checkmark$$ Substituting -3 results in a true statement.

Since $x = -3$ is not in the domain restrictions, the solution set is $\{-3\}$. ■

▶ **Think About It** A rational equation is a proportion if it has the form $\frac{a}{b} = \frac{c}{d}$, where $\frac{a}{b}$ and $\frac{c}{d}$ are rational expressions.

Solving Rational Equations and Checking for Extraneous Solutions

The zero product property can be used to identify domain restrictions or solve more complicated equations.

Zero Product Property

For any real numbers a and b, $ab = 0$ if and only if $a = 0$ or $b = 0$.

▶ **Remember** See how to apply the property with this example.

$$(x - 4)(x + 1) = 0$$
$$(x - 4) = 0 \quad \text{or} \quad (x + 1) = 0$$
$$x = 4 \qquad\qquad x = -1$$

So the solutions to the equation are $x = 4$ and $x = -1$.

EXAMPLE 2

Solve and check.

A $\dfrac{3}{x^2 + 5x + 6} + \dfrac{x - 1}{x + 2} = \dfrac{7}{x + 3}$

SOLUTION

First identify values of x that must be excluded from the domain.

$$\frac{3}{x^2 + 5x + 6} + \frac{x - 1}{x + 2} = \frac{7}{x + 3} \qquad \text{Original equation}$$

$$\frac{3}{(x + 2)(x + 3)} + \frac{x - 1}{x + 2} = \frac{7}{x + 3} \qquad \text{Factor the first denominator.}$$

If $x = -2$, then $x + 2 = 0$, which makes two denominators equal zero.
If $x = -3$, then $x + 3 = 0$, which makes two denominators equal zero.

So -2 and -3 must be excluded as possible solutions. Now solve the equation.

$$\frac{3}{(x+2)(x+3)} + \frac{x-1}{x+2} = \frac{7}{x+3}$$

Keep denominators in factored form to help identify the LCD.

$$(x+2)(x+3)\left[\frac{3}{(x+2)(x+3)} + \frac{x-1}{x+2}\right]$$

Multiply both sides by the LCD.

$$=(x+2)(x+3)\left(\frac{7}{x+3}\right)$$

$$\cancel{(x+2)}\cancel{(x+3)}\frac{3}{\cancel{(x+2)}\cancel{(x+3)}} + \cancel{(x+2)}\,(x+3)\frac{x-1}{\cancel{x+2}}$$

Distribute the LCD. Divide out common factors.

$$=(x+2)\cancel{(x+3)}\frac{7}{\cancel{x+3}}$$

$$3 + (x+3)(x-1) = (x+2)\cdot 7$$

Simplify.

$$3 + x^2 + 2x - 3 = 7x + 14$$

Multiply binomials. Distribute 7.

$$x^2 + 2x = 7x + 14$$

Simplify.

$$x^2 - 5x - 14 = 0$$

Add $-7x - 14$ to both sides.

$$(x-7)(x+2) = 0$$

Factor the trinomial.

$$x - 7 = 0 \quad \text{or} \quad x + 2 = 0$$

Zero Product Property

$$x = 7 \qquad\qquad x = -2$$

CHECK

Substitute 7 for x.

$$\frac{3}{x^2 + 5x + 6} + \frac{x - 1}{x + 2} = \frac{7}{x + 3}$$

$$\frac{3}{7^2 + 5 \cdot 7 + 6} + \frac{7 - 1}{7 + 2} \overset{?}{=} \frac{7}{7 + 3}$$

$$\frac{3}{49 + 35 + 6} + \frac{6}{9} \overset{?}{=} \frac{7}{10}$$

$$\frac{3}{90} + \frac{60}{90} \overset{?}{=} \frac{63}{90}$$

$$\frac{63}{90} = \frac{63}{90} \checkmark$$

So 7 is a solution.

Substitute -2 for x.

$$\frac{3}{x^2 + 5x + 6} + \frac{x - 1}{x + 2} = \frac{7}{x + 3}$$

$$\frac{3}{(-2)^2 + 5 \cdot (-2) + 6} + \frac{-2 - 1}{-2 + 2} \overset{?}{=} \frac{7}{-2 + 3}$$

$$\frac{3}{0} + \frac{-3}{0} \neq \frac{7}{1}$$

Here, -2 is called an extraneous solution because it does not make the original equation true. Recall that -2 was identified as a value that must be excluded as a possible solution anyway.

The solution set is $\{7\}$.

B $\dfrac{10}{n} = \dfrac{n+9}{n-4} - 3$

SOLUTION

First note that 0 and 4 must be excluded as possible solutions because each value makes a denominator equal zero. Solve the equation.

$$\frac{10}{n} = \frac{n+9}{n-4} - 3$$

$$n(n-4)\frac{10}{n} = n(n-4)\frac{n+9}{n-4} + n(n-4)(-3)$$

$$\cancel{n}(n-4)\frac{10}{\cancel{n}} = n\cancel{(n-4)}\frac{n+9}{\cancel{n-4}} + n(n-4)(-3)$$

$$(n-4)10 = n(n+9) - 3n(n-4)$$

$$10n - 40 = n^2 + 9n - 3n^2 + 12n$$

$$2n^2 - 11n - 40 = 0$$

$$(2n+5)(n-8) = 0$$

Apply the zero product property.

$$2n + 5 = 0 \qquad \text{or} \qquad n - 8 = 0$$

$$n = -\frac{5}{2} \qquad\qquad n = 8$$

CHECK

Substitute $-\dfrac{5}{2}$ for n.

$$\frac{10}{n} = \frac{n+9}{n-4} - 3$$

$$\frac{10}{-\dfrac{5}{2}} \overset{?}{=} \frac{-\dfrac{5}{2}+9}{-\dfrac{5}{2}-4} - 3$$

$$\frac{10}{-\dfrac{5}{2}} \overset{?}{=} \frac{\dfrac{13}{2}}{-\dfrac{13}{2}} - 3$$

$$\frac{10}{1} \cdot \left(-\frac{2}{5}\right) \overset{?}{=} \frac{13}{2} \cdot \left(-\frac{2}{13}\right) - 3$$

$$-4 \overset{?}{=} -1 - 3$$

$$-4 = -4 \checkmark$$

Substitute 8 for n.

$$\frac{10}{n} = \frac{n+9}{n-4} - 3$$

$$\frac{10}{8} \overset{?}{=} \frac{8+9}{8-4} - 3$$

$$\frac{5}{4} \overset{?}{=} \frac{17}{4} - \frac{12}{4}$$

$$\frac{5}{4} = \frac{5}{4} \checkmark$$

The solution set is $\left\{ -\frac{5}{2}, 8 \right\}$. ∎

Solving a Rate Problem

EXAMPLE 3

It takes 6 h for Pump A to fill a tank. It takes 4 h for Pump A and Pump B together to fill the same tank. How long would it take Pump B alone to fill the tank?

SOLUTION

Pump A alone can fill the tank in 6 h, so it fills $\frac{1}{6}$ of the tank each hour. Pumps A and B together can fill the tank in 4 h, so they fill $\frac{1}{4}$ of the tank each hour. Let x be the number of hours it takes Pump B to fill the tank alone. Then Pump B alone fills $\frac{1}{x}$ of the tank each hour. Now reason as follows: Pump A fills $\frac{1}{6}$ of the tank in 1 h, $\frac{2}{6}$ of the tank in 2 h, $\frac{3}{6}$ of the tank in 3 h, and so on. Pump B fills $\frac{1}{x}$ of the tank in 1 h, $\frac{2}{x}$ of the tank in 2 h, $\frac{3}{x}$ of the tank in 3 h, and so on.

Write an equation.

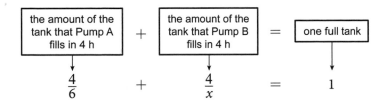

$$\frac{4}{6} + \frac{4}{x} = 1$$

Solve the equation.

$$\frac{4}{6} + \frac{4}{x} = 1$$

$$6x \cdot \frac{4}{6} + 6x \cdot \frac{4}{x} = 6x \cdot 1 \qquad \text{Multiply both sides by the LCD.}$$

$$\cancel{6}x \cdot \frac{4}{\cancel{6}} + 6\cancel{x} \cdot \frac{4}{\cancel{x}} = 6x \cdot 1 \qquad \text{Divide out common factors.}$$

$$4x + 24 = 6x \qquad \text{Simplify.}$$

$$24 = 2x$$

$$12 = x$$

Substitute 12 for x in the original equation to verify that 12 is the solution. It would take 12 h for Pump B to fill the tank alone. ▪

> ▶ **Think About It** For the equation $\frac{4}{6} + \frac{4}{x} = 1$, the value 0 must be excluded as a possible solution.

Solving a Work Problem

EXAMPLE 4

Mario can finish all the house chores twice as fast as his sister Ana can. Together, they can do the job in 2 h. How long would it take each of them working alone?

SOLUTION

Let x be the number of hours it takes Mario to do the chores alone. Mario does the job twice as fast as Ana, so Ana would take $2x$ hours to do the chores by herself. Then Mario does $\frac{1}{x}$ of the chores each hour, and Ana can do $\frac{1}{2x}$ of the chores each hour. Mario and Ana together can finish the chores in 2 h, so together they can do $\frac{1}{2}$ of the job each hour. Write an equation that combines Mario's and Ana's labor for each hour.

$$\frac{1}{x} + \frac{1}{2x} = \frac{1}{2}$$

Solve the equation.

$$\frac{1}{x} + \frac{1}{2x} = \frac{1}{2}$$

$$2x \cdot \frac{1}{x} + 2x \cdot \frac{1}{2x} = 2x \cdot \frac{1}{2} \qquad \text{Multiply both sides by the LCD.}$$

$$2x \cdot \frac{1}{x} + 2\!\!\!/x \cdot \frac{1}{2\!\!\!/x} = 2x \cdot \frac{1}{2\!\!\!/} \qquad \text{Divide out common factors.}$$

$$2 + 1 = x \qquad \text{Simplify.}$$

$$3 = x$$

Substitute 3 for x in the original equation to verify that 3 is the solution. It would take 3 h for Mario to do all the house chores alone, and it would take twice as long, or 6 h, for Ana to do the job alone. ∎

Solving for a Variable in a Real-World Rational Equation

Solving for a variable in a real-world rational equation does not always produce a numerical value. However, the steps used to solve the equation are the same.

EXAMPLE 5

One way to express the work formula is in the form $\frac{t}{a} + \frac{t}{b} = 1$, where t is the time it takes two people to complete the work, a is the time it takes Person A to complete the work alone, and b is the time it takes Person B to complete the work alone. Solve this equation for t.

SOLUTION

Multiply both sides of the equation by the least common denominator ab, making it easier to solve for t.

$$\frac{t}{a} + \frac{t}{b} = 1$$

$$ab \cdot \left(\frac{t}{a}\right) + ab \cdot \left(\frac{t}{b}\right) = ab \cdot 1 \qquad \text{Multiply both sides by the LCD.}$$

$$\cancel{a}b\left(\frac{t}{\cancel{a}}\right) + a\cancel{b}\left(\frac{t}{\cancel{b}}\right) = ab \qquad \text{Divide out common factors.}$$

$$bt + at = ab \qquad \text{Simplify.}$$

$$t(b + a) = ab \qquad \text{Distributive Property}$$

$$t(a + b) = ab \qquad \text{Commutative Property}$$

$$t = \frac{ab}{(a + b)} \qquad \text{Divide both sides by } (a + b).$$

When solved for t, the expression $\frac{t}{a} + \frac{t}{b} = 1$ is $t = \frac{ab}{(a + b)}$. ∎

Exponential and Logarithmic Functions

Topic List

The amount of light that makes it through a camera lens to expose the sensor depends on the area of the opening and the exposure time. The shutter controls the amount of time the light passes through and the exposure is a logarithmic function of the time the shutter is open.

Modeling with Exponential Equations and Expressions

Exponential equations and expressions can be used to represent quantities that grow or decay by a fixed percent at regular intervals.

Identifying Growth, Decay, and Rates of Change

An exponential function has the form $y = a(b)^x$, where a is any nonzero real number and b is the base of the function such that $b > 0$ and $b \neq 1$. When $a > 0$ and $b > 1$, the function increases or grows exponentially. When $a > 0$ and $0 < b < 1$, the function decreases or decays exponentially.

Definition
Exponential growth occurs when a quantity increases by the same percent at regular intervals over a given period of time. This situation is modeled by the equation $$y = A(1 + r)^t$$ where A is the initial amount, r is the rate of change expressed as a decimal, and t represents time.

For example, if $2500 is invested at an annual interest rate of 3% for t years, then the equation $y = 2500(1 + 0.03)^t = 2500(1.03)^t$ represents the value of the investment after t years.

Definition

Exponential decay occurs when a quantity decreases by the same percent at regular intervals over a given period of time. This situation is modeled by the equation

$$y = A(1 - r)^t$$

where A is the initial amount, r is the rate of change expressed as a decimal, and t represents time.

For example, if a bicycle tire contains 1400 in^3 of air and loses 2.5% of its air each day, then the equation $y = 1400(1 - 0.025)^t$ or $y = 1400(0.975)^t$ represents the amount of air in the tire after t days.

EXAMPLE 1

Determine whether each equation represents exponential growth or decay. Then find the rate of growth or decay.

A $y = 250(0.86)^x$

SOLUTION

Transform the equation into the form $y = A(1 + r)^t$ or $y = A(1 - r)^t$.

$$y = 250(0.86)^x$$
$$y = 250(1 - 0.14)^x$$

The equation can be rewritten in the form $y = A(1 - r)^x$, where $A = 250$ and $r = 0.14$. Because the rate is subtracted from 1, the equation represents exponential decay.

$$0.14 = \frac{14}{100} = 14\% \qquad \text{Write the rate as a percent.}$$

The rate of decay is a 14% decrease every x units of time.

B $y = 1.44^{\frac{t}{2}}$

SOLUTION

Use the properties of exponents to rewrite the equation with only t in the exponent.

$y = 1.44^{\frac{t}{2}}$

$y = 1.44^{\frac{1}{2} \cdot t}$ Rewrite the exponent.

$y = \left(1.44^{\frac{1}{2}}\right)^{t}$ Power of a Power Rule

$y = (1.2)^{t}$ Simplify.

Transform the exponential equation into the form $y = A(1 + r)^{t}$ or $y = A(1 - r)^{t}$.

$$y = (1.2)^{t}$$
$$y = (1 + 0.2)^{t}$$

The equation can be rewritten in the form $y = A(1 + r)^{t}$, where $A = 1$ and $r = 0.2$. Because the rate is added to 1, the equation represents exponential growth.

$0.20 = \dfrac{20}{100} = 20\%$ Write the rate as a percent.

The rate of growth is a 20% increase every t units of time. ■

▶ **Think About It** When an exponential model is in the form $y = a(b)^{x}$, you can tell at a glance whether it represents exponential growth or decay by examining b. If $0 < b < 1$, the model represents exponential decay. If $b > 1$, the model represents exponential growth.

Modeling with Exponential Equations

You can use exponential equations to model and solve problems.

EXAMPLE 2

The number of visitors to a state park grows at an annual rate of about 1.69%. This year, the number of visitors was 44,505.

A Write an exponential growth equation to model the situation.

SOLUTION

The initial amount is $A = 44{,}505$.

The annual growth rate is 1.69%. Write this rate as a decimal.

$$r = 1.69\% = \frac{1.69}{100} = 0.0169$$

Substitute the values of A and r into the equation $y = A(1 + r)^t$ and simplify.

$$y = 44{,}505(1 + 0.0169)^t$$
$$= 44{,}505(1.0169)^t$$

The exponential equation $y = 44{,}505(1.0169)^t$ models the number of annual visitors to the park after t years.

B According to the model, about how many visitors are expected 10 years from now?

SOLUTION

Substitute $t = 10$ in the equation and simplify.

$$y = 44{,}505(1.0169)^{10}$$
$$\approx 52{,}625$$

About 52,625 visitors are expected 10 years from now. ▮

Interpreting Exponential Expressions

You can use the properties of exponents to transform and interpret exponential expressions.

EXAMPLE 3

A deer population with population P is expected to decline according to the model $P(0.344)^{\frac{m}{4}}$, where m is the number of months. What is the monthly rate of decrease?

SOLUTION

Use the properties of exponents to rewrite the expression with only m in the exponent.

$P(0.344)^{\frac{m}{4}}$

$P(0.344)^{\frac{1}{4} \cdot m}$ Rewrite the exponent.

$P\left(0.344^{\frac{1}{4}}\right)^{m}$ Power of a Power Rule

$P(0.7658)^{m}$ Simplify.

Transform the exponential expression into the form $A(1+r)^{t}$ or $A(1-r)^{t}$.

$$P(0.7658)^{m}$$
$$P(1 - 0.2342)^{m}$$

The expression can be rewritten in the form $A(1-r)^{t}$, where $A = P$ and $r = 0.2342$. Because the rate is subtracted from 1, the expression represents exponential decay.

$0.2342 = 23.42\%$ Write the rate as a percent.

The monthly rate of decrease is 23.42%. ∎

Exponential Equations and Graphs

Exponential equations are a powerful way to model growth and decay.

Solving Exponential Equations

Definition
An **exponential equation** contains a variable in an exponent.

To solve an exponential equation, isolate the term with the variable exponent. Use properties of exponents and transformations to make the terms on each side of the equals sign have equal bases. Then compare the exponents.

EXAMPLE 1

Solve.

A $2\sqrt{2} = 4^x$

SOLUTION

Transform each side of the equation so that 2 is the base. Then use the laws of exponents to simplify.

$$2\sqrt{2} = 4^x$$

$$2^1 \cdot 2^{\frac{1}{2}} = \left(2^2\right)^x \qquad \text{Rewrite the left side using exponents.}$$

$$2^{\frac{3}{2}} = 2^{2x} \qquad \text{Apply properties of exponents.}$$

$$\frac{3}{2} = 2x \qquad \text{Set the exponents equal to each other.}$$

$$\frac{3}{4} = x \qquad \text{Divide each side by 2.}$$

B $e^{3-x} = 1$

SOLUTION

Transform each side of the equation so that e is the base. Then use the laws of exponents to simplify.

$e^{3-x} = 1$

$e^{3-x} = e^0$ Rewrite 1 as a power of e.

$3 - x = 0$ Set the exponents equal to each other.

$3 = x$ Addition Property of Equality ■

Graphing Exponential Functions

How to Graph an Exponential Function

To graph an equation of the form $f(x) = ab^x + k$,

Step 1 Determine the horizontal asymptote $y = k$.

Step 2 Plot the y-intercept $(0, a + k)$.

Step 3 Plot two other points on the graph.

Step 4 Draw a smooth curve connecting the points.

EXAMPLE 2

$f(x) = 2 \cdot 3^x - 1$

A Graph the function.

SOLUTION

Step 1 Determine the horizontal asymptote.

$$y = -1$$

Step 2 Plot the y-intercept.

$$(0, 2 + (-1)) = (0, 1)$$

Step 3 Plot two other points on the graph.

$$\left(-1, -\frac{1}{3}\right) \text{ and } (1, 5)$$

Step 4 Draw a smooth curve connecting the points.

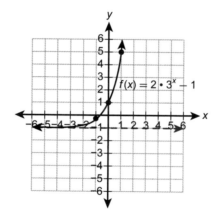

B Determine the domain and range.

SOLUTION

From the graph, you can see that x can take on any value; therefore, the domain is all real numbers. The graph also shows that the y-values are all greater than -1, so the range is $y > -1$. ■

Determining an Exponential Function

You can write an exponential function to match a situation by determining the parameters a, b, and k.

EXAMPLE 3

What is an exponential function of the form $f(x) = ab^x + k$ that contains the points $(0, 4)$ and $(1, 5)$ and has a horizontal asymptote of $y = 2$?

▶ **Think About It** $f(0)$ gives the value for the y-intercept.

SOLUTION

Step 1 Use the horizontal asymptote to determine k.

The horizontal asymptote is $y = k$, and the problem states that $y = 2$. So $k = 2$.

Step 2 Use the coordinates of the given points to determine a and b.

Substitute the values of k and the y-intercept of $(0, 4)$ into the function $f(x) = ab^x + k$. Solve for a.

$$4 = a \cdot b^0 + 2$$
$$4 = a + 2$$
$$a = 2$$

Substitute the values of a, k, and a different point, such as $(1, 5)$, into the function $f(x) = ab^x + k$. Solve for b.

$$5 = 2 \cdot b^1 + 2$$
$$3 = 2b$$
$$b = \frac{3}{2}$$

Step 3 Substitute the values of a, b, and k into $f(x) = ab^x + k$.

$$f(x) = 2 \cdot \left(\frac{3}{2}\right)^x + 2 \ \blacksquare$$

Inverses

The graphs of function inverses are reflections of each other over the line $y = x$.

Visualizing the Inverse of a Graph

Relations and graphs have inverses.

Definition

The **inverse of a relation** switches the x- and y-values of the ordered pairs of the original relation. The domain of the inverse relation is the range of the original relation. The range of the inverse relation is the domain of the original relation. The graph of the inverse of a relation is its reflection over the line $y = x$.

EXAMPLE 1

Graph the inverse of the function $f(x) = x^2 - 2$.

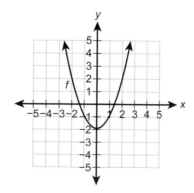

SOLUTION

To create the graph of the inverse, reflect the graph over the line $y = x$. That will switch the x- and y-values of the ordered pairs. The points $(0, -2)$ and $(-2, 2)$ on the original graph become the points $(-2, 0)$ and $(2, -2)$ on the inverse of the graph.

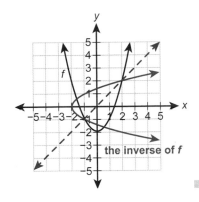

Using the Horizontal Line Test

Some functions will have inverses that are functions while others will not.

Definitions
A function f is **invertible** if its inverse is also a function.   The **inverse of a function** f is denoted by f^{-1}.

To determine whether a function f is invertible, you could use the **horizontal line test**. If a horizontal line intersects a function more than once, then the function is not invertible—that is, the inverse of the function is not a function.

However, if every horizontal line intersects a function only once, then the function is invertible.

EXAMPLE 2

Determine whether $f(x) = |x + 1|$ is invertible.

SOLUTION

Graph the function.

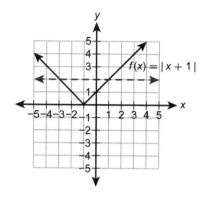

There are many horizontal lines (such as the line $y = 2$ drawn on the graph) that intersect the graph at two points. The function is not invertible because it fails the horizontal line test. ▪

Determining the Inverse of a Function

How to Determine the Inverse of a Function

Step 1 Replace $f(x)$ with y.

Step 2 Switch x and y.

Step 3 Solve the new equation for y.

Step 4 Replace y with $f^{-1}(x)$.

EXAMPLE 3

Determine the inverse of the function $f(x) = 2x - 1$.

SOLUTION
Step 1 Replace $f(x)$ with y.

$$y = 2x - 1$$

Step 2 Switch x and y.

$$x = 2y - 1$$

Step 3 Solve $x = 2y - 1$ for y.

$$y = \frac{x + 1}{2}$$

Step 4 Replace y with $f^{-1}(x)$.

$$f^{-1}(x) = \frac{x + 1}{2} \quad \blacksquare$$

Determining Functions with Restricted Domains

Some functions do not have inverses. However, they can have inverses when the domain is restricted.

EXAMPLE 4

Determine the inverse of $f(x) = x^2 - 2$, $x \geq 0$.

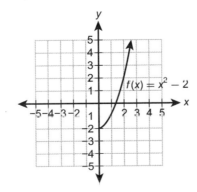

SOLUTION

The domain is $x \geq 0$, and the range is $y \geq -2$. The domain of the inverse is $x \geq -2$, and the range of the inverse is $y \geq 0$.

Determine the inverse.

$$y = x^2 - 2 \quad \Rightarrow \quad x = y^2 - 2 \qquad \text{Switch } x \text{ and } y.$$
$$y = \pm\sqrt{x + 2} \qquad \text{Solve for } y.$$

Only $y = +\sqrt{x + 2}$ has a domain of $x \geq -2$ and a range of $y \geq 0$.

Therefore, $f^{-1}(x) = \sqrt{x + 2}$. ∎

Logarithms

Just as taking a square root is the opposite of squaring a number, the opposite of raising a base to a variable power is called taking a logarithm.

A **logarithm** is the exponent to which a base would have to be raised to result in a given value. Using logarithms, you would write $2^x = 10$ as $x = \log_2 10$.

Definition

The logarithm of a with base b, **$\log_b a$**, where $b > 0$, $b \neq 1$, and $a > 0$, is defined as $\log_b a = x$ if and only if $b^x = a$.

▶ **Think About It**
NOTATION The expression $\log_b a$ is read as "log base b of a."

Converting Between Logarithmic and Exponential Forms

The definition of a logarithm can be used to convert between exponential and logarithmic forms.

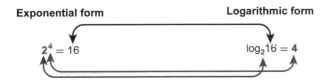

Exponential form   Logarithmic form

$$2^4 = 16 \qquad\qquad \log_2 16 = 4$$

The table shows equivalent equations written in both exponential and logarithmic forms.

Exponential form	$5^2 = 25$	$4^{-3} = \dfrac{1}{64}$	$81^{\frac{1}{2}} = 9$	$10^0 = 1$
Logarithmic form	$\log_5 25 = 2$	$\log_4\left(\dfrac{1}{64}\right) = -3$	$\log_{81} 9 = \dfrac{1}{2}$	$\log_{10} 1 = 0$

Logarithms with special bases have names.

Definitions

A **common logarithm** is a logarithm with base 10. Common logarithms, such as $\log_{10} x$, are usually written without the base, as log x.

A **natural logarithm** is a logarithm with base e. Natural logarithms, such as $\log_e x$, are often written using the notation ln x.

▶ **Remember** Like π, the number e is an irrational number.

$$e \approx 2.71828\ldots$$

EXAMPLE 1

Evaluate.

A log 0.001

SOLUTION
Since the base of the log is not stated, the base is 10. Let x be the value of log 0.001.

$\log 0.001 = x$

$\quad\quad 10^x = 0.001$ Rewrite equation in exponential form.

$\quad\quad 10^x = 10^{-3}$ Rewrite 0.001 as a power of 10.

$\quad\quad\quad x = -3$ Solve for x.

B $\ln \sqrt{e}$

SOLUTION

Since the ln notation is used, the base is e. Let x be the value of $\ln \sqrt{e}$.

$\ln \sqrt{e} = x$

$e^x = \sqrt{e}$ Rewrite equation in exponential form.

$e^x = e^{\frac{1}{2}}$ Rewrite $\sqrt{e}$ as a power of e.

$x = \dfrac{1}{2}$ Solve for x. ■

Using a Calculator to Find Common and Natural Logarithms

Calculators are programmed to calculate common and natural logarithms.

▶ **Think About It** Pietro Mengoli and Nicholas Mercator called the natural logarithm *logarithmus naturalis*.

EXAMPLE 2

Use a calculator to evaluate the logarithm to four decimal places.

A $\log 8$

SOLUTION

On a calculator, press **LOG**, type **8**), and press **ENTER**.

```
log (8)
.903089987
```

$\log 8 \approx 0.9031$

B ln 53

SOLUTION

On a calculator, press **LN**, type **53)**, and press **ENTER**.

ln (53)
3.970291914

ln 53 ≈ 3.9703 ▪

Using Logarithms in a Formula

EXAMPLE 3

The time t it takes for an investment with continuous growth rate r to double is given by the formula $t = \dfrac{\ln 2}{r}$. How many years would it take for an investment to double with a continuous rate of 3%?

SOLUTION

A rate of 3% means that $r = 0.03$. Substitute the value of r into the formula.

$$t = \frac{\ln 2}{0.003} \approx \frac{0.693}{0.03} \approx 23.1$$

It will take approximately 23 years for the investment to double. ▪

Properties of Logarithms

As with other mathematical functions, logarithms have their own unique properties.

Using Basic Properties of Logarithms

Aside from the basic definition of logarithms, there are three properties of logarithms that are frequently used.

Properties of Logarithms

Let $m > 0$, $n > 0$, and p be any real number.

Product Property of Logarithms

$$\log mn = \log m + \log n$$

Quotient Property of Logarithms

$$\log\left(\frac{m}{n}\right) = \log m - \log n$$

Power Property of Logarithms

$$\log\left(m^p\right) = p \log m$$

▶ **Think About It** All of these properties apply to logarithms with any base, including the natural logarithm, ln.

EXAMPLE 1

Write as a single logarithm.

A $\log 8 + \log 4$

SOLUTION

$$\log 8 + \log 4 = \log(8 \bullet 4) \qquad \text{Product Property of Logarithms}$$
$$= \log 32 \qquad \text{Simplify.}$$

B $\ln 15 - \ln 5 + 3 \ln 2$

SOLUTION

$$\ln 15 - \ln 5 + 3 \ln 2 = \ln\left(\frac{15}{5}\right) + 3 \ln 2 \qquad \text{Quotient Property of Logarithms}$$
$$= \ln 3 + \ln 2^3 \qquad \text{Power Property of Logarithms}$$
$$= \ln(3 \bullet 8) \qquad \text{Product Property of Logarithms}$$
$$= \ln 24 \qquad \text{Simplify.} \ \blacksquare$$

EXAMPLE 2

Write in expanded form.

A $\ln\left(\frac{3}{10}\right)$

SOLUTION

Use the quotient property of logarithms.

$$\ln\left(\frac{3}{10}\right) = \ln 3 - \ln 10$$

B $\log\left(3x^9\right)$

SOLUTION

Use the product and power properties of logarithms.

$$\log\left(3x^9\right) = \log 3 + \log\left(x^9\right) \qquad \text{Product Property of Logarithms}$$
$$= \log 3 + 9 \log x \qquad \text{Power Property of Logarithms} \ \blacksquare$$

Solving Logarithmic Equations

To solve equations involving logarithms, apply the properties of logarithms.

▶ **Think About It** If $\log a = \log b$, then $a = b$.

EXAMPLE 3

Solve for x.

A $\log x + \log 3 = \log(2x + 5)$

SOLUTION

$$\log x + \log 3 = \log(2x + 5)$$

$$\log 3x = \log(2x + 5) \qquad \text{Product Property of Logarithms}$$

$$3x = 2x + 5 \qquad \text{Equate arguments of logarithms.}$$

$$x = 5 \qquad \text{Solve for } x.$$

B $\ln(5x - 4) = 9$

SOLUTION

$$\ln(5x - 4) - 9$$

$$e^9 = 5x - 4 \qquad \text{Write in exponential form.}$$

$$e^9 + 4 = 5x$$

$$x = \frac{e^9 + 4}{5} \qquad \text{Solve for } x. \blacksquare$$

Application: Simplifying Formulas

EXAMPLE 4

The formula $\dfrac{G}{20} = \log\left(\dfrac{V}{K}\right)$ estimates the power gain G, in decibels, when V is the voltage being measured and K is a reference voltage. Show that $G = 20\log V - 20\log K$.

SOLUTION

Use the quotient property of logarithms.

$$\frac{G}{20} = \log\left(\frac{V}{K}\right)$$

$$\frac{G}{20} = \log V - \log K \qquad \text{Write the right side in expanded form.}$$

$$G = 20\log V - 20\log K \qquad \text{Multiply both sides by 20.} \ \blacksquare$$

Using Logarithms to Solve Exponential Equations

To solve an exponential equation such as $2^x = 10$, you have to use a logarithm.

Just as you use addition, multiplication, or square roots to transform and solve equations, you can use logarithms to transform and solve equations.

Using the Definition of Logarithms to Solve Exponential Equations

EXAMPLE 1

Solve. Round your answers to four decimal places if necessary.

A $3^x = 81$

SOLUTION
If you raise the base, 3, to the fourth power, you get 81.

$$3^x = 81$$
$$3^x = 3^4$$
$$x = 4$$

B $e^x = 10$

SOLUTION
There is no whole number you can raise e to and get 10 (or any other whole number greater than 1). Use the definition of the logarithm.

$$e^x = 10 \quad \Rightarrow \quad x = \log_e 10$$
$$x = \ln(10) \approx 2.3026 \ \blacksquare$$

Using Logarithmic Transformations to Solve Exponential Equations

Property of Equality for Logarithmic Equations

If a, x, and y are positive numbers and $a \neq 1$, then $\log_a x = \log_a y$ if and only if $x = y$.

EXAMPLE 2

Solve. Round your answer to four decimal places.

> ▶ **Think About It** It is customary to round the value of a logarithmic expression to four decimal places.

A $2^x = 10$

SOLUTION

$$2^x = 10$$

$\log 2^x = \log 10$ Take the common (base 10) logarithm of both sides.

$x \log 2 = \log 10$ Power Property of Logarithms

$x \log 2 = 1$ $\log_{10} 10 = 1$ because $10^1 = 10$.

$x = \dfrac{1}{\log 2}$ Divide both sides by $\log 2$.

$x \approx 3.3219$ Use a calculator to approximate the expression.

Check for reasonableness. Because $2^3 = 8$ and $2^4 = 16$, it is reasonable that $2^{3.3219} \approx 10$. You may use a calculator to verify the result.

B $5^{2n} = 101$

SOLUTION

$$5^{2n} = 101$$

$\log 5^{2n} = \log 101$ Take the common logarithm of both sides.

$2n \log 5 = \log 101$ Power Property of Logarithms

$n = \dfrac{\log 101}{2 \log 5}$ Divide both sides by 2 log 5.

$n \approx 1.4338$ Use a calculator to approximate the expression. ■

▶ **Think About It** Always solve the equation thoroughly before approximating the value of the variable. The equation $n = \dfrac{\log 101}{2 \log 5}$ gives the exact value of n; $n \approx 1.4338$ gives an approximation.

When an exponential equation contains the number e, it can be easier to take the natural logarithm of both sides to solve the equation.

▶ **Think About It** The equations in Example 2 could also have been solved using the natural logarithm. For an equation with a variable in the exponent, you can choose to use either the natural or the common logarithm.

EXAMPLE 3

Solve the equation by using logarithms. Round your answer to four decimal places.

A $e^{3a} = 9$

SOLUTION

$$e^{3a} = 9$$

$\ln e^{3a} = \ln 9$ Take the natural logarithm of both sides.

$3a \ln e = \ln 9$ Power Property of Logarithms

$3a = \ln 9$ $\ln e = 1$ because $e^1 = e$.

$a = \dfrac{\ln 9}{3}$ Divide both sides by 3.

$a \approx 0.7324$ Use a calculator to approximate the expression.

CHECK

To verify the result, substitute the approximate value in the original equation. Use a calculator to evaluate the left side of the equation.

$$e^{3a} = 9$$
$$e^{3 \, \bullet \, 0.7324} \overset{?}{\approx} 9$$
$$8.9998 \approx 9 \checkmark$$

The solution $a \approx 0.7324$ is correct.

B $7^x = e^{x+1}$

Method Using LN

$$7^x = e^{x+1}$$
$$\ln 7^x = \ln e^{x+1}$$
$$x \ln 7 = (x+1) \ln e$$
$$x \ln 7 = (x+1) \bullet 1$$
$$x \ln 7 = x + 1$$
$$x \ln 7 - x = 1$$
$$x((\ln 7) - 1) = 1$$
$$x = \frac{1}{(\ln 7) - 1}$$
$$x \approx 1.0572$$

Method Using LOG

$$7^x = e^{x+1}$$
$$\log 7^x = \log e^{x+1}$$
$$x \log 7 = (x+1) \log e$$
$$x \log 7 = x \bullet \log e + 1 \bullet \log e$$
$$x \log 7 - x \log e = \log e$$
$$x(\log 7 - \log e) = \log e$$
$$x = \frac{\log e}{\log 7 - \log e}$$
$$x \approx 1.0572$$

CHECK

To verify the result, substitute the approximate value in the original equation. Use a calculator to evaluate each side of the equation.

$$7^x = e^{x+1}$$
$$7^{1.0572} \stackrel{?}{\approx} e^{1.0572+1}$$
$$7.8242 \approx 7.8240 \checkmark$$

The calculator gives the same value, if rounded to three decimal places, for each expression. ∎

Interpreting a Calculator Error Message

EXAMPLE 4

Solve $10^x + 2 = -6$.

SOLUTION

$10^x + 2 = -6$	
$10^x = -8$	Subtract 2 from both sides.
$\log 10^x = \log(-8)$	Take the common logarithm of both sides.
$x \log 10 = \log(-8)$	Power Property of Logarithms
$x = \log(-8)$	$\log 10 = 1$

When you try to use a calculator to evaluate $\log(-8)$, the calculator gives an error. There is no real solution to the equation. ∎

▶ **Think About It** The statement $10^x = -8$ indicates that the original equation has no real solution. It is not possible for any power of 10 to be negative.

Applications: Logarithms

Logarithmic functions have applications in many scientific fields.

Chemistry Application: pH

The pH of a substance indicates its acidity. Substances that are more acidic have a lower pH than substances that are less acidic. The logarithmic function $f(x) = -\log_{10}x$ models the pH of different substances. Specifically, the function $pH = -\log_{10}\left[H^+\right]$ measures the pH of a substance, where $\left[H^+\right]$ is the hydrogen-ion concentration of the substance, measured in moles per liter.

▶ **Think About It** Pure water has a pH level of 7.0, which is considered neutral on the pH scale. You can use pH paper to test whether a substance is acidic (below 7.0 on the pH scale), alkaline (above 7.0), or neutral.

EXAMPLE 1

The pH of a brand of apple juice is 3.5. What is the $\left[H^+\right]$ for the apple juice?

SOLUTION
Use the logarithmic function $pH = -\log_{10}\left[H^+\right]$. The pH level of the juice is 3.5.

$$pH = -\log_{10}\left[H^+\right]$$
$$3.5 = -\log_{10}\left[H^+\right] \qquad \text{Substitute 3.5 for pH.}$$
$$-3.5 = \log_{10}\left[H^+\right] \qquad \text{Multiply both sides by } -1.$$
$$\left[H^+\right] = 10^{-3.5} \qquad \text{Definition of a logarithm}$$

There are $10^{-3.5}$ moles of hydrogen ions in a liter of apple juice with a pH level of 3.5. By using a calculator and rounding the result to four decimal places, you can determine that $[H^+]$ is approximately 0.0003 mole/L. ∎

> **Think About It** The value in the calculator window may read 3.16227766E−4, which means $3.16227766 \times 10^{-4}$.

Biology Application: Exponential Growth

Under the right conditions, bacteria populations grow exponentially according to the formula $N_t = N_0 e^{ct}$, where N_0 is the initial number of bacteria (at time $t = 0$), t is the number of days, and N_t is the number of bacteria after t days. The constant c is the growth factor for a particular type of bacteria in a given environment.

EXAMPLE 2

At the beginning of an experiment, a culture has 400 bacteria. Three days later, the culture has 2000 bacteria.

A Calculate the growth factor.

SOLUTION
Find the value of c by substituting the given information.

$$N_0 = 400, t = 3, N_t = 2000$$

$$N_t = N_0 e^{ct}$$

$$2000 = 400 \cdot e^{c \cdot 3}$$

$$\frac{2000}{400} = e^{3c} \qquad \text{Divide both sides by 400.}$$

$$5 = e^{3c}$$

$$\ln 5 = 3c \qquad \text{Definition of natural logarithm}$$

$$\frac{\ln 5}{3} = c \qquad \text{Divide both sides by 3.}$$

The growth factor of the function is $\frac{\ln 5}{3}$.

B Predict the number of bacteria 8 days after the beginning of the experiment.

SOLUTION

Substitute the answer from Example 1A for c and 8 for t.

$$N_t = N_0 e^{ct}$$

$$N_t = 400 \cdot e^{\frac{\ln 5}{3} \cdot 8}$$

$$N_t \approx 29{,}240 \qquad \text{Use a calculator and round to the nearest whole.}$$

There will be about 29,240 bacteria 8 days after the beginning of the experiment. ■

Physics Application: Decibels

The threshold of hearing I_0 is the intensity of the faintest sound that can be heard by the human ear. Other sound intensities I are often measured by comparing them to the threshold of hearing. The logarithmic function $R = 10 \log_{10}\left(\dfrac{I}{I_0}\right)$ can be used to find the relative intensity of a sound in decibels.

EXAMPLE 3

The sound intensity of a vacuum cleaner is about 10^8 times greater than the threshold of hearing. What is the relative intensity of a vacuum cleaner, measured in decibels?

SOLUTION

Use the logarithmic function $R = 10 \log_{10}\left(\frac{I}{I_0}\right)$. Since the sound of the vacuum cleaner is 10^8 times greater than the threshold of hearing, $I = 10^8 \cdot I_0$. Substitute $10^8 \cdot I_0$ in the equation for I.

$R = 10 \log_{10}\left(\frac{I}{I_0}\right)$

$R = 10 \log_{10}\left(\frac{10^8 \cdot I_0}{I_0}\right)$ Substitute $10^8 \cdot I_0$ for I.

$R = 10 \log_{10}\left(10^8\right)$ Simplify by using exponential form.

$R = 10 \cdot 8$

$R = 80$

The relative sound intensity of a vacuum cleaner is about 80 decibels. ■

Seismology Application: Richter Scale

The Richter scale was developed to compare the sizes of earthquakes. On the Richter scale, the magnitude of an earthquake M is related to the released energy E, in ergs, of the earthquake according to the formula

$$M = \frac{2}{3} \log_{10}\left(\frac{E}{10^{11.8}}\right).$$

EXAMPLE 4

An earthquake in the region of the Dominican Republic measured 3.2 on the Richter scale, while an earthquake near New Zealand measured 6.4. Compare the amount of energy released by these two earthquakes.

▶ **Think About It** An earthquake with magnitude between 3.5 and 5.4 on the Richter scale is felt, but rarely causes major damage. An earthquake with magnitude 7 or more is major and can cause serious damage.

SOLUTION

Use $M = \frac{2}{3} \log_{10} \left(\frac{E}{10^{11.8}} \right)$ to calculate the amount of energy released by each earthquake.

Dominican Republic earthquake:

$$3.2 = \frac{2}{3} \log_{10} \left(\frac{E}{10^{11.8}} \right)$$

$$4.8 = \log_{10} \left(\frac{E}{10^{11.8}} \right)$$

$$10^{4.8} = \frac{E}{10^{11.8}}$$

$$10^{4.8} \cdot 10^{11.8} = E$$

$$10^{16.6} = E$$

$$3.9810 \times 10^{16} \approx E$$

New Zealand earthquake:

$$6.4 = \frac{2}{3} \log_{10} \left(\frac{E}{10^{11.8}} \right)$$

$$9.6 = \log_{10} \left(\frac{E}{10^{11.8}} \right)$$

$$10^{9.6} = \frac{E}{10^{11.8}}$$

$$10^{9.6} \cdot 10^{11.8} = E$$

$$10^{21.4} = E$$

$$2.5119 \times 10^{21} \approx E$$

To compare the stronger quake to the weaker one, write the fraction.

$$\frac{2.5119 \times 10^{21}}{3.9810 \times 10^{16}} = \frac{2.5119}{3.9810} \times 10^5 \approx 6.31 \times 10^4$$

The 6.4 quake released roughly 63,100 times the energy of the 3.2 quake. ■

Nuclear Application: Calculating Half-Life

The function $f(t) = b \cdot \left(\frac{1}{2}\right)^{\frac{t}{h}}$ gives the amount remaining, in milligrams, of a radioactive sample of b milligrams that has a half-life h after a period of time t.

EXAMPLE 5

A sample of 50 mg of technetium-99m is given to a patient during a medical test. If the radioactive substance decays to 2.8 mg after 25 h, find the half-life of this substance.

▶ **Remember** The half-life of a radioactive substance is the time it takes for half of the substance to decay.

SOLUTION

$$f(t) = b \cdot \left(\frac{1}{2}\right)^{\frac{t}{h}}$$

$$2.8 = 50 \cdot \left(\frac{1}{2}\right)^{\frac{25}{h}} \qquad \text{Substitute the given values.}$$

$$0.056 = \left(\frac{1}{2}\right)^{\frac{25}{h}} \qquad \text{Divide both sides by 50.}$$

$$\log 0.056 = \log\left(\frac{1}{2}^{\frac{25}{h}}\right) \qquad \text{Take the common logarithm of both sides.}$$

$$\log 0.056 = \frac{25}{h}\log \frac{1}{2} \qquad \text{Power Property of Logarithms}$$

$$h = 25 \cdot \frac{\log \frac{1}{2}}{\log 0.056} \qquad \text{Multiply both sides by } \frac{h}{\log 0.056}.$$

Use a calculator to find an approximate value of h, the half-life of this substance. Then check the result.

$$h = 25 \cdot \frac{\log \frac{1}{2}}{\log 0.056} \approx 6$$

Recall that h and t have the same units—in this case, hours.

> ▶ **Think About It** The units for h and t must be the same.

CHECK

$$2.8 = 50\left(\frac{1}{2}\right)^{\frac{25}{h}}$$

$$2.8 \overset{?}{\approx} 50\left(\frac{1}{2}\right)^{\frac{25}{6}}$$

$$2.8 \approx 2.7841 \checkmark$$

The half-life of technetium-99m is approximately 6 h. ▪

EXAMPLE 6

Carbon-14 has a half-life of 5730 years. Archaeologists find a wooden bowl that has 40% of the normal carbon-14 levels. When you replace b in the half-life formula with 1, the formula $f(t) = \left(\frac{1}{2}\right)^{\frac{t}{h}}$ gives the percentage left after t years, where h is the half-life. What is the approximate age of the bowl?

SOLUTION

$$f(t) = \left(\frac{1}{2}\right)^{\frac{t}{h}}$$

$$0.4 = \left(\frac{1}{2}\right)^{\frac{t}{5730}} \qquad \text{Substitute the given values.}$$

$$\log 0.4 = \log\left(\frac{1}{2}^{\frac{t}{5730}}\right) \qquad \text{Take the common logarithm of both sides.}$$

$$\log 0.4 = \frac{t}{5730} \log \frac{1}{2} \qquad \text{Power Property of Logarithms}$$

$$\frac{5730}{\log\frac{1}{2}} \cdot \log 0.4 = t \qquad \text{Multiply both sides by } \frac{5730}{\log\frac{1}{2}}.$$

Use a calculator to find an approximate value of t, the age of the bowl. Then check the result.

$$t = \frac{5730}{\log\frac{1}{2}} \cdot \log 0.4 \approx 7575$$

CHECK

$$0.4 = \left(\frac{1}{2}\right)^{\frac{t}{5730}}$$

$$0.4 \stackrel{?}{\approx} \left(\frac{1}{2}\right)^{\frac{7575}{5730}}$$

$$0.4 \approx 0.39999 \checkmark$$

The wooden bowl is approximately 7575 years old. ◾

Formula Reference

pH $\text{pH} = -\log_{10}\left[\text{H}^+\right]$

Bacteria Growth $N_t = N_0 e^{ct}$

Decibel Scale for Sound Intensity $R = 10\log_{10}\left(\frac{I}{I_0}\right)$

Richter Scale for Earthquake Energy $M = \frac{2}{3}\log_{10}\left(\frac{E}{10^{11.8}}\right)$

Half-Life $f(t) = b \bullet \left(\frac{1}{2}\right)^{\frac{t}{h}}$

Graphing Logarithmic Functions

Common logarithmic functions have base 10, while natural logarithmic functions have base e.

Definitions

If x is a positive real number, then

- $f(x) = \log x$ is a **common logarithmic function with base 10**.
- $g(x) = \ln x$ is a **natural logarithmic function with base e**.

Both of these logarithmic functions have domain $x > 0$ and a vertical asymptote at $x = 0$.

Logarithmic functions are related to exponential functions. In fact, a logarithmic function is always the inverse of some exponential function, so their graphs have similar shapes.

How to Graph a Logarithmic Function

Step 1 Find any x- or y-intercepts.

Step 2 Give the domain and the equation of the vertical asymptote.

Step 3 Make a table of values to find points on the graph.

Step 4 Draw a smooth curve using the vertical asymptote and points on the graph as a guide.

EXAMPLE 1

EXAMPLE 1

Graph $f(x) = \ln(x + 1)$.

SOLUTION

Step 1 Find any x- or y-intercepts.

To find the x-intercept, set $f(x) = 0$ and solve for x.

$$0 = \ln(x + 2)$$
$$e^0 = x + 2$$
$$1 = x + 2$$
$$-1 = x$$

To find the y-intercept, set $x = 0$ and solve for $f(x)$.

$$f(x) = \ln(0 + 1)$$
$$= \ln 1$$
$$= 0$$

The x-intercept is $x = -1$, and the y-intercept is $y = 0$.

Step 2 Give the domain and the equation of the vertical asymptote.

Find the domain of $f(x)$ by solving the inequality $x + 1 > 0$.

$$x + 1 > 0$$
$$x > -1$$

Find the vertical asymptote by solving $x + 1 = 0$.

$$x + 1 = 0$$
$$x = -1$$

The domain is $x > -1$, and the vertical asymptote is the line $x = -1$.

▶ **Remember** You can only take the logarithm of a positive real number. The logarithm of 0 or a negative real number does not exist.

Step 3 Make a table of values to find points on the graph.

x	$f(x) = \ln(x + 1)$
0	$\ln(0 + 1) = \ln 1 = 0$
1	$\ln(1 + 1) = \ln 2 \approx 0.69$
4	$\ln(4 + 1) = \ln 5 \approx 1.6$

Step 4 Draw a smooth curve using the vertical asymptote and points on the graph as a guide.

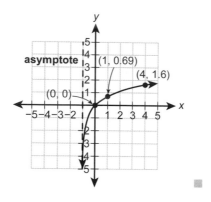

▶ **Think About It** The graph never actually touches the vertical asymptote.

EXAMPLE 2

Graph $f(x) = 5\log(2.3 - x)$.

SOLUTION

Step 1 Find any x- or y-intercepts.

To find the x-intercept, set $f(x) = 0$ and solve for x.

$$0 = 5\log(2.3 - x)$$
$$0 = \log(2.3 - x)$$
$$10^0 = 2.3 - x$$
$$1 = 2.3 - x$$
$$x = 1.3$$

To find the y-intercept, set $x = 0$ and solve for $f(x)$.

$$f(x) = 5\log(2.3 - 0)$$
$$= 5\log(2.3 - 0)$$
$$= 5\log(2.3)$$
$$\approx 1.8$$

The x-intercept is $x = 1.3$, and the y-intercept is $y \approx 1.8$.

Step 2 Give the domain and the equation of the vertical asymptote.

Find the domain of $f(x)$ by solving the inequality $2.3 - x > 0$.

$$2.3 - x > 0$$
$$-x > -2.3$$
$$x < 2.3$$

Find the vertical asymptote by solving $2.3 - x = 0$.

$$2.3 - x = 0$$
$$-x = -2.3$$
$$x = 2.3$$

The domain is $x < 2.3$, and the vertical asymptote is the line $x = 2.3$.

Step 3 Make a table of values to find points on the graph.

x	$f(x) = 5\log(2.3 - x)$
-3	$5\log(2.3 - (-3)) = 5\log 5.3 \approx 3.6$
-1	$5\log(2.3 - (-1)) = 5\log 3.3 \approx 2.6$
2	$5\log(2.3 - 2) = 5\log 0.3 \approx -2.6$

Step 4 Draw a smooth curve using the vertical asymptote and points on the graph as a guide.

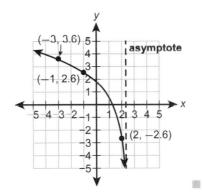

Radians and Trigonometric Functions

Topic List

Robotic arms are critical to manufacturers on earth as well as to astronauts, scientists, and engineers working in outer space. The software that manipulates robotic arms uses trigonometry to put the arms in exactly the right position.

Right Triangle Trigonometry

Right triangles can be solved using trigonometric ratios and the Pythagorean theorem.

Using Similarity in Right Triangles

Definition

Two triangles are **similar** if their corresponding angles are congruent and their corresponding side lengths are proportional.

Because the lengths of corresponding sides of similar triangles are proportional, the ratios of corresponding side lengths are equal.

▶ **Think About It** When making statements about similarity and congruence, always name figures according to their corresponding parts.

EXAMPLE 1

What is the value of the ratio $\dfrac{f}{e}$ in $\triangle DEF$?

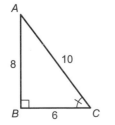

> ▶ **Remember** To indicate the length of a segment, use the names of its endpoints without a segment symbol over them. For example, AB indicates the length of $\overline{AB}$.

SOLUTION

$\triangle ABC$ and $\triangle DEF$ are right triangles with $\angle B \cong \angle E$ and $\angle C \cong \angle F$. Because two angles of $\triangle ABC$ are congruent to two angles of $\triangle DEF$, the third pair of angles, $\angle A$ and $\angle D$, must also be congruent.

Therefore, the triangles are similar, with $\overline{AB}$ corresponding to $\overline{DE}$ and $\overline{AC}$ corresponding to $\overline{DF}$, which means that $\dfrac{AB}{AC} = \dfrac{DE}{DF} = \dfrac{f}{e} = \dfrac{8}{10} = \dfrac{4}{5}$. ■

Determining Trigonometric Ratios in Right Triangles

The ratios of side lengths in right triangles are properties of the angles of the triangle. They are called trigonometric ratios and have specific names.

Definitions

For any acute angle of a right triangle,

- The **sine (sin)** of an angle is the ratio of the length of the leg opposite the angle to the length of the hypotenuse.

- The **cosine (cos)** of an angle is the ratio of the length of the leg adjacent to the angle to the length of the hypotenuse.

- The **tangent (tan)** of an angle is the ratio of the length of the leg opposite the angle to the length of the leg that is adjacent to the angle.

In △ABC,

- $\sin A = \dfrac{\text{opposite}}{\text{hypotenuse}} = \dfrac{a}{c}$

- $\cos A = \dfrac{\text{adjacent}}{\text{hypotenuse}} = \dfrac{b}{c}$

- $\tan A = \dfrac{\text{opposite}}{\text{adjacent}} = \dfrac{a}{b}$

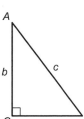

▶ **Think About It** The hypotenuse will always be the side opposite the right angle. But which sides are adjacent and opposite depends on which acute angle is referenced.

EXAMPLE 2

In a right triangle, θ is an acute angle and $\sin \theta = \dfrac{2}{5}$. Determine $\cos \theta$ and $\tan \theta$.

SOLUTION

Step 1 Draw the triangle and choose an acute angle to label θ. Since $\sin \theta = \dfrac{\text{opposite}}{\text{hypotenuse}}$, label the opposite side with length 2, and the hypotenuse with length 5.

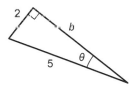

Step 2 To calculate $\cos \theta$ and $\tan \theta$, you must first determine the missing side length, b. Use the Pythagorean theorem, with $a = 2$ and $c = 5$.

$$a^2 + b^2 = c^2$$
$$2^2 + b^2 = 5^2$$
$$4 + b^2 = 25$$
$$b^2 = 21$$
$$b = \sqrt{21}$$

Step 3 Use the definitions to find the unknown ratios.

$$\cos A = \frac{\text{adjacent}}{\text{hypotenuse}} = \frac{\sqrt{21}}{5}$$

$$\tan A = \frac{\text{opposite}}{\text{adjacent}} = \frac{2}{\sqrt{21}} = \frac{2\sqrt{21}}{\sqrt{21} \cdot \sqrt{21}} = \frac{2\sqrt{21}}{21} \ \blacksquare$$

Applying Trigonometric Ratios

You can use trigonometric ratios to solve for angle measures and side lengths in a variety of situations. After you read a problem, draw and label a triangle that models the scenario. Then set up an equation involving the appropriate trigonometric ratio and solve for the unknown measure.

EXAMPLE 3

The shadow of a vertical building is 16.6 m long when the angle of elevation of the sun is 32.8°. What is the height of the building to the nearest tenth of a meter?

SOLUTION

Draw a right triangle that models the situation. Label the unknown height as h.

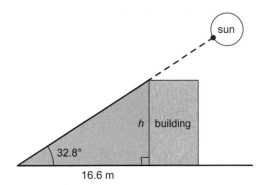

The angle of elevation, 32.8°, is a known value. The unknown height, h, is opposite that angle. The shadow length, 16.6 m, is the length of the side adjacent to the angle. Use the tangent since it is the ratio that involves the opposite and adjacent side lengths.

$$\tan(32.8°) = \frac{h}{16.6}$$
$$\tan(32.8°) \cdot 16.6 = h$$
$$10.7 \approx h$$

The building is approximately 10.7 m high. ■

Radians and Degrees

Radian measure is related to the length of the arc of a circle that is intercepted by an angle.

Determining Arc Length

Arc length is part of the circumference of a circle. The arc length of a full circle, which measures 360°, is the same as the circle's circumference of $2\pi r$ units.

For an arc intercepted by an angle of any measure, you can use proportionality to determine its length.

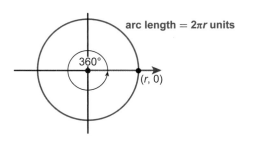

arc length = $2\pi r$ units

360°

$(r, 0)$

Arc Length Proportionality Property

The length of an arc is proportional to the measure of its central angle.

An arc intercepted by a 180° angle is a semicircle, so its length is equal to one-half the circumference of a circle. That length is $s = \frac{1}{2}(2\pi r) = \pi r$. You can also use a proportion to determine the length between the arc length s and the measure of the central angle, 180°.

$$\frac{\text{arc length}}{2\pi r} = \frac{\text{degrees}}{360°}$$

$$\frac{s}{2\pi r} = \frac{180°}{360°}$$

$$2\pi r \cdot \frac{s}{2\pi r} = \frac{180°}{360°} \cdot 2\pi r$$

$$s = \frac{1}{2} \cdot 2\pi r$$

$$s = \pi r$$

arc length = πr units

180°

$(r, 0)$

EXAMPLE 1

What is the length s of the arc on a circle with a radius of r units that is intercepted by a central angle of 90°?

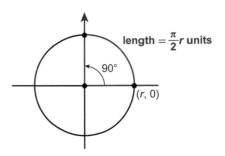

length $= \frac{\pi}{2}r$ units

90°

$(r, 0)$

SOLUTION

An arc intercepted by a 90° angle is a quarter circle, so its length is equal to one-fourth the circumference of the circle.

That length is $s = \frac{1}{4}(2\pi r) = \frac{\pi}{2}r$. ▪

▶ **Remember** You can also use a proportion to determine the arc length of the 90° angle.

$$\frac{s}{2\pi r} = \frac{90°}{360°}$$

$$2\pi r \cdot \frac{s}{2\pi r} = \frac{90°}{360°} \cdot 2\pi r$$

$$s = \frac{1}{4} \cdot 2\pi r$$

$$s = \frac{\pi}{2}r$$

EXAMPLE 2

What is the measure of the central angle on a circle with radius 40 cm that intercepts a 120 cm arc?

▶ **Remember** Arc length is a distance; it is part of the circumference of a circle.

SOLUTION

Use a proportion between the arc length and the unknown angle θ.

$$\frac{\theta}{360°} = \frac{120}{2\pi(40)}$$ Set up the proportion.

$$360° \cdot \frac{\theta}{360°} = \frac{120}{80\pi} \cdot 360°$$ Multiply both sides by 360°.

$$\theta \approx 171.89°$$ Use a calculator to simplify.

The angle measure is approximately 171.89°. ▪

Defining Radian Measure

The circumference of a unit circle is $2\pi(1)$, or 2π units. It is the same as the arc length on a unit circle with a central angle of 360°. Now look at an arc that is a semicircle. It is intercepted by a 180° angle. The length of the arc is one-half of the circumference of the circle. One-half of 2π is π. So an arc on the unit circle with a 180° central angle has a length of π units.

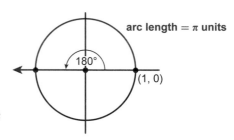

arc length $= \pi$ units

180°

(1, 0)

If an arc on the unit circle intercepted by an angle has a length of x units, then the angle itself is said to have a measure of x radians. Therefore, because the arc length of one full unit circle is 2π, the radian measure of 360° is 2π.

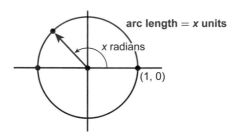

arc length $= x$ units

x radians

(1, 0)

EXAMPLE 3

What is the radian measure x of an angle that intercepts a quarter circle of radius 1?

▶ **Q&A**

Q What is the degree measure of a quarter circle?

A 90°

SOLUTION

The angle has a measure in radians that is equal to $\frac{1}{4}$ of the radian measure of the entire unit circle. The radian measure of the full circle is 2π. Take $\frac{1}{4}$ of 2π to get $x = \frac{1}{4}(2\pi) = \frac{\pi}{2}$ radians. ▪

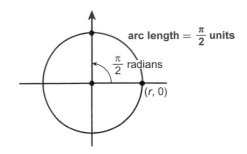

Converting Between Degrees and Radians

If you know an angle's degree measure, you can figure out its radian measure and vice versa.

The radian measure of an entire circle, which has a degree measure of 360°, is equal to 2π. The radian measure of one-half of a circle, which measures 180°, is equal to one-half of 2π, which is π. Just as degree measure and arc length are proportional, degree measure and radian measure are proportional.

Degrees-Radians Proportionality Property

Let θ be the measure of an angle in degrees and x be the measure of the angle in radians.

$$\frac{\theta}{180°} = \frac{x}{\pi}$$

You can solve the proportion for degrees (θ) by multiplying both sides by 180° to get $\theta = \frac{x}{\pi}(180°) = x\left(\frac{180°}{\pi}\right)$. You can likewise solve for radians (x) by multiplying both sides by π to get $x = \frac{\theta}{180°}(\pi) = \theta\left(\frac{\pi}{180°}\right)$.

How to Convert Between Degrees and Radians

To convert radians to degrees, multiply a radian measure by $\frac{180°}{\pi}$.

To convert degrees to radians, multiply a degree measure by $\frac{\pi}{180°}$.

EXAMPLE 4

A What is the measure of $-135°$ in radians? Give your answer in terms of π.

SOLUTION

Multiply by $\frac{\pi}{180°}$ and simplify.

$$-135°\left(\frac{\pi}{180°}\right) = -\frac{3\pi}{4}$$

> ▶ **Think About It** A counterclockwise rotation generates a positive angle measure (in degrees or radians), while a clockwise rotation generates a negative measure.

B What is the measure of $\frac{5\pi}{6}$ in degrees?

SOLUTION

Multiply by $\frac{180°}{\pi}$ and simplify.

$$\frac{5\pi}{6}\left(\frac{180°}{\pi}\right) = \frac{5}{1}\left(\frac{30°}{1}\right) = 150° \ \blacksquare$$

> ▶ **Think About It** When no unit of measure is specified for an angle, radian measure is understood. For example, $\frac{\pi}{6}$ and 3.5 are both radian measures.

EXAMPLE 5

Determine the indicated measure.

> ▶ **Remember** Complementary angles have measures that sum to 90°. Supplementary angles have measures that sum to 180°.

A the complement of $\frac{3\pi}{8}$

SOLUTION

First determine the measure of a 90° angle in radians.

$$90°\left(\frac{\pi}{180°}\right) = \frac{\pi}{2}$$

Then subtract $\frac{3\pi}{8}$ from that measure.

$$\frac{\pi}{2} - \frac{3\pi}{8} = \frac{4\pi}{8} - \frac{3\pi}{8} = \frac{\pi}{8}$$

B the supplement of $\frac{3\pi}{8}$

SOLUTION

First determine the measure of a 180° angle in radians.

$$180°\left(\frac{\pi}{180°}\right) = \pi$$

Then subtract $\frac{3\pi}{8}$ from that measure.

$$\pi - \frac{3\pi}{8} = \frac{8\pi}{8} - \frac{3\pi}{8} = \frac{5\pi}{8} \quad \blacksquare$$

▶ **Think About It** Unless otherwise indicated, always give measures in the units provided in a problem.

Angles in Standard Position

An angle in standard position is in the same quadrant as its terminal side.

Determining the Quadrant in Which an Angle Lies

Definitions

An angle is in **standard position** on the coordinate plane when its vertex is at the origin and its initial side is along the positive horizontal axis.

Quadrantal angles are angles in standard position that have their terminal sides along the horizontal or vertical axis.

▶ **Remember** The initial side of an angle is the ray from which the rotation of an angle starts. The terminal side of an angle is the ray at which the rotation of an angle stops.

Examples of quadrantal angles are 0°, 90°, 180°, 270°, and 360°. These degree measures are equivalent to radian measures of 0, $\frac{\pi}{2}$, π, $\frac{3\pi}{2}$, and 2π, respectively.

▶ **Remember** The first quadrant of the coordinate plane is between the positive horizontal axis and the positive vertical axis. The second, third, and fourth quadrants are located counterclockwise from the first quadrant, respectively.

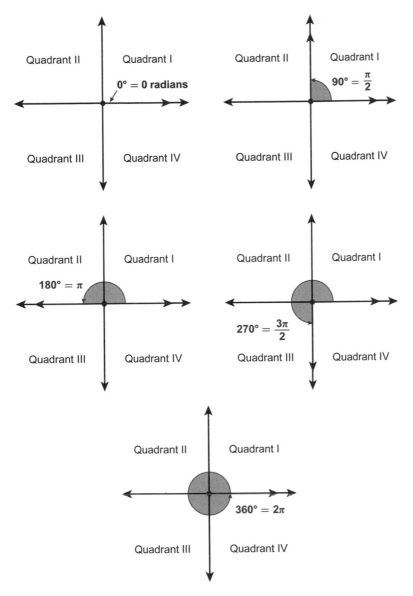

An angle in standard position that is not quadrantal lies in the quadrant in which its terminal side lies.

Angles and Quadrants

The quadrant in which an angle θ lies can be determined by its measure.

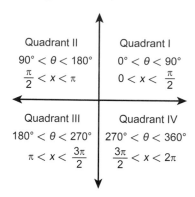

Quadrant II
$90° < \theta < 180°$
$\dfrac{\pi}{2} < x < \pi$

Quadrant I
$0° < \theta < 90°$
$0 < x < \dfrac{\pi}{2}$

Quadrant III
$180° < \theta < 270°$
$\pi < x < \dfrac{3\pi}{2}$

Quadrant IV
$270° < \theta < 360°$
$\dfrac{3\pi}{2} < x < 2\pi$

EXAMPLE 1

Determine the quadrant in which the angle lies.

There are no units given for the angle measures in these examples, so they are understood to be in radians.

A $\dfrac{4\pi}{5}$

SOLUTION

Note that $\dfrac{4\pi}{5}$ is the same as $\dfrac{4}{5}$ of π. The fraction $\dfrac{4}{5}$ is between $\dfrac{1}{2}$ and 1.

So $\dfrac{4\pi}{5}$ is between the quadrantal angles $\dfrac{\pi}{2}$ $\left(\text{or } \dfrac{1}{2} \text{ of } \pi\right)$ and π. The terminal

side of the angle is therefore in Quadrant II, so $\dfrac{4\pi}{5}$ lies in Quadrant II.

> ▶ **Think About It** Radian measures of angles given in terms of π
> can be thought of as fractional or integer multiples of π. To help visualize
> the standard position of such an angle, think about where it lies with
> respect to π.
>
> For example, $\dfrac{7\pi}{6}$ is the same as $1\dfrac{1}{6}$ times π. It is located in the
>
> third quadrant, $\dfrac{1}{6}$ of the way between π and 2π.

SOLUTION

Since the measure is not expressed in terms of π, convert it to degrees to determine the quadrantal angles between which it lies.

$$5.2\left(\frac{180°}{\pi}\right) \approx 298°$$

The measure 298° is between 270° and 360°, so the angle lies in Quadrant IV. ▪

Generating and Identifying Coterminal Angles

Definition
Coterminal angles are angles in standard position that have the same terminal side but have different amounts of rotation. Their angles differ by a multiple of 360°, or 2π radians.

A simple example of coterminal angles is the quadrantal angles 0° (0 radians) and 360° (2π). Their measures differ by 360°, or 2π radians, but they both terminate on the positive horizontal axis.

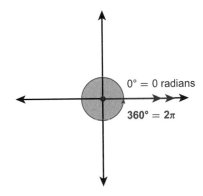

$0° = 0$ radians

$360° = 2\pi$

How to Generate Coterminal Angles

Use the following expressions to determine the measures of angles that are coterminal with a given angle. Let n be an integer.

For angles in degrees, use $\theta + 360°n$.
For angles in radians, use $x + 2\pi n$.

You can add or subtract multiples of $360°$, or 2π, to determine the measures of angles coterminal with a given angle.

▶ **Q&A**

Q What is the degree measure of the angle between $-360°$ and $0°$ that is coterminal with $90°$?

A $-270°$

EXAMPLE 2

Determine the measures of a positive angle and a negative angle that are coterminal with $\dfrac{13\pi}{4}$.

SOLUTION

The measure is in radians, so subtract multiples of 2π.

$$\frac{13\pi}{4} - 2\pi = \frac{13\pi}{4} - \frac{8\pi}{4} = \frac{5\pi}{4} \qquad \text{positive angle}$$

$$\frac{13\pi}{4} - 2(2\pi) = \frac{13\pi}{4} - \frac{16\pi}{4} = -\frac{3\pi}{4} \qquad \text{negative angle} \blacksquare$$

EXAMPLE 3

Draw $-\frac{11\pi}{3}$ in standard position.

SOLUTION

Find an angle that is coterminal with $-\frac{11\pi}{3}$, but is between 0 and 2π.

Step 1 Add 2π as many times as you have to until you get to a value that is between 0 and 2π.

$$-\frac{11\pi}{3} + 2\pi = -\frac{11\pi}{3} + \frac{6\pi}{3} = -\frac{5\pi}{3}$$

$$-\frac{5\pi}{3} + 2\pi = -\frac{5\pi}{3} + \frac{6\pi}{3} = \frac{\pi}{3}$$

Step 2 Determine the quadrant in which the terminal side lies. The angle $\frac{\pi}{3}$ is between quadrantal angles 0 and $\frac{\pi}{2}$, so it lies in Quadrant I.

Step 3 Draw the angle as coterminal with $\frac{\pi}{3}$. Label the angle $-\frac{11\pi}{3}$. ▪

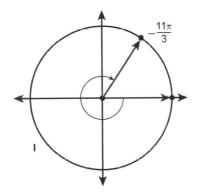

▶ **Think About It** Show rotation with an arrow pointing in the clockwise direction when drawing angles with negative measure.

Applying Coterminal Angles

EXAMPLE 4

A fishing reel has 6 m of fishing line hanging from it, perpendicular to the positive horizontal axis that passes through the center of the reel, as shown in the first figure.

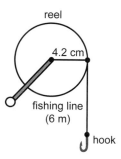

The fishing reel is rotated counterclockwise until the line is completely wrapped around the reel. The hook is now right up against the reel, as shown in the second figure.

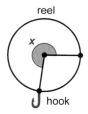

What is the measure of angle x to the nearest hundredth of a radian?

SOLUTION

The reel rotates until the remaining 6 m of fishing line are wrapped around it, which generates an arc length of 6 m.

Step 1 Arc length and angle measure are proportional. Set up a proportion between the angle x and the arc length of 6 m.

$$\frac{x}{2\pi} = \frac{6}{2\pi(0.42)}$$

$$2\pi(0.42) \cdot \frac{x}{2\pi} = \frac{6}{2\pi(0.42)} \cdot 2\pi(0.42)$$

$$0.42x = 6$$

$$x \approx 142.8571$$

▶ **Think About It** To ensure better accuracy, round to the indicated place value after converting to the desired units.

▶ **Q&A**

Q How many full rotations does the fishing reel make?

A about 22

Step 2 The angle x is between 0 and 2π and is coterminal with 142.8571 radians. It is the difference of 142.8571 and a multiple of 2π. The quotient of 142.8571 and 2π is approximately 22.74. Subtract 22 multiples of 2π from 142.8571 to get $142.8571 - 22(2\pi) \approx 4.64$.

The measure of angle x is approximately 4.64 radians. ▪

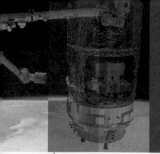

The Unit Circle

Trigonometric function values correspond to coordinates of points on the unit circle.

Identifying Points on the Unit Circle

Let P be a point located at the intersection of the terminal side of angle x and the unit circle. The length of the side of $\triangle POQ$ that is adjacent to x is the horizontal coordinate of P. The length of the side that is opposite x is the vertical coordinate of P.

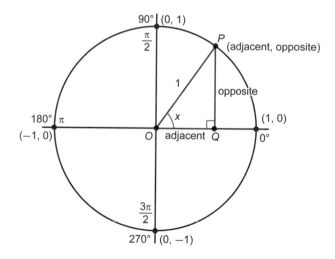

Using the side lengths of $\triangle POQ$, you can establish the following ratios:

$$\cos x = \frac{\text{adjacent}}{\text{hypotenuse}} = \frac{\text{adjacent}}{1} = \text{adjacent side length}$$

$$\sin x = \frac{\text{opposite}}{\text{hypotenuse}} = \frac{\text{opposite}}{1} = \text{opposite side length}$$

For any point (a, b) on the unit circle that lies on the terminal side of an angle x in standard position, $a = \cos x$ and $b = \sin x$. For points on the unit circle, the horizontal axis is the cosine axis, and the vertical axis is the sine axis.

EXAMPLE 1

What is the point on the unit circle that lies on the terminal side of an angle in standard position with a measure of $\frac{\pi}{6}$?

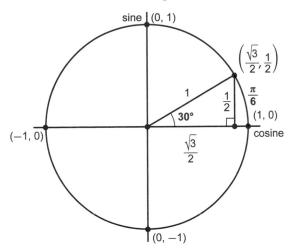

SOLUTION

A $\frac{\pi}{6}$ radian angle measure is equivalent to 30°. The reference triangle is therefore a 30°-60°-90° special right triangle with hypotenuse 1, and legs with side lengths $\frac{\sqrt{3}}{2}$ and $\frac{1}{2}$.

The horizontal coordinate is the length of the horizontal leg.

$$\cos\left(\frac{\pi}{6}\right) = \frac{\sqrt{3}}{2}$$

The vertical coordinate is $\sin\left(\frac{\pi}{6}\right) = \frac{1}{2}$.

The coordinate pair of the point with a measure of $\frac{\pi}{6}$ is $\left(\frac{\sqrt{3}}{2}, \frac{1}{2}\right)$. ■

Defining Trigonometric Functions

From the point $(1, 0)$ on the unit circle, move a distance of x units along the circle's circumference and stop at a point $P(a, b)$. Because P is on the unit circle, the real number x is the arc length from $(1, 0)$ to P and is equal to the radian measure of the angle that intercepts the arc. So a, the horizontal coordinate of P, is equal to $\cos x$ and b, the vertical coordinate of P, is equal to $\sin x$.

The movement x units from $(1, 0)$ along the unit circle takes you to a unique point (a, b) on the unit circle with coordinates $(\cos x, \sin x)$. Therefore, every real number x is paired with one and only one point $(\cos x, \sin x)$ on the graph of the unit circle. Because $a = \cos x$ and $b = \sin x$ are unique for any real number x, they can be defined as functions of x.

▶ **Remember** Distance is a length, so it is a real number.

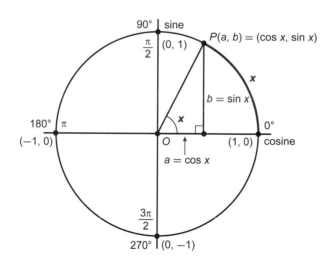

Definitions

Let x be the radian measure of the angle that intercepts the unit circle at (a, b). Then

$$\cos x = a \text{ and } \sin x = b$$

are trigonometric functions of x.

You have seen the tangent of x defined as the ratio of the side length opposite the angle x to the side length adjacent to x. With the unit circle, you can see that the tangent ratio for a radian angle measure x is $\tan x = \dfrac{\sin x}{\cos x}$.

Definition

Let x be the radian measure of the angle that intercepts the unit circle at (a, b). Then

$$\tan x = \frac{\sin x}{\cos x} = \frac{b}{a}$$

is a trigonometric function of x for all values of x that do not result in the cosine being zero.

Determining Trigonometric Function Values for Multiples of $\frac{\pi}{6}$, $\frac{\pi}{4}$, and $\frac{\pi}{3}$

You can find values of trigonometric functions for any angle measure or real number if you know the coordinates of the point on the unit circle that corresponds to that number. The point on the unit circle that corresponds with $\frac{\pi}{6}$ is $\left(\dfrac{\sqrt{3}}{2}, \dfrac{1}{2} \right)$, so $\cos\left(\dfrac{\pi}{6} \right) = \dfrac{\sqrt{3}}{2}$ and $\sin\left(\dfrac{\pi}{6} \right) = \dfrac{1}{2}$. Use $\tan x = \dfrac{\sin x}{\cos x}$

to get $\tan\left(\dfrac{\pi}{6} \right) = \dfrac{\sin\left(\dfrac{\pi}{6} \right)}{\cos\left(\dfrac{\pi}{6} \right)} = \dfrac{\dfrac{1}{2}}{\dfrac{\sqrt{3}}{2}} = \dfrac{\sqrt{3}}{3}$.

To determine the sine, cosine, and tangent of $\frac{\pi}{4}$, or 45°, draw a 45°-45°-90° triangle in Quadrant I of the unit circle.

The point that corresponds to $\frac{\pi}{4}$ is therefore $\left(\frac{\sqrt{2}}{2}, \frac{\sqrt{2}}{2}\right)$, which means that

$$\cos\left(\frac{\pi}{4}\right) = \sin\left(\frac{\pi}{4}\right) = \frac{\sqrt{2}}{2} \text{ and } \tan\left(\frac{\pi}{4}\right) = \frac{\sin\left(\frac{\pi}{4}\right)}{\cos\left(\frac{\pi}{4}\right)} = \frac{\frac{\sqrt{2}}{2}}{\frac{\sqrt{2}}{2}} = 1.$$

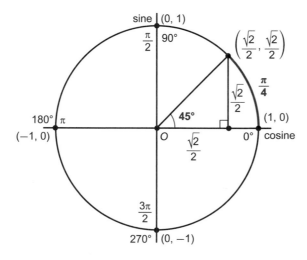

To determine the trigonometric function values for $\frac{\pi}{3}$, use a 30°-60°-90° special right triangle, but use $\frac{\pi}{3}$, or 60°, as the reference angle.

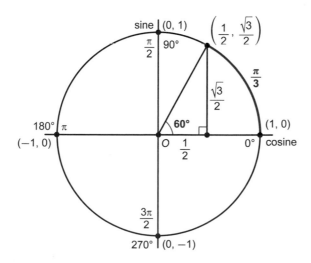

When you move among the quadrants of the unit circle on the coordinate plane, the absolute values of the trigonometric functions of respective multiples of $\frac{\pi}{6}$, $\frac{\pi}{4}$, and $\frac{\pi}{3}$ are the same. The function values differ only by a sign.

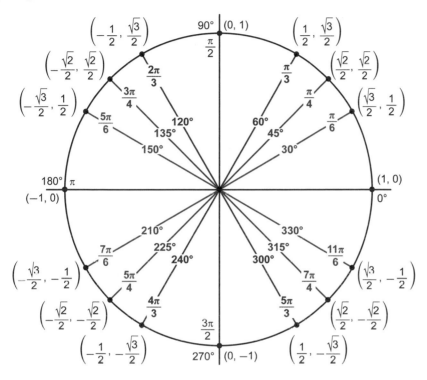

EXAMPLE 2

Use the unit circle to find the exact value of $\sin\left(-\frac{2\pi}{3}\right)$.

► **Remember** Negative measures are generated by rotating clockwise.

SOLUTION

To determine the location of $-\frac{2\pi}{3}$, start at the positive horizontal axis. Then rotate $\frac{2\pi}{3}$ radians in the negative (clockwise) direction, which takes you into the third quadrant to the same point as $\frac{4\pi}{3}$. On the unit circle, $\frac{4\pi}{3}$ corresponds to the point $\left(-\frac{1}{2}, -\frac{\sqrt{3}}{2}\right)$. So $\sin\left(-\frac{2\pi}{3}\right) = -\frac{\sqrt{3}}{2}$. ∎

> ▶ **Think About It** When locating the position of a measure using the unit circle, verify that the absolute value of the angle measure and its positive coterminal angle measure add to 2π. In this example,
> $$\frac{2\pi}{3} + \frac{4\pi}{3} = \frac{6\pi}{3} = 2\pi.$$

EXAMPLE 3

In which quadrant does x lie if $\sin x < 0$ and $\tan x > 0$?

SOLUTION

Look at the unit circle.

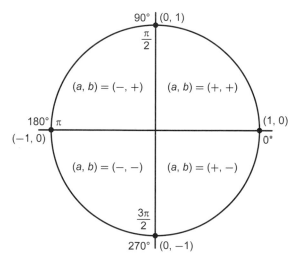

If x corresponds to the point (a, b) on the unit circle, then $\sin x = b$, which is negative in Quadrants III and IV. You can use $\tan x = \frac{b}{a}$ to see that $\tan x$ is positive when b and a have the same sign, which occurs in Quadrants I and III. The quadrant in which both conditions are true is Quadrant III. Therefore, x lies in Quadrant III. ∎

Trigonometric Identities

Identities are useful for determining unknown trigonometric function values.

Using the Pythagorean Identity

The triangle shown on the unit circle is a right triangle with leg lengths $a = \cos \theta$ and $b = \sin \theta$ and a hypotenuse of length 1.

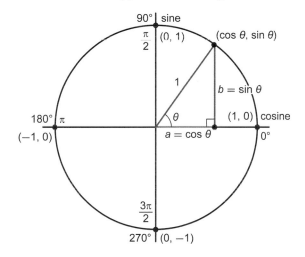

By the Pythagorean theorem, $a^2 + b^2 = 1$. You can substitute $\sin \theta$ for b and $\cos \theta$ for a to get $\sin^2 \theta + \cos^2 \theta = 1$.

▶ **Think About It** The expression $\sin^2 \theta$ is the same as $(\sin \theta)^2$, and $\cos^2 \theta$ is the same as $(\cos \theta)^2$. The first way of writing the expressions is often used to emphasize that the entire function, not just the angle or input value, is being squared.

> ▶ **Think About It** The unit circle has a radius of 1 unit. The equation of the unit circle is therefore $y^2 + x^2 = 1$. This equation is another way that you can derive the equation that leads to the Pythagorean identity $\sin^2 \theta + \cos^2 \theta = 1$.

Pythagorean Identity

For any angle θ,

$$\sin^2 \theta + \cos^2 \theta = 1.$$

This identity is called a **Pythagorean identity** because the equation that leads to it comes from the Pythagorean theorem.

EXAMPLE 1

The angle θ lies in Quadrant IV and $\cos \theta = \frac{3}{4}$. Determine the function value.

A $\sin \theta$

SOLUTION

Use the Pythagorean identity.

$\sin^2 \theta + \cos^2 \theta = 1$

$\sin^2 \theta + \left(\frac{3}{4}\right)^2 = 1$ Substitute $\frac{3}{4}$ for $\cos \theta$.

$\sin^2 \theta + \frac{9}{16} = 1$ Square $\frac{3}{4}$.

$\sin^2 \theta = \frac{7}{16}$ Subtract $\frac{9}{16}$ from both sides.

$\sin \theta = \pm\frac{\sqrt{7}}{4}$ Square Root Property

In Quadrant IV, sine is negative, so $\sin \theta = -\frac{\sqrt{7}}{4}$.

B tan θ

SOLUTION

Use the equation $\tan \theta = \dfrac{\sin \theta}{\cos \theta}$.

$$\tan \theta = \frac{\sin \theta}{\cos \theta} = \frac{\dfrac{-\sqrt{7}}{4}}{\dfrac{3}{4}} = -\frac{\sqrt{7}}{3} \ \blacksquare$$

Using Other Trigonometric Identities

Properties
For any angle θ, $$\sin(-\theta) = -\sin \theta$$ $$\cos(-\theta) - \cos \theta$$ $$\tan(-\theta) = -\tan \theta$$

To see why the first two properties make sense, look at the unit circle. The angle $-\theta$ has a measure that is the absolute value of the measure of angle θ. Point A on the terminal side of θ is $(\cos \theta, \sin \theta)$. Point B on the terminal side of $-\theta$ is $(\cos(-\theta), \sin(-\theta))$.

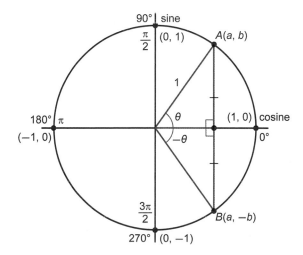

The value of $\cos(-\theta)$ is the same as the value of $\cos \theta$ because both angles have the same horizontal coordinate. So $\cos(-\theta) = \cos \theta$.

However, the value of $\sin(-\theta)$ is the opposite of the value of $\sin \theta$ because the vertical coordinate of $-\theta$ is the opposite of the vertical coordinate of θ. So $\sin(-\theta) = -\sin \theta$.

EXAMPLE 2

Determine $\cos \theta$ when $\sin(-\theta) = \dfrac{2}{5}$ and $\tan \theta = \dfrac{2\sqrt{21}}{21}$.

SOLUTION

Step 1 Determine $\sin \theta$ using the property $\sin(-\theta) = -\sin \theta$.

$$\sin \theta = -\sin(-\theta) = -\frac{2}{5}$$

Step 2 Solve $\tan \theta = \dfrac{\sin \theta}{\cos \theta}$ for $\cos \theta$.

$$\tan \theta = \frac{\sin \theta}{\cos \theta}$$

$$\cos \theta \bullet \tan \theta = \frac{\sin \theta}{\cos \theta} \bullet \cos \theta \qquad \text{Multiply both sides by } \cos \theta.$$

$$\cos \theta \bullet \tan \theta = \sin \theta \qquad \text{Simplify.}$$

$$\frac{\cos \theta \bullet \tan \theta}{\tan \theta} = \frac{\sin \theta}{\tan \theta} \qquad \text{Divide both sides by } \tan \theta.$$

$$\cos \theta = \frac{\sin \theta}{\tan \theta} \qquad \text{Simplify.}$$

Step 3 Use $\sin \theta = -\dfrac{2}{5}$ and $\tan \theta = \dfrac{2\sqrt{21}}{21}$ to determine $\cos \theta$.

$$\cos \theta = \frac{\sin \theta}{\tan \theta} = \frac{-\dfrac{2}{5}}{\dfrac{2\sqrt{21}}{21}} = -\frac{\sqrt{21}}{5}$$

Proving Identities

To prove that an identity is true, transform one or both sides of the equation so that they are identical.

Strategies for Proving Trigonometric Identities

Here are some tips to keep in mind when proving identities:

- Try to rewrite the more complicated side of the equation so that it is identical to the less complicated side. If both sides are fairly complicated, rewrite both sides so they are identical to the same simpler expression.

- Try writing $\tan \theta$ in terms of $\sin \theta$ and $\cos \theta$.

- If there is a mixture of $\sin^2$ and $\cos^2$, then use the Pythagorean identity to get just one or the other.

EXAMPLE 3

$$\sin^2 \theta \left(1 + \frac{1}{\tan^2 \theta} \right) = 1$$

SOLUTION

Rewrite the left side so that it is identical to the right side.

$$\sin^2 \theta \left(1 + \frac{1}{\tan^2 \theta} \right) = 1$$

$$\sin^2 \theta \left(1 + \frac{1}{\frac{\sin^2 \theta}{\cos^2 \theta}} \right) = 1 \qquad \text{Substitute } \frac{\sin \theta}{\cos \theta} \text{ for } \tan \theta.$$

$$\sin^2 \theta \left(1 + \frac{\cos^2 \theta}{\sin^2 \theta} \right) = 1 \qquad \text{Simplify.}$$

$$\sin^2 \theta + \cos^2 \theta = 1 \qquad \text{Distribute.}$$

$$1 = 1 \qquad \text{Pythagorean Identity} \ \blacksquare$$

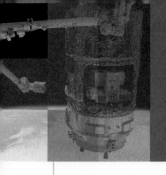

Trigonometric Functions of Any Angle

Trigonometric functions are defined for angles of any measure.

Defining Trigonometric Functions for Angles on Circles with Radius *r*

You can determine the trigonometric functions of an angle θ given a point (a, b) on its terminal side, even if the point does not lie on the unit circle. The circle shown has radius r. The angle θ is in standard position, and the point $P(a, b)$ lies on its terminal side. A segment from P to the horizontal axis at point Q creates right triangle PQO with the origin.

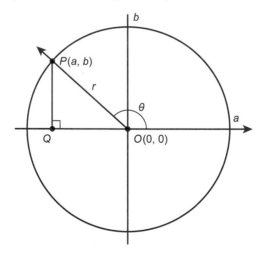

The distance r between points $P(a, b)$ and $O(0, 0)$ can be determined using the distance formula.

$$r = \sqrt{(a-0)^2 + (b-0)^2} = \sqrt{a^2 + b^2}$$

330 RADIANS AND TRIGONOMETRIC FUNCTIONS

Then the trigonometric functions of θ are determined by the side lengths of triangle PQO.

Definition

Let (a, b) be a point other than the origin on the terminal side of an angle θ in standard position. The distance from the point to the origin is

$$r = \sqrt{a^2 + b^2}.$$

The **trigonometric functions** of θ are defined as follows:

$$\sin \theta = \frac{b}{r} \qquad \cos \theta = \frac{a}{r} \qquad \tan \theta = \frac{b}{a} \ (a \neq 0)$$

▶ **Think About It** The point (a, b) cannot be the origin because that leads to a value of r equal to 0. In that case, the values of sine and cosine have 0 in the denominator and are therefore undefined. If only the horizontal coordinate is 0, then $\tan \theta$ is undefined.

EXAMPLE 1

Let $(-4, -11)$ be on the terminal side of an angle θ. Determine the exact value of the trigonometric ratio.

A $\sin \theta$

SOLUTION
Determine r.

$$r = \sqrt{(-4)^2 + (-11)^2} = \sqrt{16 + 121} = \sqrt{137}$$

$$\sin \theta = \frac{b}{r} = \frac{-11}{\sqrt{137}} = \frac{-11\sqrt{137}}{137}$$

B $\cos \theta$

SOLUTION

$$\cos \theta = \frac{a}{r} = \frac{-4}{\sqrt{137}} = \frac{-4\sqrt{137}}{137}$$

C $\tan \theta$

SOLUTION

$$\tan \theta = \frac{b}{a} = \frac{-11}{-4} = \frac{11}{4} \ \blacksquare$$

▶ **Think About It** Pay attention to the sign of each horizontal and vertical coordinate. While the value of r does not depend on the signs, the function values do.

Using the Equation of a Line

If the terminal side of an angle x is given as an equation of a line, determine the trigonometric functions of the angle by graphing the line and then determining a point on the line.

▶ **Think About It** It is often customary to use a variable such as x from the English alphabet for an angle measured in radians and a variable such as θ from the Greek alphabet for an angle measured in degrees.

EXAMPLE 2

The terminal side of an angle x in standard position coincides with the line $7a + 3b = 0$ in Quadrant IV. Determine $\cos x$.

SOLUTION

Step 1 Solve the equation for b.

$$7a + 3b = 0$$
$$3b = -7a$$
$$b = -\frac{7}{3}a$$

Step 2 Graph the angle with its terminal side in Quadrant IV.

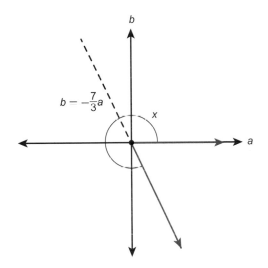

Step 3 In Quadrant IV a is positive. Choose a positive value of a to determine the coordinates of a point (a, b) on the terminal side of x.

When $a = 3$, $b = -\frac{7}{3}a = -\frac{7}{3}(3) = -7$.

The point $(3, -7)$ is on the terminal side of the angle.

Step 4 Determine r.

$$r = \sqrt{3^2 + (-7)^2} = \sqrt{9 + 49} = \sqrt{58}$$

Step 5 Use the definition of $\cos x$.

$$\cos x = \frac{a}{r} = \frac{3}{\sqrt{58}} = \frac{3\sqrt{58}}{58}$$

Using Reference Angles

Every nonquadrantal angle in standard position is associated with a reference angle.

Definition

A **reference angle** x' for an acute angle x is the positive acute angle made by the terminal side of x and the horizontal axis.

To determine the reference angle for an angle x, draw the angle in standard position, and then draw the acute angle coinciding with x that has its initial or terminal side on the horizontal axis.

▶ **Think About It** If an angle measure is greater than 2π or $360°$, first determine the measure of an angle that is coterminal with the given angle, and then determine its reference angle.

EXAMPLE 3

Determine the measure of the reference angle for $\dfrac{9\pi}{8}$.

SOLUTION
Graph the angle.

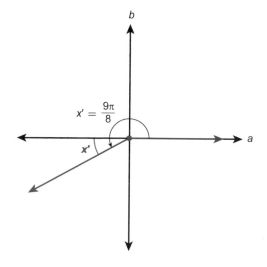

Remember State the measure of an angle in the units given in the problem unless otherwise directed.

The measure of the reference angle x' is the difference between $\frac{9\pi}{8}$ and the angle π made by the negative horizontal axis.

$$x' = \frac{9\pi}{8} - \pi = \frac{9\pi}{8} - \frac{8\pi}{8} = \frac{\pi}{8} \blacksquare$$

Q&A

Q What is the measure of $\frac{9\pi}{8}$ in degrees?

A 202.5°

Inverse Trigonometric Functions

A trigonometric function has an inverse when its domain is restricted so that it is one-to-one.

Defining the Inverse Function of $y = \sin x$

Definition
In a **one-to-one function**, every element of the domain corresponds to exactly one element of the range.

When you look at the unit circle, you can see several values of $\sin x$ for which there is more than one input that results in that same output. Look at $\sin \frac{\pi}{6} = \frac{1}{2}$ and $\sin \frac{5\pi}{6} = \frac{1}{2}$ as an example. Because the inputs $\frac{\pi}{6}$ and $\frac{5\pi}{6}$ both give the output $\frac{1}{2}$, $y = \sin x$ is not a one-to-one function. However, when the inputs are restricted to values from $-\frac{\pi}{2}$ and $\frac{\pi}{2}$, $\sin x$ is strictly increasing.

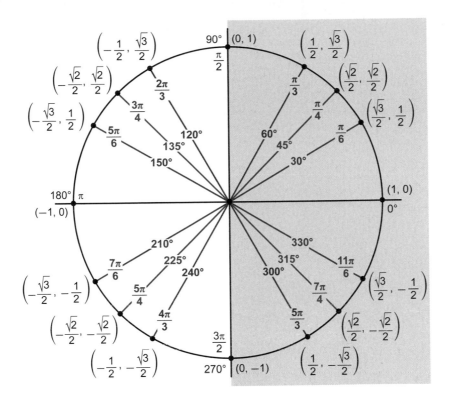

In this interval, the values of sin x do not repeat. The function is therefore one-to-one when its domain is restricted to values between $-\frac{\pi}{2}$ and $\frac{\pi}{2}$, inclusive. So it is possible to define an inverse function of sin x on this interval.

Definition

The **arcsine (arcsin) function** $y = \arcsin x$ if and only if

$$\sin y = x$$

where $-1 \le x \le 1$ and $-\frac{\pi}{2} \le y \le \frac{\pi}{2}$.

Another way of stating this definition is "The inverse function of $y = \sin x$ is $y = \arcsin x$ as long as sin x is restricted to input values from $-\frac{\pi}{2}$ to $\frac{\pi}{2}$."

EXAMPLE 1

Determine the exact value of $\arcsin\left(\dfrac{-\sqrt{3}}{2}\right)$ in radians.

SOLUTION

You want to determine an angle θ such that $\sin\theta = \left(\dfrac{-\sqrt{3}}{2}\right)$.

Look on the unit circle in the interval from $-\dfrac{\pi}{2}$ to $\dfrac{\pi}{2}$ and locate the angle with a sine value of $\dfrac{-\sqrt{3}}{2}$.

The angle $-\dfrac{\pi}{3}$ has a sine value of $\dfrac{-\sqrt{3}}{2}$, so $\arcsin\left(\dfrac{-\sqrt{3}}{2}\right) = -\dfrac{\pi}{3}$. ■

Defining the Inverse Function of $y = \cos x$

The cosine function can also be restricted so that it is one-to-one. From 0 to $\dfrac{\pi}{2}$, the interval indicated by the shaded region, cosine is a decreasing function as it takes on all values from −1 to 1. It is therefore one-to-one from 0 to $\dfrac{\pi}{2}$. So cosine has an inverse function when its domain is restricted to this interval.

Definition

The **arccosine (arccos) function** $y = \arccos x$ if and only if

$$\cos y = x$$

where $-1 \leq x \leq 1$ and $0 \leq y \leq \pi$.

You can set up equations involving inverse trigonometric functions based on triangle side lengths and angles.

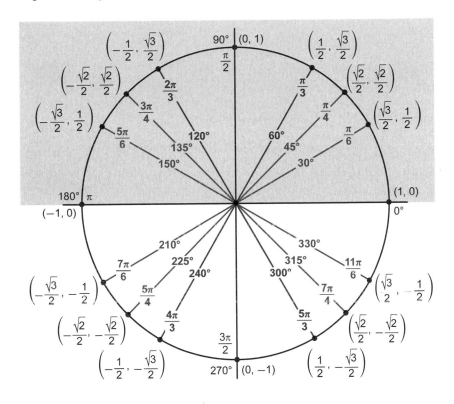

EXAMPLE 2

Write θ as a function of x.

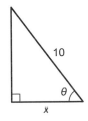

SOLUTION

Side length x is adjacent to angle θ, and the hypotenuse of the triangle is 10. So start with cos θ, which involves the ratio of the adjacent side length to the length of the hypotenuse. Then use the definition of arccosine.

$$\cos \theta = \frac{x}{10}$$

$$\theta = \arccos\left(\frac{x}{10}\right)$$

You can use reference angles to evaluate expressions involving inverse trigonometric functions. ■

▶ **Think About It** When you are asked to write one variable as a function of another variable, the function equation should end up with the first variable isolated on one side. In this case, θ is the variable to be isolated.

EXAMPLE 3

Use a calculator to determine arcsin(0.6) to the nearest hundredth of a radian.

SOLUTION

Make sure that your calculator is in radian mode. Then enter the expression **arcsin(0.6)** and press **ENTER**.

$$\arcsin(0.6) \approx 0.6435 \;■$$

▶ **Think About It** On a scientific calculator, enter the value, then select the **Inv** or **Shift** button and then the trig function. For instance, 0.6, then **Inv**, and then **sin**$^{-1}$.

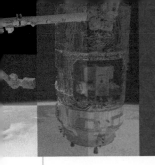

Solving Trigonometric Equations

You can use inverse functions to solve trigonometric equations that arise in real-world applications.

Solving a Trigonometric Equation Analytically

How to Use a Trigonometric Equation to Solve a Real-World Problem

Step 1 Sketch the scenario, labeling the given and unknown values.

Step 2 Write an equation using a trigonometric function that involves the unknown value.

Step 3 Use an inverse trigonometric function to solve for the unknown value.

Using an Inverse Trig Function to Solve an Application Problem

EXAMPLE

Francois is flying a kite. He has let out all 100 m of his kite string, and the kite is directly above a spot that is 15 m away from where Francois is standing. What is the angle of elevation of the kite, to the nearest degree, from his location?

SOLUTION

Step 1 Sketch the scenario, labeling the unknown angle as θ.

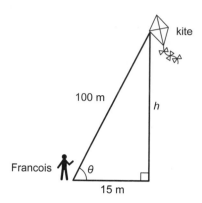

Step 2 The known side lengths are for the hypotenuse and the leg adjacent to θ, so write an equation in terms of $\cos \theta$.

$$\cos \theta = \frac{15}{100}$$

Step 3 Solve the equation using arccosine.

$$\cos \theta = \frac{15}{100}$$

$$\theta = \arccos\left(\frac{15}{100}\right)$$

$$\theta \approx 81.37°$$

The angle of elevation of the kite is about 81°. ▪

Graphs of Sinusoidal Functions

Topic List

A vibrating string, a seismic wave, and an ocean wave all can be modeled with sinusoidal functions. You can see the repetitive pattern in these periodic phenomena and model them with periodic trigonometric functions.

Sinusoidal Graphs

Period, midline, and amplitude are some of the key characteristics of sinusoidal functions.

Identifying Characteristics of Sinusoidal Graphs

Any sine or cosine function has a graph that resembles the one shown. These functions are called **sinusoidal functions**.

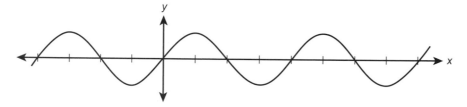

Here is sinusoidal $f(x)$ graphed on the interval $(0, 2\pi)$.

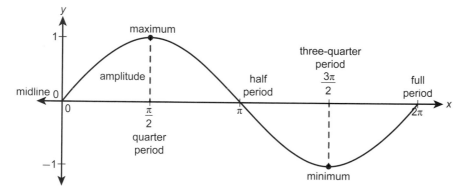

Notice that the maximum height the function reaches is 1. So the maximum is 1. The function's minimum height is -1, so the minimum is -1.

Remember Recall that the period of a function is the smallest interval where the function repeats itself. In the case of $f(x)$, the period is 2π.

Definitions

The **midline** of a sinusoidal function is the horizontal line that is halfway between the maximum and the minimum. The equation of the midline of a sinusoidal function is

$$y = \frac{\text{maximum} + \text{minimum}}{2} .$$

The **amplitude** of a sinusoidal function is one-half the distance between the maximum and minimum values.

$$\text{amplitude} = \frac{\text{maximum} - \text{minimum}}{2}$$

▶ **Remember** If the minimum y-value is -1 and the maximum y-value is 1, then the range of the function is $[-1, 1]$.

EXAMPLE

Determine the period, minimum, maximum, midline, and amplitude of the function.

A

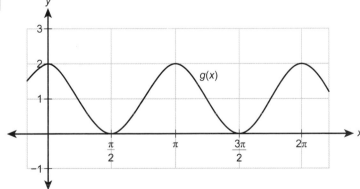

SOLUTION

Since the graph of $g(x)$ repeats itself every π, the period is π. The lowest y-value the function takes on is 0, so the minimum is 0. The maximum value the function reaches is 2, so the maximum is 2.

$$\text{equation of midline: } y = \frac{\text{maximum} + \text{minimum}}{2} = \frac{2 + 0}{2} = 1$$

$$\text{amplitude} = \frac{\text{maximum} - \text{minimum}}{2} = \frac{2 - 0}{2} = 1$$

▶ **Q&A**

Q What is the range of $g(x)$ from Example A?

A $[0, 2]$

B

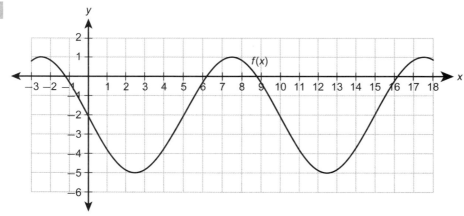

SOLUTION

The period is 10 since the function repeats every 10. The minimum is −5, and the maximum is 1.

$$\text{equation of midline: } y = \frac{1 + (-5)}{2} = -2$$

$$\text{amplitude} = \frac{1 - (-5)}{2} = 3 \ \blacksquare$$

Sinusoidal Graphs: Amplitude

The amplitude is the height of a sinusoidal function above the midline.

Defining the Sine Function

Recall some key points from the unit circle for sine.

Angle (in radians)	0	$\frac{\pi}{2}$	π	$\frac{3\pi}{2}$	2π
Sine ratio	0	1	0	-1	0

Now consider the angles as inputs (x-values) and the sine ratios as outputs (y-values). Plot those points, and draw a smooth curve through them. You will see that the result is a sinusoidal function, $f(x) = \sin x$.

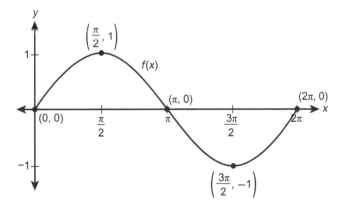

Since you can find the sine of any angle measure, the graph extends horizontally in both directions without end. Therefore, the domain of $f(x) = \sin x$ is $(-\infty, \infty)$.

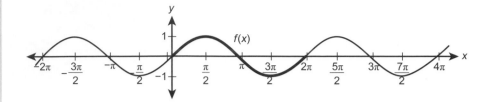

Since the graph repeats every 2π, the period of $f(x) = \sin x$ is 2π. Also, since $\sin(0) = 0$, the graph of $f(x) = \sin x$ passes through the origin $(0, 0)$.

The x-intercepts occur whenever sine is equal to zero $(x = \ldots -2\pi, -\pi, 0, \pi, 2\pi, \ldots)$, so the x-intercepts occur at $x = n\pi$ where n is an integer.

Inspecting the graph reveals that a maximum is $\left(\dfrac{\pi}{2}, 1\right)$ and a minimum is $\left(\dfrac{3\pi}{2}, -1\right)$. Therefore, the range of $f(x) = \sin x$ is $[-1, 1]$.

The midline is halfway between the minimum y-value $(y = -1)$ and the maximum y-value $(y = 1)$, so the equation of the midline is $y = 0$. Since the amplitude is the height above the midline, the amplitude is equal to 1.

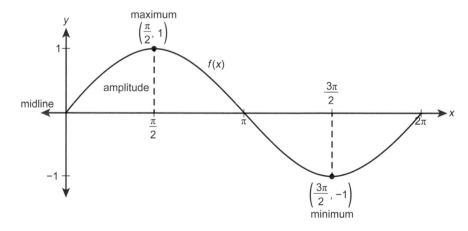

EXAMPLE 1

Determine the amplitude of $g(x) = 2 \sin x$, which is graphed.

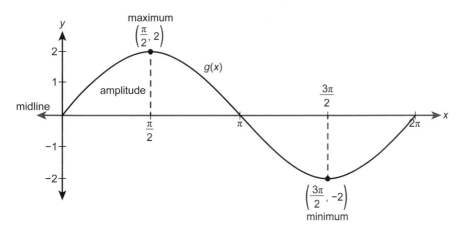

SOLUTION

Notice that $g(x) = 2 \sin x$ has the same basic shape as $f(x) = \sin x$ but is stretched vertically by a factor of 2. Since the maximum is 2 and the minimum is -2, the amplitude of $g(x) = 2 \sin x$ is 2. ■

Formula for the Amplitude of a Sinusoidal Function

The amplitude of a sinusoidal function can be found directly from the function equation. For $f(x) = A \sin x$,

$$\text{amplitude} = |A|$$

where $A \neq 0$.

EXAMPLE 2

Determine the amplitude of $h(x) = -\dfrac{3}{2} \sin x$.

SOLUTION

Since the function is in the form $h(x) = A \sin x$ and $A = -\dfrac{3}{2}$, the amplitude is $\left| -\dfrac{3}{2} \right| = \dfrac{3}{2}$.

Confirm this result by graphing it.

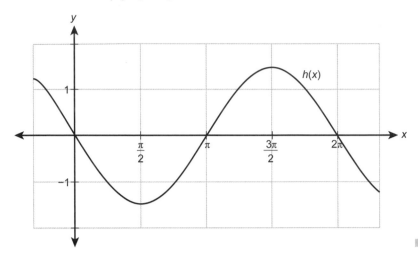

Notice that compared to the parent function $f(x) = \sin x$, the graph of $h(x) = -\frac{3}{2} \sin x$ is stretched vertically and is also reflected over the x-axis, which occurs because $A < 0$. The graph of $h(x) = A \sin x$ is the result of reflecting the function $y = |A| \sin x$ over the x-axis if $A < 0$.

Defining the Cosine Function

Recall some key points from the unit circle for cosine.

Angle (in radians)	0	$\frac{\pi}{2}$	π	$\frac{3\pi}{2}$	2π
Cosine ratio	1	0	-1	0	1

When graphed using a smooth curve (where x = angle measures, y = cosine ratios), you get the graph of the cosine function, $f(x) = \cos x$.

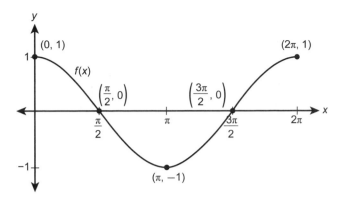

Just like the sine function, this pattern repeats and extends horizontally in both directions, so the domain of $f(x) = \cos x$ is $(-\infty, \infty)$, and the period is 2π. Notice that the range of $f(x) = \cos x$ is also $[-1, 1]$, as with the sine function.

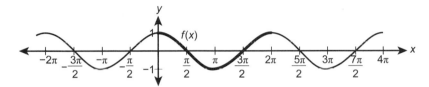

The midline is also at $y = 0$, and the amplitude is 1.

> **Think About It** Since the graph of $f(x) = \cos x$ is symmetric about the y-axis, it has even symmetry $f(-x) = f(x)$.

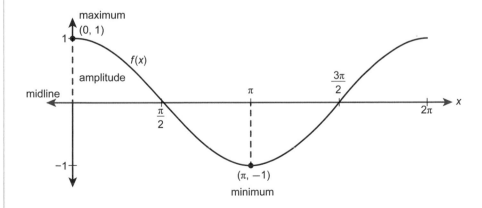

However, note the following differences for the cosine function:

- The y-intercept is $(0, 1)$.

- A maximum occurs at $(0, 1)$, and a minimum is at $(\pi, -1)$.

- The x-intercepts occur where the cosine function is equal to zero, which are the odd multiples of $\frac{\pi}{2}$: $x = \left\{ \ldots -\frac{3\pi}{2}, -\frac{\pi}{2}, \frac{\pi}{2}, \frac{3\pi}{2}, \ldots \right\}$. So the x-intercepts occur when $x = \frac{n\pi}{2}$, where n is an odd integer.

EXAMPLE 3

Determine the amplitude and the equation in the form $g(x) = A \cos x$.

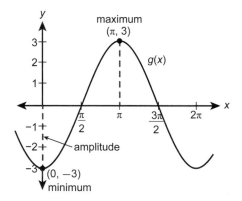

▶ Q&A

Q What is the range shown in Example 3?

A $[-3, 3]$

SOLUTION

$$\text{amplitude} = \frac{\text{maximum} - \text{minimum}}{2} = \frac{3 - (-3)}{2} = 3$$

Since the graph is reflected over the x-axis, $A < 0$ in the form $f(x) = A \cos x$. So the equation of the function is $g(x) = -3 \cos x$. ■

EXAMPLE 4

Determine the amplitude of $f(x) = 3.5 \cos x$.

SOLUTION

Since the function is in the form $f(x) = A \cos x$ and $A = 3.5$, the amplitude is $|3.5| = 3.5$. ∎

Sinusoidal Graphs: Period

The interval over which a sinusoidal graph repeats itself is its period.

Determining the Period of Sine Functions

Recall that the period of a function is the smallest interval over which the function repeats itself. For the parent sine function, $f(x) = \sin x$, the period is 2π.

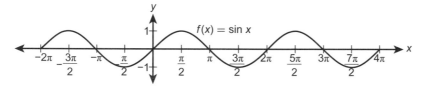

Compare the graph of the parent function $f(x)$ to the graph of $g(x) = \sin 2x$.

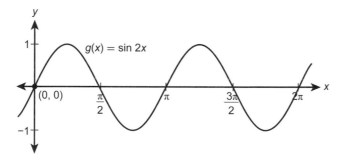

Notice that the period for $g(x) = \sin 2x$ is π. The graph has the same basic shape as $f(x) = \sin x$ but has been compressed horizontally by a factor of $\frac{1}{2}$.

Formula for the Period of Sine

For $f(x) = \sin Bx$, period $= \dfrac{2\pi}{B}$ where $B > 0$.

The function $f(x) = \sin 2x$ is in the form $f(x) = \sin Bx$, so its period is

$\dfrac{2\pi}{B} = \dfrac{2\pi}{2} = \pi$, which is one-half the period of the sine function.

EXAMPLE 1

Use the formula for period to determine the period of

$g(x) = \sin\left(\dfrac{x}{3}\right)$. Then graph the function to check your answer.

▶ **Think About It** Another way to define period is as the smallest real number p that makes $f(x) = f(x + p)$.

SOLUTION

Rewrite the function in the form $g(x) = \sin Bx$.

$$g(x) = \sin\left(\dfrac{x}{3}\right) = \sin\left(\dfrac{1}{3}x\right)$$

Since $B = \dfrac{1}{3}$, period $= \dfrac{2\pi}{\dfrac{1}{3}} = 6\pi$.

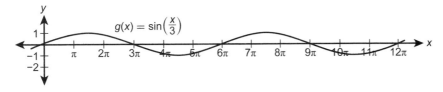

The graph also repeats every 6π, so the period is 6π. ■

Determining the Period of Cosine Functions

Recall that the period of the cosine function, $f(x) = \cos x$, is also 2π.

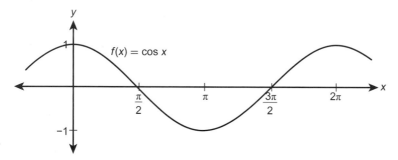

As with sine functions, the period of cosine functions can be found using a formula.

Formula for the Period of Cosine

For $f(x) = \cos Bx$, period $= \dfrac{2\pi}{B}$ where $B > 0$.

EXAMPLE 2

Use the formula for period to determine the period of $h(x) = \cos 4x$. Then graph the function to check your answer.

SOLUTION

The function is in the form $h(x) = \cos Bx$.

Since $B = 4$, period $= \dfrac{2\pi}{B} = \dfrac{2\pi}{4} = \dfrac{\pi}{2}$.

The graph repeats every $\dfrac{\pi}{2}$, so the period is $\dfrac{\pi}{2}$.

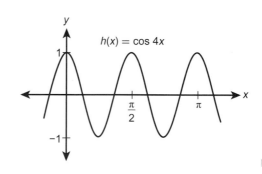

EXAMPLE 3

Determine the period of $f(x) = \cos \pi x$.

SOLUTION

Since $B = \pi$, period $= \dfrac{2\pi}{\pi} = 2.$ ■

Determining Frequency

Definition

The **frequency** of a sinusoidal function is the number of periods per unit. A function's frequency is the reciprocal of its period.

Formula for Frequency

For $f(x) = \sin Bx$ and $f(x) = \cos Bx$, frequency $= \dfrac{1}{\text{period}} = \dfrac{B}{2\pi}$ where $B > 0$.

EXAMPLE 4

Determine the frequency of $g(x) = \sin 4x$.

SOLUTION

Determine the period. Since $B = 4$, period $= \dfrac{2\pi}{4} = \dfrac{\pi}{2}$. Take the reciprocal of the period.

$$\text{frequency} = \dfrac{1}{\dfrac{\pi}{2}} = \dfrac{2}{\pi} \ \blacksquare$$

EXAMPLE 5

Write the equation of a function in the form $f(x) = \cos Bx$ that has a frequency of $\frac{2}{3}$.

SOLUTION

$$\text{frequency} = \frac{2}{3} = \frac{B}{2\pi}$$

Solve for B.

$$4\pi = 3B$$

$$\frac{4\pi}{3} = B$$

An equation of the function is $f(x) = \cos\left(\frac{4\pi x}{3}\right)$. ∎

Sinusoidal Graphs: Vertical Shift

Adding a constant to a sinusoidal function causes a vertical shift.

Determining Vertical Shifts of the Sine Function

Compare the graph of $g(x) = \sin x + 2$ to $f(x) = \sin x$.

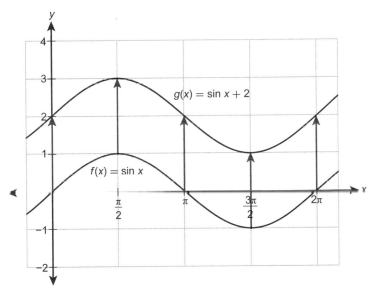

The graph of $g(x) = \sin x + 2$ is a translation up 2 units of $f(x) = \sin x$.

Vertical Translation of a Sine Function

Compared to the parent function $f(x) = \sin x$, $g(x) = \sin x + C$ is a vertical translation by C units such that

$C > 0$: shift up C units.

$C < 0$: shift down $|C|$ units.

In the graph of $g(x) = \sin x + 2$, the equation of the midline is $y = 2$. For any function $g(x) = \sin x + C$, the equation of the midline is $y = C$.

EXAMPLE 1

Write an equation for the graph in the form $g(x) = \sin x + C$.

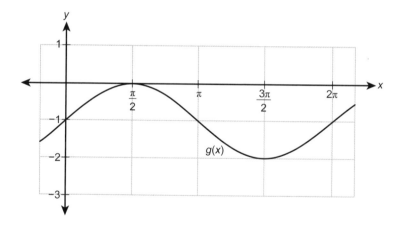

SOLUTION

Since the graph is a 1-unit shift down of $f(x) = \sin x$, $C = -1$. So the equation is $g(x) = \sin x - 1$. ▪

Determining Vertical Shifts of the Cosine Function

As with a sine function, a vertical shift of a cosine function can be found using a formula.

Also, the equation of the midline of $g(x) = \cos x + C$ is $y = C$.

EXAMPLE 2

Use the graph of the cosine function as reference and the function $g(x)$ shown to write the equation of the function in the form $g(x) = \cos x + C$.

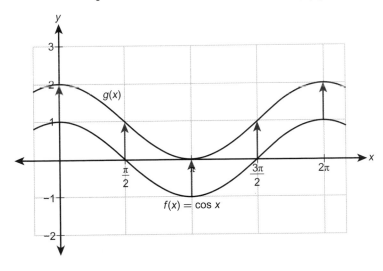

SOLUTION

Since the cosine function has been shifted up by 1 unit, $C = 1$. So the transformed function is $g(x) = \cos x + 1$. ■

Sinusoidal Family of Functions

The amplitude, period, and vertical shift of a sinusoidal function can be determined from its equation.

Determining Sinusoidal Function Transformations

Sinusoidal functions in the form $f(x) = A \sin Bx + C$ or $f(x) = A \cos Bx + C$ have the following characteristics:

amplitude $= |A|$, where $A \neq 0$

period $= \dfrac{2\pi}{B}$, where $B > 0$

frequency $= \dfrac{1}{\text{period}} = \dfrac{B}{2\pi}$ equation of midline: $y = C$

If $C > 0$, there is a vertical shift up C units.

If $C < 0$, there is a vertical shift down $|C|$ units.

EXAMPLE 1

Determine the midline, amplitude, maximum value, minimum value, period, and frequency of the function.

A $g(x) = 3 \sin 2x + 1$

SOLUTION

Since $C = 1$, the equation of the midline is $y = 1$. Since $A = 3$, the amplitude is 3. So the maximum is 3 units above the midline at $y = 4$ and the minimum is 3 units below at $y = -2$.

Since $B = 2$, period $= \dfrac{2\pi}{2} = \pi$, and frequency $= \dfrac{1}{\pi}$.

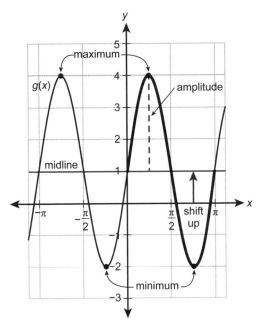

B $h(x) = -2\cos\left(\dfrac{\pi x}{2}\right) - 3$

SOLUTION

Since $C = -3$, the equation of the midline is $y = -3$. Since $A = -2$, the amplitude is $|-2| = 2$. Also, since $A < 0$, $h(x)$ is reflected across the midline. The minimum is 2 units below the midline at $y = -5$. The maximum is 2 units above the midline at $y = -1$.

Since $B = \frac{\pi}{2}$, period $= \frac{2\pi}{\frac{\pi}{2}} = 4$, and frequency $= \frac{1}{4}$.

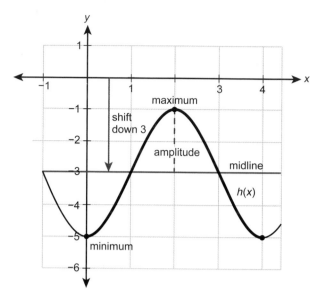

EXAMPLE 2

Graph the function $v(x) = -3\cos\left(\frac{x}{2}\right) + 2$, and then determine the midline, amplitude, maximum value, minimum value, period, and frequency.

SOLUTION

To graph a sinusoidal function, start by finding the maximum and minimum values.

Since $C = 2$, the equation of the midline is $y = 2$. The amplitude is $|A| - |-3| = 3$. The maximum is 5 and the minimum is -1. Draw dashed lines for the maximum, minimum, and midline.

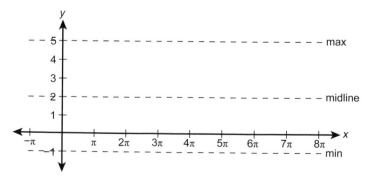

$A < 0$, so the graph is flipped when compared to $y = \cos x$. The period is $\dfrac{2\pi}{\frac{1}{2}} = 4\pi$. Start the graph at $x = 0$, and then mark the end of one period at

$x = 4\pi$. The cosine function starts at a maximum or minimum, and this one has $A < 0$, so mark a minimum at $x = 0$, another at $x = 4\pi$, and another at 8π. Mark maximum values halfway between the minima at $x = 2\pi$ and $x = 6\pi$.

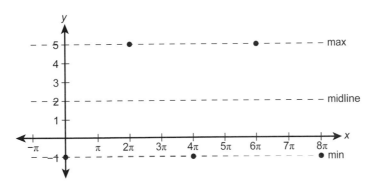

Connect the points with a smooth sinusoidal curve.

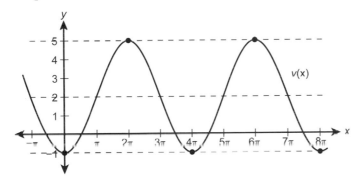

Creating Trigonometric Models

You can write the equation of a sinusoidal function if you know its characteristics.

EXAMPLE 1

Write the equation of a function in the form $y = A \sin Bx + C$ or $y = A \cos Bx + C$ for the given characteristics.

A frequency $= \dfrac{4}{\pi}$; amplitude $= 2.25$; midline: $y = 4.5$; y-intercept: $(0, 4.5)$; $A > 0$

SOLUTION

To write a function with the given characteristics, determine the values of A, B, and C.

Since amplitude $= 2.25$, $|A| = 2.25$. The equation of the midline is $y = 4.5$, so $C = 4.5$. You can use the frequency formula to determine B.

$$\text{frequency} = \frac{B}{2\pi}$$

$$\frac{4}{\pi} = \frac{B}{2\pi}$$

$$B = 8$$

Since the y-intercept is on the midline, substitute the values of A, B, and C into the sine function.

$$y = 2.25 \sin(8x) + 4.5$$

B period $= 24$; absolute minimum $= 5$; absolute maximum $= 12$;
y-intercept: $(0, 12)$; $A > 0$

SOLUTION

Determine the values of A, B, and C.

$$\text{amplitude} = \frac{\text{maximum} - \text{minimum}}{2} = \frac{12 - 5}{2} = 3.5$$

So $|A| = 3.5$.

$$\text{period} = \frac{2\pi}{B}$$

$$24 = \frac{2\pi}{B}$$

$$24B = 2\pi$$

$$B = \frac{\pi}{12}$$

$$\text{equation of midline: } y = \frac{\text{maximum} + \text{minimum}}{2} = \frac{12 + 5}{2} = 8.5$$

So $C = 8.5$.

Since the y-intercept is a maximum, substitute the values of A, B, and C into the cosine function.

$$y = 3.5 \cos\left(\frac{\pi x}{12}\right) + 8.5 \ ■$$

EXAMPLE 2

The Singapore Flyer is a 165 m tall Ferris wheel that takes 30 min to make 1 full revolution. Assuming you start at ground level, determine the equation of a sinusoidal function, where your height in meters (y) is a function of time in hours (x).

SOLUTION

Determine the values of A, B, and C. Since the Ferris wheel starts a revolution from ground level, both the minimum and the y-intercept are $(0, 0)$. Since the Ferris wheel is 165 m tall, the maximum is 165.

$$\text{amplitude} = \frac{\text{maximum} - \text{minimum}}{2} = \frac{165 - 0}{2} = 82.5$$

So $|A| = 82.5$.

$$\text{period} = \frac{2\pi}{B}$$

$$0.5 = \frac{2\pi}{B}$$

$$0.5B = 2\pi$$

$$B = 4\pi$$

▶ **Think About It** The period is 30 min = 0.5 h.

$$\text{equation of midline: } y = \frac{\text{maximum} + \text{minimum}}{2} = \frac{165 + 0}{2} = 82.5$$

So $C = 82.5$.

Since you start at the Ferris wheel's minimum value, a cosine function with $A < 0$ should be used. Substitute the values you found for A, B, and C into the cosine function.

$$y = -82.5\cos(4\pi x) + 82.5 \ \blacksquare$$

Interpreting Trigonometric Models

Many natural phenomena can be modeled using sinusoidal functions.

Real-world situations, such as temperature fluctuations, tidal cycles, and simple harmonic motion can be modeled using sine and cosine functions.

EXAMPLE 1

The average daily maximum temperature for Johannesburg, South Africa, can be modeled by the sinusoidal function

$$y = 8.65 \cos\left(\frac{\pi x}{6}\right) + 69.5$$

where y is the temperature $(°F)$ and x is the month $(x = 0$ corresponds to January).

A Determine the period of the function.

SOLUTION
Use technology to graph the function.

Since the function is in the form $f(x) = A \cos Bx + C$, $B = \frac{\pi}{6}$ and period $= \frac{2\pi}{\frac{\pi}{6}} = 12$. So the period is 12 months, which is consistent with the graph.

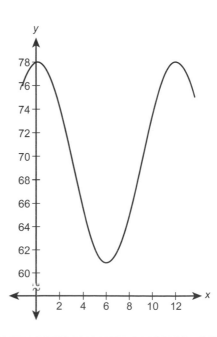

B What is the average daily temperature during November?

SOLUTION

Substitute 10 for x in the function equation and simplify.

$$y = 8.65 \cos\left(\frac{\pi(10)}{6}\right) + 69.5 = 73.83$$

The average daily temperature during November is 73.83°F.

C What is the minimum average temperature, and during what month does this temperature occur?

SOLUTION

The minimum temperature can be found by subtracting the amplitude $(A = 8.65)$ from the midline value (69.5), so the minimum temperature is $69.5 - 8.65 = 60.85$. You can see from the graph that the minimum temperature of 60.85° occurs during July $(x = 6)$. ▪

EXAMPLE 2

The movement of a weight bobbing up and down on a spring is called simple harmonic motion. The weight's vertical position over time can be modeled by a sinusoidal function. The graph shows the vertical height of the object in feet (y) as a function of time in seconds (t). Write an equation for the function.

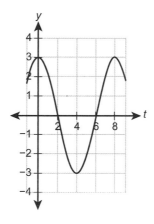

SOLUTION

Determine which trigonometric function best models the graph.

Since a maximum occurs on the y-axis, the curve is best modeled by

$f(t) = A \cos Bt + C$.

▶ **Think About It** A graph that starts at the midline is best modeled by sine, and a graph that starts at a maximum or minimum is best modeled by cosine.

Determine the values of A, B, and C. The midline is the t-axis $(y = 0)$, so $C = 0$. The maximum height reached above the midline is 3, so the amplitude, A, is 3. Also, the period is 8, so B can be found using the period formula.

$$\text{period} = \frac{2\pi}{B}$$

$$8 = \frac{2\pi}{B}$$

$$8B = 2\pi$$

$$B = \frac{\pi}{4}$$

Substitute the values for A, B, and C into the cosine function.

$$y = 3\cos\left(\frac{\pi t}{4}\right) \ \blacksquare$$

EXAMPLE 3

The tide chart shows the hourly tide levels (in meters) in the Bay of Fundy in St. John, New Brunswick, Canada. Create a sinusoidal model that depicts the tide level (y) as a function of time (x).

Hour	0	1	2	3	4	5	6	7	8	9	10	11	12
Tide levels (m)	4.5	3.0	1.8	1.4	1.8	3.0	4.5	6.1	7.2	7.6	7.2	6.1	4.5

SOLUTION

Determine the values of A, B, and C.

To determine C, use the midline formula.

$$\text{equation of midline} = y = \frac{\text{maximum} + \text{minimum}}{2} = \frac{7.6 + 1.4}{2} = 4.5$$

So $C = 4.5$.

To determine A, find the amplitude. Use the formula.

$$\text{amplitude} = \frac{\text{maximum} - \text{minimum}}{2} = \frac{7.6 - 1.4}{2} = 3.1$$

So $|A| = 3.1$. Also, the water level initially decreases, so $A = -3.1$.

The water starts at the midline and then after there is a minimum and a maximum level, the tide returns to the midline value after 12 h, so the period is 12.

Use the period formula to solve for B.

$$\text{period} = \frac{2\pi}{B}$$

$$12 = \frac{2\pi}{B}$$

$$12B = 2\pi$$

$$B = \frac{\pi}{6}$$

Since the midline value occurs where $x = 0$, a sine curve works best.

Substitute the values for A, B, and C into the sine function.

$$y = -3.1 \sin\left(\frac{\pi x}{6}\right) + 4.5 \;\blacksquare$$

Properties of Sinusoidal Graphs

Trigonometric functions can model periodic phenomena.

EXAMPLE

The tides on the French island of Mont Saint-Michel in the Couesnon River can be approximated by a sinusoidal function.

A Write an equation modeling the height of the tides if the high tide of 12.5 m occurs every 12 h and it is now low tide when the river is 0.5 m below sea level.

SOLUTION

Let y = water level (meters) and x = time (hours).

$$\text{equation of midline: } y = \frac{12.5 + (-0.5)}{2} = 6$$

So $C = 6$.

$$\text{amplitude} = \frac{12.5 - (-0.5)}{2} = 6.5$$

The tide returns to the maximum after 12 h, so the period is 12.

To find B, solve for B in the period formula.

$$\text{period} = \frac{2\pi}{B}$$

$$12 = \frac{2\pi}{B}$$

$$12B = 2\pi$$

$$B = \frac{\pi}{6}$$

Since the function starts at a minimum, a cosine function where $A < 0$ works best, so $A = -6.5$. Thus, the equation that models the tides is

$$y = -6.5 \sin\left(\frac{\pi x}{6}\right) + 6.$$

B Sketch the graph of the function for the first 24 h.

SOLUTION

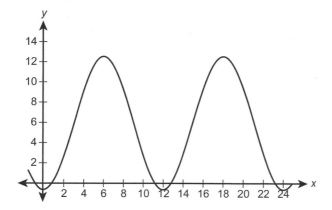

C If the daily mail delivery can only be made by boat when the water is above 6 m, between what times can the mail delivery be made if the initial low tide occurs at midnight?

SOLUTION

Since the midline is $y - 6$, you must find the intersections of the curve with the midline. Using the graph, the intersections occur at $x = 3, 9, 15,$ and 21 during the first 24 h.

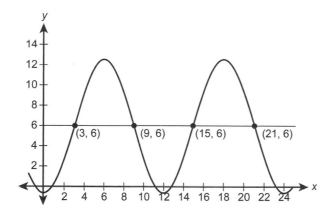

The curve is above the midline on the intervals $(3, 9)$ and $(15, 21)$, so the boat can make the delivery to the island between 3 a.m. and 9 a.m., and between 3 p.m. and 9 p.m. ▪

Periodic Functions

Many real-world phenomena occur in cycles.

Some graphs are periodic. Periodic graphs are formed by cycles, or regular intervals of repeating patterns.

Analyzing a Periodic Function

Definitions

In a periodic function, the **period** is the length of one cycle. The **amplitude** is half the difference between the maximum and minimum output values.

▶ **Think About It** A cycle is the shortest complete repeating pattern in a graph.

EXAMPLE 1

Identify the period and amplitude of the function.

A

SOLUTION

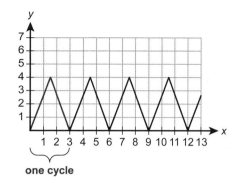

one cycle

The highlighted cycle extends from $x = 0$ to $x = 3$. The period is $3 - 0$, or 3.
The maximum y-value is 4 and the minimum y-value is 0. The amplitude is

$$\frac{4 - 0}{2} = 2.$$

B

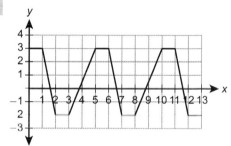

SOLUTION

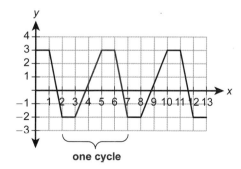

one cycle

The highlighted cycle extends from $x = 2$ to $x = 7$. The period is $7 - 2$, or 5.
The maximum y-value is 3 and the minimum y-value is –2. The amplitude is

$$\frac{3 - (-2)}{2} = \frac{5}{2} = 2.5.$$ ■

Determining the Period of a Data Set

EXAMPLE 2

Determine whether the data set is approximately periodic.
If so, estimate the period and the amplitude.

The table shows the times and heights of the tides for Barren Island, in the
Chesapeake Bay, during a given time span.

Time (h)	5.76	11.76	18.01	24.56	30.56	36.68	42.68	49.25
Height (ft)	1.4	0.4	1.6	0.3	1.5	0.4	1.6	0.3

Tide High and Low, Inc. 2013

SOLUTION

Look for patterns. The tides alternate between high tides at about 1.5 ft and
low tides at about 0.35 ft. The times are all approximately 6.25 h apart.

The data set is periodic. The period is about 6.25 h + 6.25 h = 12.5 h.

The amplitude is about $\dfrac{1.5 - 0.3}{2}$ ft $= \dfrac{1.2}{2}$ ft $= 0.6$ ft. ▪

Graphing a Trigonometric Function

A trigonometric function, or trig function, has a trigonometric ratio in its
function rule. Trigonometric functions are periodic functions.

You can graph a trigonometric function on a graphing calculator or by using
an online tool.

Analyzing a Trigonometric Function

EXAMPLE 3

Identify the period and amplitude of the sine function.

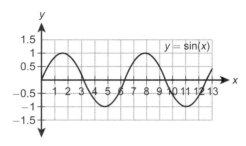

SOLUTION

One cycle extends from $x = 0$ to $x \approx 6.25$. The period is about 6.25. The maximum y-value is 1 and the minimum y-value is -1.

The amplitude is $\dfrac{1 - (-1)}{2} = \dfrac{2}{2} = 1.$ ■

> **Think About It** Some graphing tools will show the x-values in terms of π.

The exact period of the sine function in Example 3 is 2π. The value of π is approximately 3.14, so the value of 2π is approximately 6.28.

Application: Simple Harmonic Motion

The motion created by an object shifting back and forth by regular amounts is an example of **simple harmonic motion**. Simple harmonic motion can be modeled by sine and cosine functions, called **sinusoids**.

Imagine a weight on the end of a spring as the spring is compressed upward and then released. The weight would spring down below its initial, or resting, position, and then up above it. This would continue indefinitely in the absence of friction.

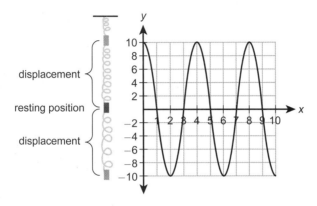

The graph shows the height y, in centimeters, of the weight, at a given number of seconds, x.

Compare the graph to the table.

Time (s)	0	1	2	3	4	5	6	7	8
Displacement (cm)	10	0	−10	0	10	0	−10	0	10

The weight's displacement at any moment is its distance from its resting position. Its maximum displacement is the graph's amplitude: 10 cm. From its resting position, the time it takes the weight to bounce one direction, then the other, and then return to its resting position is the period: 4 s.

The **frequency** of a periodic graph is the reciprocal of its period and gives the number of cycles in one unit of time. For the spring, the frequency of $\frac{1}{4}$ indicates that the weight completes one-fourth of a cycle in 1 s.

Application: Circular Motion

Suppose a fly lands on the end of the second hand of a clock at 7:45. The graph of its vertical movement for the next 2 min would form a periodic function because it would move up and down in regular intervals.

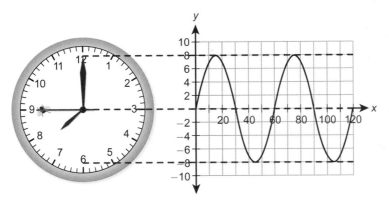

Compare the graph to the table.

Time (s)	0	15	30	45	60	75	90	105	120
Height (in.)	0	8	0	−8	0	8	0	−8	0

The length of the second hand is the graph's amplitude: 8 in. The time it takes for the fly to travel around the clock and return to its original position is the period: 60 s.

> **Q&A**
>
> **Q** How many degrees does the fly turn per second?
>
> **A** 6°/s

More Function Types

Topic List

Astronomers have used power functions to describe solar activity, the initial masses of stars, and the relationship between how long it takes a planet to orbit the sun and the planet's distance from the sun. Function graphs help scientists make sense of complicated processes.

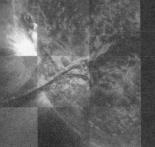

Graphing Quadratic Functions

A **quadratic function** is a second-degree polynomial function.

Standard Form of a Quadratic Function

The standard form of a quadratic function is $f(x) = ax^2 + bx + c$, where $a \neq 0$. The graph of a quadratic function is called a **parabola**.

One way to graph a quadratic function is to create a table of ordered pairs, plot the points, and then draw a smooth curve through those points. As you study the following examples, recall that y and $f(x)$ are used interchangeably.

Using a Table to Graph a Quadratic Function

EXAMPLE 1

Graph the function.

A $y = x^2$

SOLUTION

x	-2	-1	0	1	2
y	4	1	0	1	4

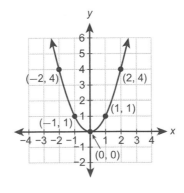

B $y = -2x^2 + 2x + 4$

SOLUTION

x	−2	−1	0	1	2
y	−8	0	4	4	0

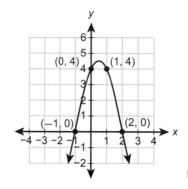

The point $(-2, -8)$ is not shown.

Graphing Quadratic Functions in Standard Form

All quadratic function graphs have in common the following characteristics, which can be used to create accurate graphs.

Properties of Quadratic Function Graphs

The graph of $f(x) = ax^2 + bx + c$ is a parabola with these characteristics:

- It opens up when $a > 0$; it opens down when $a < 0$.

- It has y-intercept c, so $(0, c)$ is a point on the graph.

- It has a vertex with x-coordinate $-\dfrac{b}{2a}$.

- It has an axis of symmetry with equation $x = -\dfrac{b}{2a}$.

  The axis of symmetry is the vertical line through the vertex. It separates the graph into two halves that are reflections (mirror images) of each other.

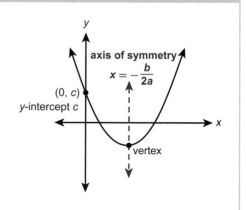

EXAMPLE 2

Graph $y = 3x^2 - 12x + 6$.

SOLUTION

First identify the coefficients a, b, and c.

$$y = 3x^2 - 12x + 6$$

$$a = 3 \quad b = -12 \quad c = 6$$

The leading coefficient a is positive, so the parabola opens up, not down.

The x-coordinate of the vertex is $-\dfrac{b}{2a} = -\dfrac{(-12)}{2 \cdot 3} = 2$. To find the y-coordinate of the vertex, substitute 2 for x.

$$y = 3x^2 - 12x + 6 = 3 \cdot 2^2 \quad 12 \cdot 2 + 6 = -6$$

The vertex, V, is $(2, -6)$, and the equation of the axis of symmetry is $x = 2$.

The y-intercept is $c = 6$, so $(0, 6)$ is a point on the graph. The reflection image of $(0, 6)$ over the axis of symmetry is $(4, 6)$, which is also on the graph.

Choose any value for x and substitute it to find one more point on the parabola. If $x = 1$, then $y = 3 \cdot 1^2 - 12 \cdot 1 + 6 = -3$. So $(1, -3)$ is on the graph, and its reflection image $(3, -3)$ is also on the graph.

Draw a smooth curve through all five points, including the vertex.

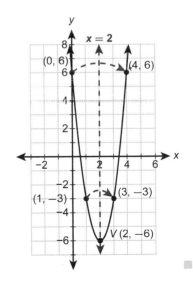

Determining the Number of Zeros of a Quadratic Function

Using properties of quadratic functions can help you determine how many times the graph of a given function crosses the x-axis.

Zeros of a Polynomial Function

The **zeros of a polynomial function** $f(x)$ are the **roots** (solutions) of the equation $f(x) = 0$. The real zeros are the x-intercepts of the graph of $f(x)$.

Number of Real Zeros of a Quadratic Function

A quadratic function can have no, one, or two real zeros.

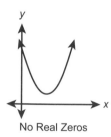

No Real Zeros

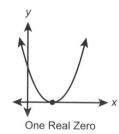

One Real Zero

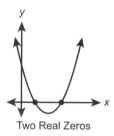

Two Real Zeros

EXAMPLE 3

Determine the number of real zeros of the quadratic function.

A $y = x^2 + 6x + 9$

SOLUTION

$a = 1$, $b = 6$, and $c = 9$. Since $a > 0$, the parabola opens up.

Use a and b to find the x-coordinate of the vertex, and then substitute to find the y-coordinate.

$$x = -\frac{b}{2a} = -\frac{6}{2 \cdot 1} = -3$$

$$y = x^2 + 6x + 9 = (-3)^2 + 6 \cdot (-3) + 9 = 9 - 18 + 9 = 0$$

The vertex is $(-3, 0)$. The vertex is a zero of the function and because the parabola opens up, the vertex is also the lowest point on the graph. Therefore, it is the only real zero. Sketch the graph to verify.

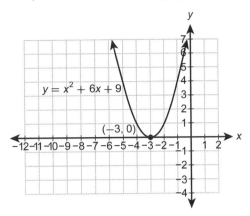

B $y = x^2 + 2$

SOLUTION

$a = 1$, $b = 0$, and $c = 2$. Since $a > 0$, the parabola opens up.

Use a and b to find the x-coordinate of the vertex, and then substitute to find the y-coordinate.

$$x = -\frac{b}{2a} = -\frac{0}{2 \cdot 1} = 0$$

$$y - x^2 + 2 = 0^2 + 2 = 2$$

The vertex is $(0, 2)$. Since the parabola opens up, the vertex is the lowest point on the graph. Therefore, the function has no real zeros. Sketch the graph to verify.

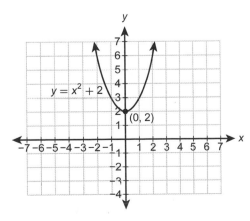

C $y = -x^2 + 4x - 1$

SOLUTION

$a = -1$, $b = 4$, and $c = -1$. Since $a < 0$, the parabola opens down.

Use a and b to find the x-coordinate of the vertex, and then substitute to find the y-coordinate.

$$x = -\frac{b}{2a} = -\frac{4}{2 \cdot (-1)} = 2$$

$$y = -x^2 + 4x - 1 = -2^2 + 4 \cdot 2 - 1 = -4 + 8 - 1 = 3$$

The vertex is $(2, 3)$. Since the parabola opens down, the vertex is the highest point. The graph must cross the x-axis at two points. Therefore, the function has two real zeros. Sketch the graph to verify.

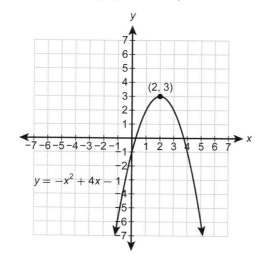

Graphing Quadratic Functions in Factored Form

Using the factored form of a quadratic function can help you graph the function.

Factored Form of a Quadratic Function

The factored form of a quadratic function is $f(x) = a(x - r_1)(x - r_2)$.
The graph of $f(x) = a(x - r_1)(x - r_2)$ is a parabola with these characteristics:

- It opens up if $a > 0$; it opens down if $a < 0$.

- It has x-intercepts r_1 and r_2.

- It has an axis of symmetry with equation $x = \dfrac{r_1 + r_2}{2}$ (halfway between the x-intercepts).

▶ **Think About It** The x-intercepts of the graph of $f(x)$ are the roots of the equation $f(x) = 0$. By the zero product property, if $a(x - r_1)(x - r_2) = 0$, then $x - r_1 = 0$ or $x - r_2 = 0$. Solving these two equations for x gives the roots $x = r_1$ and $x = r_2$.

EXAMPLE 4

Use the factored form to graph the function.

A $y = x^2 - 2x - 3$

SOLUTION

Factor the trinomial.

$$y = x^2 - 2x - 3 = (x + 1)(x - 3)$$

Since $a = 1$, the parabola opens up. Since $r_1 = -1$ and $r_2 = 3$,

the x-intercepts are -1 and 3. Since $\dfrac{r_1 + r_2}{2} = \dfrac{-1 + 3}{2} = \dfrac{2}{2} = 1$,

the equation of the axis of symmetry is $x = 1$. Since the axis of symmetry passes through the vertex, the x-coordinate of the vertex must be 1. Substitute 1 for x in the function to find the y-coordinate of the vertex.

$$y = x^2 - 2x - 3 = 1^2 - 2 \bullet 1 - 3 = 1 - 2 - 3 = -4$$

The vertex, V, is $(1, -4)$.

Find two more points, such as $(0, -3)$ and its reflection, $(2, -3)$. Then sketch the curve through all the points.

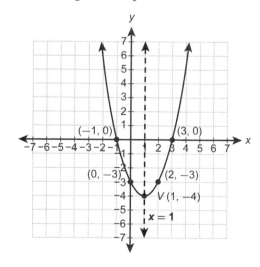

B $y = -0.4x^2 + 0.4x + 4.8$

SOLUTION

Factor out -0.4 and then factor the trinomial.

$$y = -0.4x^2 + 0.4x + 4.8 = -0.4\left(x^2 - x - 12\right) = -0.4(x - 4)(x + 3)$$

Since $a = -0.4$, the parabola opens down. Since $r_1 = 4$ and $r_2 = -3$,

the x-intercepts are 4 and -3. Since $\dfrac{r_1 + r_2}{2} = \dfrac{4 + (-3)}{2} = \dfrac{1}{2} = 0.5$,

the equation of the axis of symmetry is $x = 0.5$. Since the axis of symmetry passes through the vertex, the x-coordinate of the vertex must be 0.5. Substitute 0.5 for x in the function to find the y-coordinate of the vertex.

$$y = -0.4(x - 4)(x + 3) = -0.4(0.5 - 4)(0.5 + 3) = 4.9$$

The vertex, V, is $(0.5, 4.9)$.

Find two more points, such as $(2, 4)$ and its reflection, $(-1, 4)$. Then sketch the curve through all the points.

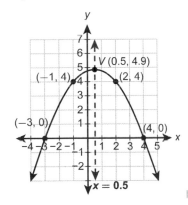

Absolute Value Functions

A **family of functions** is a group of functions with the same fundamental characteristics.

Definition

An **absolute value function** is a function whose rule contains an absolute value expression.

▶ **Remember** The absolute value of a number is its distance from zero on the number line.

The basic function in a family of functions is called the **parent function**. The parent function of the absolute value family of functions is $f(x) = |x|$. A table of ordered pairs and the graph of the function are shown.

x	$|x|$	$f(x)$
-3	$|-3|$	3
-2	$|-2|$	2
-1	$|-1|$	1
0	$|0|$	0
1	$|1|$	1
2	$|2|$	2
3	$|3|$	3

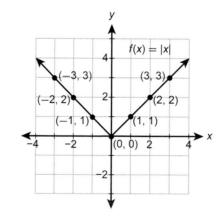

The graph is made up of two pieces—two rays that extend from a common vertex, forming a V-shape. All absolute value functions are V-shaped. Their vertex position, orientation, and width, however, can vary.

Graphing Absolute Value Functions by Plotting Points

Graph $f(x) = |x - 4| - 3$.

> ▶ **Think About It** Choose x-values that allow you to determine the position of the vertex as well as both rays.

SOLUTION
Make a table of values and plot the ordered pairs.

x	$|x-4|-3$	$f(x)$
1	$|1-4|-3$	0
2	$|2-4|-3$	-1
3	$|3-4|-3$	-2
4	$|4-4|-3$	-3
5	$|5-4|-3$	-2
6	$|6-4|-3$	-1
7	$|7-4|-3$	0

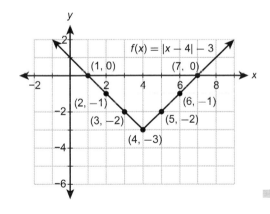

Translating Absolute Value Functions

Graphing an absolute value function by plotting points can take some guess-and-check work to determine which values in the domain you should use. In a family of functions, however, once you know the graph of the parent function, you can use transformations to graph related functions.

Recall from geometry that a **transformation** is a one-to-one mapping between two sets of points. One type of transformation is a **translation**, or slide. You can translate a function horizontally, vertically, or both.

Graphs of Absolute Value Functions

Absolute Value Function Graph Family: $f(x) = |x - h| + k$

When $f(x) = |x|$ is translated k units vertically and h units horizontally, the function becomes $g(x) = |x - h| + k$. The vertex shifts from $(0, 0)$ to (h, k).

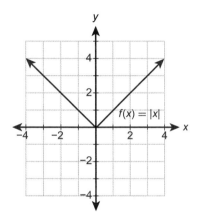

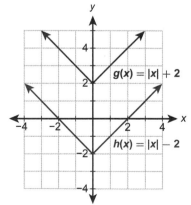

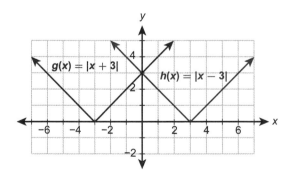

If k is positive, then the vertex is shifted up. If k is negative, then the vertex is shifted down.

If h is positive, then the vertex is shifted right. If h is negative, then the vertex is shifted left.

It may seem odd that a negative sign before h indicates a translation to the right and a positive sign indicates a translation to the left. The key is the minus sign in $g(x) = |x - h| + k$. For a translation 3 units to the left, $h = -3$ and $k = 0$ in the general form $g(x) = |x - h| + k$. In that case, the function is written $g(x) = |x - (-3)| = |x + 3|$.

EXAMPLE 2

Graph the function.

A $g(x) = |x - 2|$

SOLUTION

The graph is a horizontal translation of the parent function, 2 units to the right. You can write the function as $g(x) = |x - 2| + 0$; the vertex (h, k) is located at $(2, 0)$.

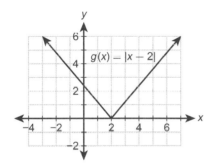

B $h(x) = |x + 1| - 2$

SOLUTION

The graph is a vertical and horizontal translation of the parent function. It is translated 1 unit left and 2 units down. You can write the function as $h(x) = |x - (-1)| + (-2)$; the vertex is located at $(-1, -2)$.

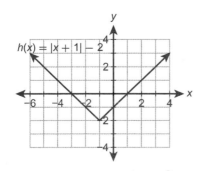

Describing Graphs of Absolute Value Functions

When the absolute value expression in the parent function $f(x) = |x|$ is multiplied by -1, the graph is reflected across the x-axis, making an upside-down V-shape. You can write this function as $g(x) = -1|x|$ or $g(x) = -|x|$.

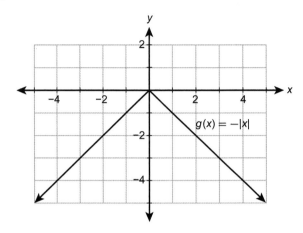

If the absolute value expression is multiplied by any factor other than 1 or -1, the graph becomes narrower or wider. For $g(x) = a|x|$, the graph becomes wider (or vertically compressed) if $0 < |a| < 1$ and narrower (or vertically stretched) if $|a| > 1$.

Compare the graphs of $g(x) = \frac{1}{4}|x|$ and $h(x) = 4|x|$ to $f(x) = |x|$.

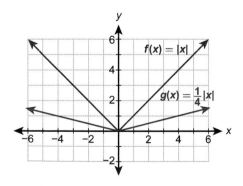
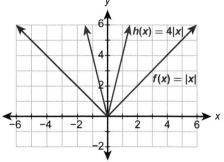

EXAMPLE 3

Describe how the graph of the function differs from the graph of $f(x) = |x|$. Then determine the domain and range.

A $g(x) = 0.8|x|$

SOLUTION

Because $|a|$ is between 0 and 1, the graph will be wider than the graph of the parent function. The vertex remains at $(0, 0)$.

domain: $\{x \mid x \in \mathbb{R}\}$, range: $\{y \mid y \geq 0\}$

B $g(x) = 3|x - 8|$

SOLUTION

The graph is translated 8 units to the right. Because $|a| > 1$, the graph will be narrower than the graph of the parent function.

domain: $\{x \mid x \in \mathbb{R}\}$, range: $\{y \mid y \geq 0\}$

C $g(x) = -2|x| + 5$

SOLUTION

The graph is translated 5 units up. Because $|a| > 1$, the graph will be narrower than the graph of the parent function. Because a is negative, the shape of the graph is an upside-down V.

domain: $\{x \mid x \in \mathbb{R}\}$, range: $\{y \mid y \leq 5\}$ ■

Finding the Equation of an Absolute Value Function

EXAMPLE 4

Write the equation of $g(x)$, which is graphed.

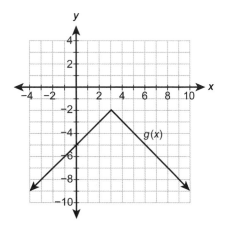

SOLUTION

The vertex is located at $(3, -2)$. Using the parent function $f(x) = |x|$ as a reference, the horizontal and vertical translations indicate that $h = 3$ and $k = -2$.

The graph, which moves up or down 1 unit for every horizontal move of 1 unit, is neither narrower nor wider than that of the parent function, so $|a| = 1$. Because the graph is upside-down, $a = -1$, making the equation $g(x) = -|x - 3| - 2$. ■

Reciprocal Power Functions

A power function is a function of the form $f(x) = ax^n$, where $a \neq 0$ and n is a positive integer.

The functions $f(x) = x$, $g(x) = x^2$, and $h(x) = x^3$ are power functions.

Graphing a Reciprocal Power Function

Definition

A **reciprocal power function** is a power function that has the power of x in the denominator of a rational function. The functions $f(x) = \dfrac{1}{x}$, $g(x) = \dfrac{1}{x^2}$, and $h(x) = \dfrac{1}{x^3}$ are reciprocal power functions.

EXAMPLE 1

Graph $f(x) = \dfrac{1}{x}$.

SOLUTION

Use a table to find several ordered pairs in the function. Include some fractional values between $x = -1$ and $x = 1$ so that you know what happens on either side of and near $x = 0$, where $f(x)$ is undefined.

x	-3	-2	-1	$-\dfrac{1}{2}$	$-\dfrac{1}{3}$	0	$\dfrac{1}{3}$	$\dfrac{1}{2}$	1	2	3
$f(x)=\dfrac{1}{x}$	$-\dfrac{1}{3}$	$-\dfrac{1}{2}$	-1	-2	-3	undefined	3	2	1	$\dfrac{1}{2}$	$\dfrac{1}{3}$

This graph is called a rectangular hyperbola. The two distinct sections of the graph are called branches.

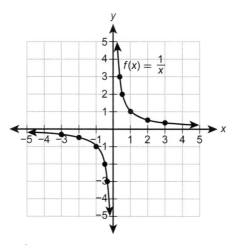

The function $f(x) = \dfrac{1}{x}$ is not defined for $x = 0$, so zero is excluded from the domain of the function. Notice that the graph gets closer and closer to the x-axis as the x-values approach positive infinity and negative infinity. Also, the graph gets closer and closer to the y-axis as the x-values get closer to zero. ■

▶ **Think About It** "$f(x)$ approaches b" means the values of $f(x)$ get closer and closer to b.

"$f(x)$ approaches ∞" means the values of $f(x)$ increase without bound.

"$f(x)$ approaches $-\infty$" means the values of $f(x)$ decrease without bound.

Definitions

The line $y = b$ is a **horizontal asymptote** of the graph of the function f if $f(x)$ approaches b as x approaches ∞ or $-\infty$.

The line $x = a$ is a **vertical asymptote** of the graph of the function f if $f(x)$ approaches ∞ or $-\infty$ as x approaches a, either from the left or the right.

Therefore, for $f(x) = \dfrac{1}{x}$, the x-axis (or $y = 0$) is a horizontal asymptote, and the y-axis (or $x = 0$) is a vertical asymptote.

Finding the Domain and Range of a Reciprocal Power Function

EXAMPLE 2

Determine the domain and range of the function.

A $f(x) = \dfrac{3}{x^2}$

SOLUTION
Find domain restrictions by setting the denominator equal to zero.

$$x^2 = 0$$
$$x = 0$$

If $x = 0$, then the denominator equals 0. So the domain is the set of all real numbers except 0. In set notation, the domain is

$$\{x \mid x \in \mathbb{R} \text{ and } x \neq 0\}.$$

Use some reasoning about the function to determine the range. Since x is squared, $f(x)$ can never be negative and $f(x)$ cannot equal 0. So the range is the set of all real numbers greater than 0,

$$\{y \mid y > 0\}.$$

B $g(x) = \dfrac{5}{2x^3}$

SOLUTION

Find domain restrictions by setting the denominator equal to zero.

$$2x^3 = 0$$
$$x^3 = 0$$
$$x = 0$$

The domain is the set of all real numbers except 0. In set notation, the domain is

$$\{x \mid x \in \mathbb{R} \text{ and } x \neq 0\}.$$

Use some reasoning about the function to determine the range. Since x is cubed, $g(x)$ can be negative or positive and $g(x)$ cannot equal 0. So the range is the set of all real numbers except 0,

$$\{y \mid y \in \mathbb{R} \text{ and } y \neq 0\}. \ \blacksquare$$

All reciprocal power functions of the form $f(x) = \dfrac{a}{x^n}$, where n is even, have the same domain and range. The domain is $\{x \mid x \in \mathbb{R} \text{ and } x \neq 0\}$. When a is positive, the range is $\{y \mid y > 0\}$, and when a is negative, the range is $\{y \mid y < 0\}$.

All reciprocal power functions of the form $f(x) = \dfrac{a}{x^n}$, where n is odd, have the same domain $\{x \mid x \in \mathbb{R} \text{ and } x \neq 0\}$ and range $\{y \mid y \in \mathbb{R} \text{ and } y \neq 0\}$.

Recognizing the Reciprocal Power Function Family of Graphs

Reciprocal Power Function Graph Family

Reciprocal Power Function Graph Family: $f(x) = \dfrac{a}{x^n}$

Equations of the form $f(x) = \dfrac{a}{x^n}$ are reciprocal power functions with a

horizontal asymptote at $y = 0$ and a vertical asymptote at $x = 0$.

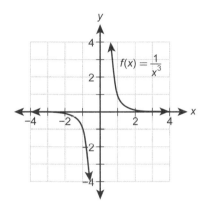

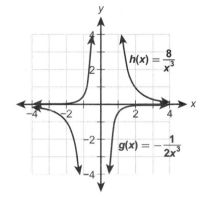

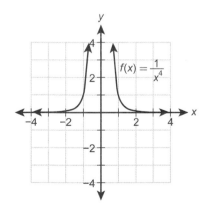

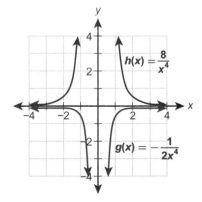

These graphs are graphs of the parent functions.

If you change the parameter a, you get curves that vary in their distance from the origin.

A negative a-value will reflect the graph across the x-axis.

Reciprocal power functions with odd powers have the same general shape, and reciprocal power functions with even powers have the same general shape. All reciprocal power functions have the x- and y-axes as asymptotes.

Graphing a Simple Reciprocal Power Function

EXAMPLE 3

Graph $f(x)$ and $g(x)$ on the same coordinate system. Compare the two graphs.

$$f(x) = \frac{1}{x^2}$$

$$g(x) = \frac{1}{3x^2}$$

SOLUTION

In both graphs, the domain is the set of all real numbers except 0.

$$\{x \mid x \in \mathbb{R} \text{ and } x \neq 0\}$$

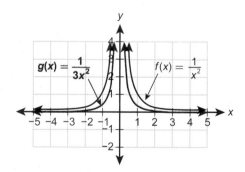

▶ **Think About It** Values for x that make the denominator zero are excluded from the domain of $f(x)$. Since these are places where $f(x)$ is not defined, they may indicate a vertical asymptote. In functions such as $f(x) = \frac{1}{x^2}$, the value of $f(x)$ is always greater than zero, which may indicate a horizontal asymptote at $y = 0$.

Each graph has two branches, one for positive x-values and one for negative x-values. Each graph has a vertical asymptote whose equation is $x = 0$ and a horizontal asymptote whose equation is $y = 0$. ■

Finding the Equation from a Graph

EXAMPLE 4

Find the equation for the reciprocal power function of the form $f(x) = \dfrac{a}{x^n}$ that has this graph.

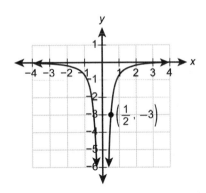

SOLUTION

$f(x) = \dfrac{a}{x^2}$ Start with the general form of the equation.

$-3 = \dfrac{a}{\left(\dfrac{1}{2}\right)^2}$ Substitute the coordinates of the known point.

$-\dfrac{3}{4} = a$ Solve for a.

The equation of the function is $f(x) = -\dfrac{3}{4x^2}$. ■

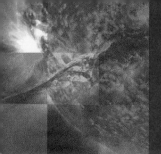

Graphing Rational Functions

Any function that can be written as the quotient of two polynomials can be called a **rational function**.

Finding the Domain of a Rational Function

Many rational functions have restricted domains because an expression is undefined if its denominator equals 0.

EXAMPLE 1

Determine the domain of the rational function.

A $f(x) = \dfrac{x+5}{x^2 - 3x - 28}$

SOLUTION

Find domain restrictions by setting the denominator equal to 0.

$$x^2 - 3x - 28 = 0$$
$$(x-7)(x+4) = 0$$
$$x - 7 = 0 \quad \text{or} \quad x + 4 = 0$$

If $x = 7$ or $x = -4$, then the denominator equals 0. The domain is the set of all real numbers except 7 and -4. You can state the domain in set notation.

$$\{x \in \mathbb{R}, x \neq 7 \text{ and } x \neq -4\}$$

B $g(x) = \dfrac{2}{x^2 + 1}$

SOLUTION

Find domain restrictions by setting the denominator equal to 0.

$$x^2 + 1 = 0$$
$$x^2 = -1$$

The equation $x^2 = -1$ has no real solution, so there are no restrictions on the domain. The domain is the set of all real numbers. In set notation, the domain is $\{x \mid x \in \mathbb{R}\}$. ■

Recognizing the Rational Function Family of Graphs

Equations of the form $f(x) = \dfrac{a}{x - h} + k$ are rational functions with one horizontal asymptote at $y = k$ and one vertical asymptote at $x = h$.

Rational Function Graph Family: $f(x) = \dfrac{a}{x-h} + k$

Each change in the value of a or b results in a different transformation of the parent graph, $f(x) = \dfrac{1}{x^n}$.

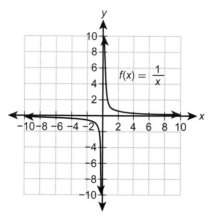

This graph is the graph of the parent function.

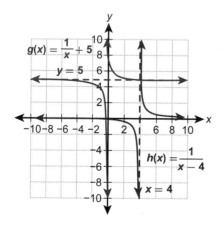

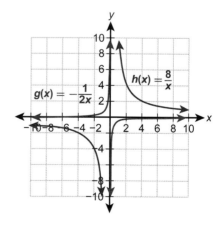

As h changes, the vertical asymptote shifts h units to the left or right.

As k changes, the horizontal asymptote shifts k units up or down.

If you change only the parameter a, you get curves that vary in their distance from the origin.

A negative a-value will reflect the graph across the x-axis.

Graphing Rational Functions

EXAMPLE 2

Graph the function.

A $y = \dfrac{1}{x + 6}$

SOLUTION

▸ **Think About It** $\dfrac{1}{\text{little}} = \text{big}$

$\dfrac{1}{\text{big}} = \text{little}$

If x is close to -6, then $\dfrac{1}{x + 6}$ is far from 0. If x is very big or very small, then $\dfrac{1}{x + 6}$ is close to 0. The domain of $y = \dfrac{1}{x + 6}$ is $\{x \mid x \in \mathbb{R}, x \neq -6\}$.

The range of $y = \dfrac{1}{x + 6}$ is $\{y \mid y \subset \mathbb{R}, y \neq 0\}$. The line $x = -6$ is a vertical asymptote. The line $y = 0$ is a horizontal asymptote.

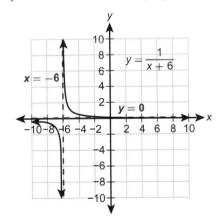

B $f(x) = \frac{4}{x} - 3$

SOLUTION

The domain of $f(x) = \frac{4}{x} - 3$ is $\{x \mid x \in \mathbb{R}, x \neq 0\}$ because the denominator cannot equal 0. The range of $f(x) = \frac{4}{x} - 3$ is $\{y \mid y \in \mathbb{R}, y \neq -3\}$ because $\frac{4}{x}$ can never be 0, so $\frac{4}{x} - 3$ can never be -3.

▶ **Think About It** Any fraction $\frac{a}{b}$ equals zero if and only if a equals zero. So $\frac{4}{x}$ can never equal zero since 4 is not equal to zero.

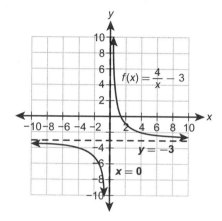

Since 4 is greater than 1, the curve of the graph is farther away from the intersection of the asymptotes.

C $f(x) = \dfrac{2}{x-3} + 1$

SOLUTION

The domain is $\{x \mid x \in \mathbb{R}, x \neq 3\}$ because 3 is a zero of the denominator.

> ▶ **Think About It** A "zero of the denominator" is just a zero of the polynomial that is in the denominator.

The range of $f(x) = \dfrac{2}{x-3} + 1$ is $\{y \mid y \in \mathbb{R}, y \neq 1\}$ because $\dfrac{2}{x-3}$ can never be 0, so $\dfrac{2}{x-3} + 1$ can never be 1.

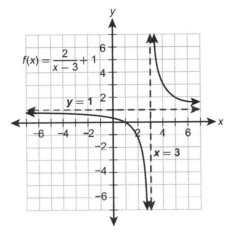

The lines $x = 3$ and $y = 1$ are asymptotes. ■

Finding the Equation When Given a Graph of a Rational Function in the Family $f(x) = \dfrac{a}{x - h} + k$

EXAMPLE 3

Find the equation in the family $f(x) = \dfrac{a}{x - h} + k$ for the graph of the function.

A

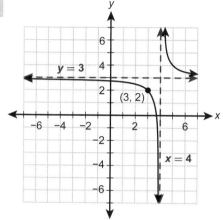

SOLUTION

Step 1 There is a horizontal asymptote at $y = 3$ and a vertical asymptote at $x = 4$. The equation of the graph so far is $f(x) = \dfrac{a}{x - 4} + 3$.

Step 2 Substitute the point $(3, 2)$ into the equation.

$2 = \dfrac{a}{3 - 4} + 3$ Substitute.

$2 = -a + 3$ Simplify.

$a = 1$ Solve.

The equation of the graph is $f(x) = \dfrac{1}{x - 4} + 3$.

B

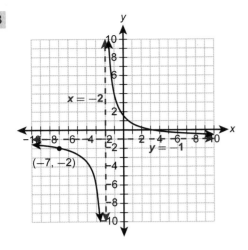

SOLUTION

Step 1 There is a horizontal asymptote at $y = -1$ and a vertical asymptote at $x = -2$. The equation of the graph so far is $f(x) = \dfrac{a}{x+2} - 1$.

Step 2 Substitute the point $(-7, -2)$ into the equation.

$$-2 = \dfrac{a}{-7+2} - 1 \qquad \text{Substitute.}$$

$$-1 = -\dfrac{a}{5} \qquad \text{Simplify.}$$

$$5 = a \qquad \text{Solve.}$$

The equation of the graph is $f(x) = \dfrac{5}{x+2} - 1$. ■

Graphing Rational Functions Not in the Family $f(x) = \dfrac{a}{x-h} + k$

EXAMPLE 4

Graph the function.

A $y = \dfrac{x^2 - 9}{x + 3}$

SOLUTION

Factor and identify the zeros of the numerator and denominator.

$$y = \frac{x^2 - 9}{x + 3} = \frac{(x + 3)(x - 3)}{x + 3} \quad \longleftarrow \quad \text{The zeros are } x = -3 \text{ and } x = 3.$$
$$\longleftarrow \quad \text{The zero is } x = -3.$$

For this function, **−3** is a zero of both the numerator and the denominator, so there is a **hole at $x = -3$**. Meanwhile, **3** is a zero of only the numerator, so the **x-intercept is 3**, and $(3, 0)$ is on the graph. There are no zeros of only the denominator, so there is no vertical asymptote. The degree of the numerator is greater than the degree of the denominator $(2 > 1)$, so there is no horizontal asymptote. If you divide out the common factor $x + 3$, you get the linear function $f(x) = x - 3$.

To graph $y = \dfrac{x^2 - 9}{x + 3}$, you can graph $f(x) = x - 3$, but you must put an open dot at $(-3, -6)$.

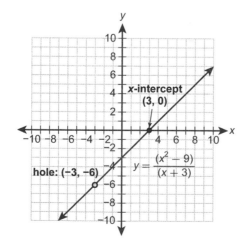

B $f(x) = \dfrac{1}{(x-3)^2}$

SOLUTION

If x is close to 3, then $\dfrac{1}{(x-3)^2}$ is far from 0. If x is far from 3,

then $\dfrac{1}{(x-3)^2}$ is close to 0. If $x = 3$, then the denominator is zero

and the function is undefined, so the domain of $f(x) = \dfrac{1}{(x-3)^2}$ is

$\{x \mid x \in \mathbb{R}, x \neq 3\}$. The numerator is positive and the denominator
is a squared value, so it has to be positive as well, so the range is
$\{y \mid y \in \mathbb{R}, y > 0\}$. Because $(x-3)$ is in the denominator, there is one
vertical asymptote at $x = 3$. The degree of the numerator is 0 and the degree
of the denominator is 2. Because $0 < 2$, the x-axis, $y = 0$, is the horizontal
asymptote.

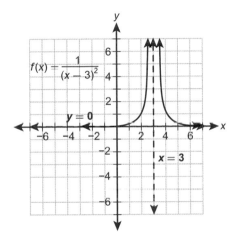

Graphing Radical Functions

A **radical function** of the form $f(x) = a\sqrt[n]{x - h} + k$, where n is an integer greater than 1, is in a family of functions whose parent function is $f(x) = \sqrt[n]{x}$.

Graphing a Square Root Function

If $n = 2$, the family contains square root functions.

EXAMPLE 1

Graph $f(x) = \sqrt{x}$.

SOLUTION

Use a table to find several ordered pairs of the function. Include only nonnegative values for x because $\sqrt{x}$ is undefined if x is negative. For convenience, choose perfect squares for x.

▶ **Think About It** Every positive real number has two square roots. For example, the two square roots of 9 are 3 and -3. But the $\sqrt{}$ symbol indicates only the principal (nonnegative) square root. Therefore, $\sqrt{9} = 3$.

x	0	1	4	9	16
f(x)	0	1	2	3	4

domain: $\{x \mid x \geq 0\}$

range: $\{y \mid y \geq 0\}$

The graph looks like the top half of a sideways parabola.

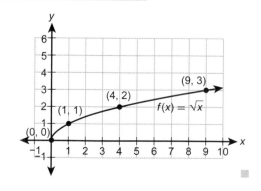

Graphing a Cube Root Function

If $n = 3$, the family contains cube root functions.

Graph $f(x) = \sqrt[3]{x}$.

SOLUTION

Use a table to find several ordered pairs of the function. Negative numbers have cube roots, so include negative values for x. For convenience, choose integer values for x that have integer cube roots.

x	-27	-8	-1	0	1	8	27
$f(x)$	-3	-2	-1	0	1	2	3

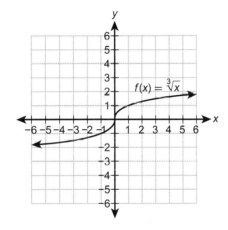

domain: $\{x \mid x \in \mathbb{R}\}$

range: $\{y \mid y \in \mathbb{R}\}$ ▪

Graphing Families of nth Root Functions

Every radical function of the form $f(x) = a\sqrt[n]{x - h} + k$ is a transformation of a parent function $f(x) = \sqrt[n]{x}$.

Square Root Functions

Square Root Function Graph Family: $f(x) = a\sqrt{x - h} + k$

Each change in the value of a, h, or k results in a different transformation of the parent graph, $f(x) = \sqrt{x}$.

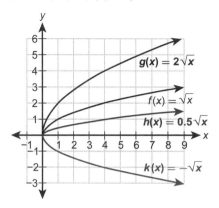

Changing only the parameter a causes the parent function to reflect, stretch, or compress.

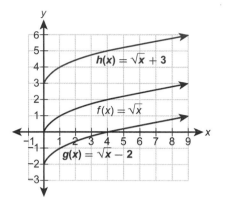

Changing only the parameter k causes the parent function to shift up or down on the y-axis.

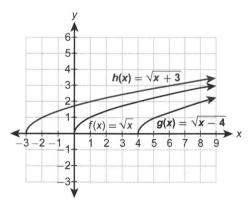

Changing only the parameter h causes the parent function to shift left or right on the x-axis.

Cube Root Functions

Cube Root Function Graph Family: $f(x) = a\sqrt[3]{x - h} + k$

Each change in the value of a, h, or k results in a different transformation of the parent graph, $f(x) = \sqrt[3]{x}$.

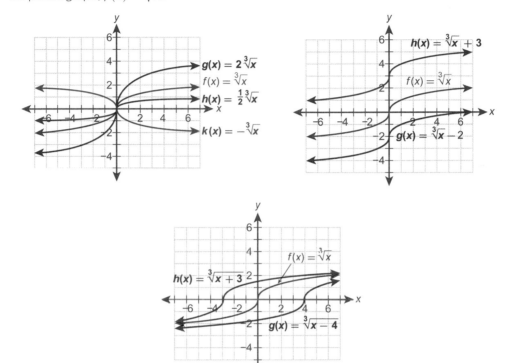

All graphs of functions with even roots look similar, and all graphs of functions with odd roots look similar. The only way to tell the graphs apart is to look at specific ordered pairs.

To transform the graph of $f(x) = \sqrt[n]{x}$ by changing more than one parameter, first decide whether or not to reflect it across the x-axis. Then apply each transformation to the graph obtained from the previous transformation.

Graphing a Square Root Function and Identifying the Domain and Range

EXAMPLE 3

For the function $g(x) = -3\sqrt{x+1} - 2$:

A Graph the function.

SOLUTION

Step 1 Describe how to obtain the graph by transforming the graph of $f(x) = \sqrt{x}$.

$g(x) = -3\sqrt{x+1} - 2$ is in the form $g(x) = a\sqrt{x-h} + k$, with $a = -3$, $h = -1$, and $k = -2$.

Parameter	Transformation
$a < 0$	Reflect the graph of $f(x) = \sqrt{x}$ across the x-axis.
$a = -3$	Stretch vertically by a factor of $\lvert -3 \rvert = 3$.
$h = -1$	Translate 1 unit to the left.
$k = -2$	Translate 2 units down.

Step 2 Make a table of values. Then plot points and sketch the graph. If you choose x-values so that $x + 1$ is a perfect square, then calculating corresponding y-values becomes easy. For example,

$$g(8) = -3\sqrt{8+1} - 2 = -3\sqrt{9} - 2 = -3 \cdot 3 - 2 = -11.$$

x	$g(x)$
-1	-2
0	-5
3	-8
8	-11

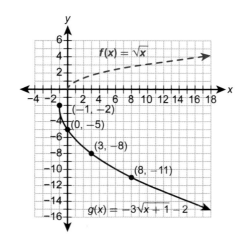

B Identify the function's domain and range.

SOLUTION

domain: The radicand is $x + 1$. The radicand in a square root expression must be nonnegative, so solve the inequality $x + 1 \geq 0$. The solution set of $x + 1 \geq 0$ is given by $x \geq -1$. The domain, then, is $\{x \mid x \geq -1\}$.

range: Since $\sqrt{x + 1} \geq 0$, $-3\sqrt{x + 1} \leq 0$ and $-3\sqrt{x + 1} - 2 \leq -2$. The range is $\{y \mid y \leq -2\}$. ∎

Verify that the domain and range are reasonable, based on the graph.

Graphing a Cube Root Function and Identifying the Domain and Range

EXAMPLE 4

For the function $g(x) = \frac{1}{2}\sqrt[3]{x - 1} + 3$:

A Graph the function.

SOLUTION

Step 1 Describe how to obtain the graph by transforming the graph of $f(x) = \sqrt[3]{x}$.

$g(x) = \frac{1}{2}\sqrt[3]{x - 1} + 3$ is in the form $g(x) = a\sqrt[3]{x - h} + k$, with $a = \frac{1}{2}$, $h = 1$, and $k = 3$.

Parameter	Transformation
$a = \dfrac{1}{2}$	Compress the graph of $f(x) = \sqrt[3]{x}$ vertically by a factor of $\dfrac{1}{2}$.
$h = 1$	Translate 1 unit to the right.
$k - 3$	Translate 3 units up.

Step 2 Make a table of values. Then plot points and sketch the graph.

x	g(x)
−7	2
0	2.5
1	3
2	3.5
9	4

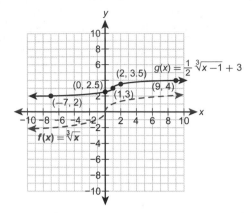

▶ **Think About It** If you choose x-values for your table that make x − 1 an integer whose cube root is an integer, then corresponding function values are easy to calculate. For example,

$$g(-7) = \frac{1}{2}\sqrt[3]{-7-1} + 3$$

$$= \frac{1}{2}\sqrt[3]{-8} + 3$$

$$= \frac{1}{2} \cdot (-2) + 3 = 2$$

B Identify the function's domain and range.

SOLUTION

domain: The index of the radical is 3, an odd integer. So the radicand $x - 1$ can be positive, negative, or zero. $\sqrt[3]{x-1}$ is defined for all real values of x. The domain is $\{x \mid x \in \mathbb{R}\}$.

range: Since x can be any real number, all of the following expressions can be any real number: $x - 1, \sqrt[3]{x-1}, \frac{1}{2}\sqrt[3]{x-1}$, and $\frac{1}{2}\sqrt[3]{x-1} + 3$. The range is $\{y \mid y \in \mathbb{R}\}$. ∎

Piecewise Functions

Some functions, such as absolute value functions, can be defined in pieces.

The functions in the following examples are piecewise functions.

Definition
A **piecewise function** is a function defined using different rules for different intervals of the domain.

Graphing a Special Piecewise Function

EXAMPLE 1

Graph the piecewise function $f(x) = \begin{cases} -x & \text{if } x \leq 0 \\ x & \text{if } x > 0 \end{cases}$.

SOLUTION

Create a table of ordered pairs for the first piece in the function.

x	-3	-2	-1	0
$f(x)$	3	2	1	0

The domain of the first piece includes 0 because it is defined for $x \leq 0$.

Create a table of ordered pairs for the second piece in the function.

x	1	2	3	4
f(x)	1	2	3	4

The domain of the second piece includes all numbers greater than 0.

Plot the points from both tables. Since both pieces of the function are linear, connect the points of each piece with a ray, starting at $(0, 0)$.

Together, the pieces of the graph form the graph of the absolute value function, $f(x) = |x|$.

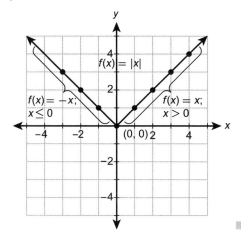

Writing an Absolute Value Function as a Piecewise Function

EXAMPLE 2

Write the absolute value function $f(x) = |x + 4|$ as a piecewise function.

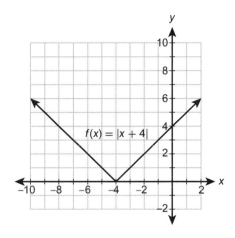

SOLUTION

There are two pieces.

The piece on the left is a ray with a boundary point at $(-4, 0)$. Study the table of ordered pairs for points of that piece and determine a rule.

Each range value is 4 subtracted from the opposite of the domain value: $f(x) = -x - 4$.

x	−7	−6	−5	−4
f(x)	3	2	1	0

The piece on the right is also a ray with a boundary point at $(-4, 0)$. Study the table of ordered pairs for points of that piece and determine a rule.

Each range value is 4 added to the domain value: $f(x) = x + 4$.

x	-4	-3	-2	-1
$f(x)$	0	1	2	3

Put both rules together. Include the boundary point in only one of the pieces.

$$f(x) = \begin{cases} -x - 4 \text{ if } x \leq -4 \\ x + 4 \text{ if } x > -4 \end{cases}$$

Graphing a Piecewise Function

EXAMPLE 3

Graph the function $g(x) = \begin{cases} 2x \text{ if } x < 1 \\ 1 \text{ if } x = 1. \\ x + 3 \text{ if } x > 1 \end{cases}$

SOLUTION

The domain is divided into three intervals.

For the interval $x < 1$, make a table of values. Although 1 is not included in this interval, use 1 as a value in the table. The point that has 1 as its x-coordinate will be a boundary for this section of the graph. Use an open circle when graphing the boundary point.

x	$g(x) = 2x$
-2	$2(-2) = -4$
-1	$2(-1) = -2$
0	$2(0) = 0$
1	$2(1) = 2$

For the value $x = 1$, $g(x) = 1$, so graph the point $(1, 1)$.

For the interval $x > 1$, make a table of values. Again, 1 is not included in this interval, but use 1 as a value in the table and use an open circle when graphing the boundary point.

x	g(x) = x + 3
1	1 + 3 = 4
2	2 + 3 = 5
3	3 + 3 = 6
4	4 + 3 = 7

Graph the function.

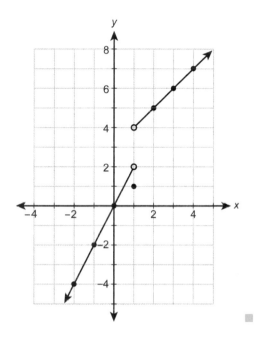

▶ **Remember** Use open circles for < and >. Use closed circles for ≤ and ≥.

Writing a Rule for a Piecewise Function

EXAMPLE 4

A Write a rule for the graphed piecewise function.

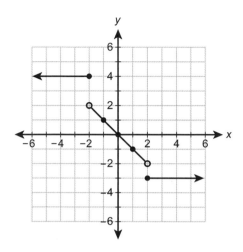

SOLUTION

The left piece is a horizontal ray that extends to the left without end from the point $(-2, 4)$. So it has a constant function value of 4, and the interval of domain values is given by the inequality $x \le -2$. The rule for this piece is $f(x) = 4$.

The center piece is a line segment that slants down from the point $(-2, 2)$ to the point $(2, -2)$. However, the open circles at $(-2, 2)$ and $(2, -2)$ indicate that these two points are not included in this piece of the graph. Therefore, the interval of domain values is given by the compound inequality $-2 < x < 2$. To find a rule for this piece, create a chart and look for a pattern.

x	-1	0	1
y	1	0	-1

Because y is the opposite of x, the rule is $y = -x$, or $f(x) = -x$.

The right piece is a horizontal ray that extends to the right without end from the point $(2, -3)$. So it has a constant function value of -3, and the interval of domain values is given by the inequality $x \geq 2$. The rule for this piece is $f(x) = -3$.

Altogether, the rule for the function is $f(x) = \begin{cases} 4 \text{ if } x \leq -2 \\ -x \text{ if } -2 < x < 2. \\ -3 \text{ if } x \geq 2 \end{cases}$

B Write a rule for the graphed piecewise function.

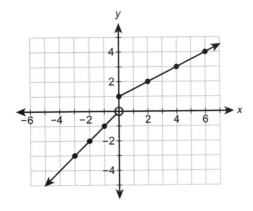

SOLUTION

The left piece is a ray that slants down to the left without end from the point $(0, 0)$, but it does not include $(0, 0)$. To find a rule for this piece, create a chart and look for a pattern.

x	-1	-2	-3
y	-1	-2	-3

The rule is $y = x$, or $f(x) = x$.

The right piece is a ray that slants up to the right without end from the point $(0, 1)$ and includes $(0, 1)$. Find a rule for this piece.

x	0	2	4	6
y	1	2	3	4

The rule is $y = \frac{1}{2}x + 1$, or $f(x) = \frac{1}{2}x + 1$.

The rule for the function is $f(x) = \begin{cases} x \text{ if } x < 0 \\ \frac{1}{2}x + 1 \text{ if } x \geq 0 \end{cases}$.

Finding Function Values of a Piecewise Function

EXAMPLE 5

Find $g(-5), g(-3), g(1)$, and $g(4)$ for the function g.

$$g(x) = \begin{cases} x - 1 \text{ if } x < -3 \\ x^2 - 1 \text{ if } -3 \leq x \leq 3 \\ 2x + 1 \text{ if } x > 3 \end{cases}$$

SOLUTION

Because -5 is in the interval $x < -3$, $g(-5) = -5 - 1 = -6$; -3 is in the interval $-3 \leq x \leq 3$, so $g(-3) = (-3)^2 - 1 = 9 - 1 = 8$; 1 is in the interval $-3 \leq x \leq 3$, so $g(1) = 1^2 - 1 = 1 - 1 = 0$. Since 4 is in the interval $x > 3$, $g(4) = 2 \cdot 4 + 1 = 8 + 1 = 9$.

Step Functions

One type of piecewise function is the step function.

Definition

A **step function** is a function defined using a rule that produces a constant value for each designated interval of the domain.

As the name implies, the graph of a step function looks like a set of stairs. Each step is just a line segment with an open or a closed circle on each end. Where the segments are placed and how long they are, as well as whether each endpoint is open or closed, depends on the particular function.

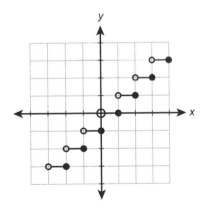

The Greatest Integer Function

The **greatest integer function**, denoted by $f(x) = \lfloor x \rfloor$, assigns the greatest integer less than or equal to each real number in an interval.

▶ **Think About It**

NOTATION The greatest integer function may also be given by $f(x) = \lfloor x \rfloor$ or $f(x) = \mathrm{int}(x)$. It is sometimes called the floor function.

EXAMPLE 1

Graph the function $f(x) = \lfloor x \rfloor$ over the interval $-3 \le x \le 3$.

SOLUTION

Make a table of values to examine how the function behaves. The function will behave the same way in each unit interval.

x	$f(x) = \lfloor x \rfloor$
-2.6	-3
-2	-2
-1.3	-2
0	0
0.7	0
1	1
1.2	1
1.5	1
1.9	1
2	2

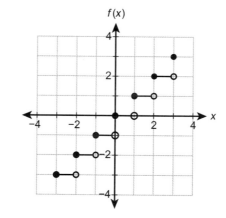

Graphs of Greatest Integer Functions

Greatest Integer Function Graph Family: $f(x) = a \lfloor x \rfloor + k$

Each change in the values of a or k results in a different transformation of the parent graph, $f(x) = \lfloor x \rfloor$.

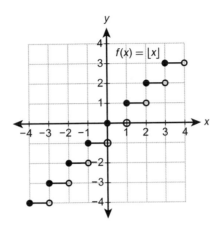

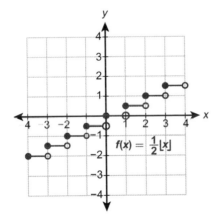

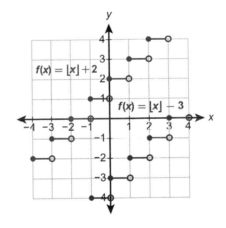

Changing only the parameter a causes the function to stretch or compress.

Changing only the parameter k causes the function to shift up or down the y-axis.

The Least Integer Function

The **least integer function**, denoted by $f(x) = \lceil x \rceil$, assigns the least integer greater than or equal to each real number in an interval.

EXAMPLE 2

Write a rule for $f(x) = \lceil x \rceil$ over the interval $-2 \leq x \leq 2$.

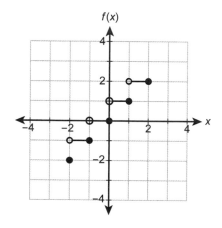

SOLUTION

There are four segments. The left endpoint of each segment is graphed with an open circle; the right endpoint is graphed with a solid circle.

To every real number in the interval $(-2, -1]$, the function assigns the value -1. The rule for this piece is $f(x) = -1$. That is to say, -1 is the least integer greater than or equal to every number in the interval $(-2, -1]$.

x	-2	-1.8	-1	-0.3	0	0.5	1	1.6	2
$f(x) = \lceil x \rceil$	-2	-1	-1	0	0	1	1	2	2

The rule for the function is

$$f(x) = \begin{cases} -2 \text{ if } x = -2 \\ -1 \text{ if } -2 < x \leq -1 \\ 0 \text{ if } -1 < x \leq 0. \\ 1 \text{ if } 0 < x \leq 1 \\ 2 \text{ if } 1 < x \leq 2 \end{cases}$$

Graphs of Least Integer Functions

Least Integer Function Graph Family: $f(x) = a \lceil x \rceil + k$

Each change in the values of a or k results in a different transformation of the parent graph, $f(x) = \lceil x \rceil$.

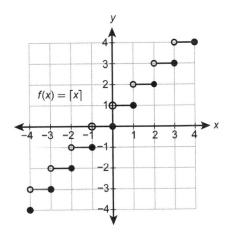

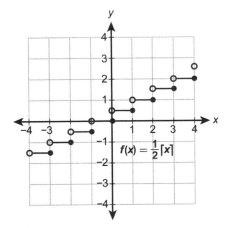

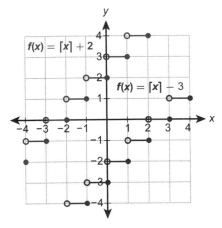

Changing only the parameter a causes the function to stretch or compress.

Changing only the parameter k causes the function to shift up or down on the x-axis.

Analyzing the Graph of the Nearest Integer Function

The **nearest integer function**, denoted by $\text{nint}(x)$, assigns the nearest integer to each real number in an interval. To avoid confusion for numbers such as -1.5 and 3.5, the function assigns the nearest even integer to each input value. So $\text{nint}(-1.5) = -2$, while $\text{nint}(3.5) = 4$. The nearest integer for numbers in the interval $[-0.5, 0.5]$ is zero.

> ▶ **Think About It** The nearest integer function is sometimes called the round function.

EXAMPLE 3

Graph the function $f(x) = \text{nint}(x)$ over the interval $-2.5 \le x \le 2.5$. Explain the pattern of horizontal segments on the graph.

SOLUTION

Study a table of values of the function for x in the interval $-2.5 \le x \le -1.5$. The value of the function for every real number in this interval, including the endpoints, is -2. The horizontal segment on the graph for this interval will include the endpoints -2.5 and -1.5.

x	$f(x) = \text{nint}(x)$
-2.5	-2
-2.3	-2
-2.0	-2
-1.8	-2
-1.5	-2

Next, study a table of values of the function for x in the interval $-1.5 \leq x \leq -0.5$. The values assigned to the endpoints of this interval are not the same as the value assigned to the other numbers in the interval. Therefore, the horizontal segment on the graph for this interval will not include the endpoints -1.5 and -0.5.

x	$f(x) = \text{nint}(x)$
-1.5	-2
-1.3	-1
-1.0	-1
-0.8	-1
-0.5	0

On the graph of the nearest integer function, the segments alternate between those including endpoints (solid circles) and those excluding the endpoints (open circles). This alternating pattern is a result of the rule to round each number to the nearest even integer.

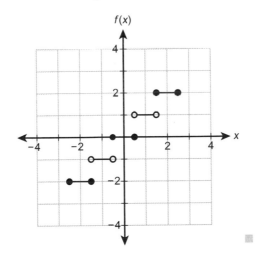

Logistic Growth

A logistic growth function can be used to model population growth.

Logistic Growth Functions

A **logistic growth function** is a function of the form

$$f(x) = \frac{C}{1 + Ae^{-Bx}}$$

where A, B, and C are all positive constants.

Evaluating Logistic Growth Functions

EXAMPLE 1

Evaluate $f(x) = \dfrac{200}{1 + 4e^{-1.2x}}$.

A $f(0)$

SOLUTION

$$f(0) = \frac{200}{1 + 4e^{-1.2(0)}} = \frac{200}{1 + 4e^{0}} = \frac{200}{1 + 4} = 40$$

B $f(1)$

SOLUTION

$$f(1) = \frac{200}{1 + 4e^{-1.2(1)}} = \frac{200}{1 + 4e^{-1.2}} \approx 90.712 \ \blacksquare$$

Graphing Logistic Growth Functions

Unlike exponential growth functions, where the value of $f(x)$ increases without bound as x increases, a logistic growth function $f(x) = \dfrac{C}{1 + Ae^{-Bx}}$ has an upper bound at $y = C$.

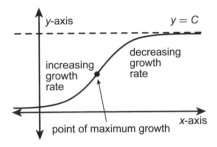

Graphs of Logistic Growth Functions

The graph of a logistic growth function $f(x) = \dfrac{C}{1 + Ae^{-Bx}}$ has the following features:

- The y-intercept is $\dfrac{C}{1 + A}$.

- The lines $y - 0$ and $y = C$ are horizontal asymptotes.

- The point of maximum growth is $\left(\dfrac{\ln A}{B}, \dfrac{C}{2} \right)$.

- To the left of the point of maximum growth, the rate of growth is increasing.

- To the right of the point of maximum growth, the rate of growth is decreasing.

EXAMPLE 2

For the function $f(x) = \dfrac{6}{1 + 2e^{-0.5x}}$:

A Identify the y-intercept.

SOLUTION

$A = 2 \qquad C = 6$

The y-intercept is $\dfrac{C}{1+A} = \dfrac{6}{1+2} = 2.$

B Identify the asymptotes.

SOLUTION

The lines $y = 0$ and $y = 6$ are asymptotes.

C Identify the point of maximum growth rate.

SOLUTION

The point of maximum growth is $\left(\dfrac{\ln A}{B}, \dfrac{C}{2}\right).$

$A = 2 \qquad B = 0.5 \qquad C = 6$

The point of maximum growth rate is $\left(\dfrac{\ln A}{B}, \dfrac{C}{2}\right) = \left(\dfrac{\ln 2}{0.5}, \dfrac{6}{2}\right) \approx (1.4, 3).$

D Make a table of values and sketch the graph.

SOLUTION

x	-2	2	4	6
$f(x)$	0.9	3.5	4.7	5.5

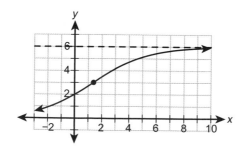

Solving Logistic Growth Functions

EXAMPLE 3

Given the function $f(x) = \dfrac{20}{1 + 2e^{-2x}}$, find the value of x when $f(x) = 8$.

SOLUTION

$$f(x) = \frac{20}{1 + 2e^{-2x}}$$

$$8 = \frac{20}{1 + 2e^{-2x}}$$

$$8\left(1 + 2e^{-2x}\right) = 20$$

$$8 + 16e^{-2x} = 20$$

$$16e^{-2x} = 12$$

$$e^{-2x} = 0.75$$

$$-2x = \ln 0.75$$

$$x = -\frac{1}{2}\ln 0.75$$

$$x \approx 0.1438$$

$x \approx 0.1438$ when $f(x) = 8$ ∎

Using Function Models

Topic List

Automotive engineers use wooden and clay models to test their designs. Many people use mathematical models to test assumptions, view patterns in data, and make good decisions.

Linear/Quadratic Systems

Linear and quadratic equations can share points that are solutions to both equations.

Definition

A **system of equations** is a group of two or more equations in the same variables.

A system of equations that consists of one linear and one quadratic equation can share two points, one point, or no points. The points of intersection for the linear and quadratic graphs represent ordered pairs that are solutions to both equations.

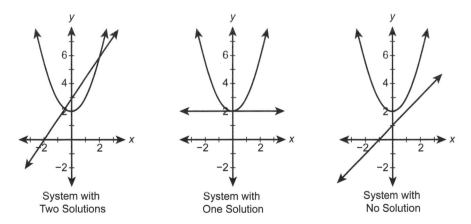

| System with Two Solutions | System with One Solution | System with No Solution |

The solutions to a linear/quadratic system of equations are ordered pairs. The ordered pairs can be determined by graphing the equations on the coordinate plane or by finding the solution using substitution.

Solving by Graphing

EXAMPLE 1

Use a graph to find the solution to the linear/quadratic system.

$$y = x^2 + 1$$
$$y - x = 1$$

SOLUTION

Create a table of ordered pairs for each equation.

$$y = x^2 + 1$$

x	−2	−1	0	1	2
y	5	2	1	2	5

$$y - x = 1$$

x	−1	0	2	1	4
y	0	1	3	2	2

Graph each equation.

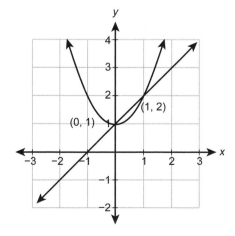

The linear and quadratic equations in the system share two points. The solution to the system consists of the ordered pairs $(0, 1)$ and $(1, 2)$. ▪

Solving by Substitution

EXAMPLE 2

Use substitution to find the solution to the linear/quadratic system.

$$y = x^2 - 2x + 2$$
$$y - 2x = -2$$

SOLUTION

Solve the linear equation for y.

$y - 2x = -2$

$y - 2x + 2x = -2 + 2x$ Add $2x$ to both sides.

$y = 2x - 2$ Simplify.

Substitute the expression for y into the quadratic equation.

$y = x^2 - 2x + 2$

$2x - 2 = x^2 - 2x + 2$ Substitute.

$2x - 2 - 2x = x^2 - 2x + 2 - 2x$ Subtract $2x$ from both sides.

$-2 = x^2 - 4x + 2$ Simplify.

$-2 + 2 = x^2 - 4x + 2 + 2$ Add 2 to both sides.

$0 = x^2 - 4x + 4$ Simplify.

$0 = (x - 2)(x - 2)$ Perfect square trinomial

$x - 2 = 0$ Zero Product Property

$x - 2 + 2 = 0 + 2$ Add 2 to both sides.

$x = 2$ Simplify.

Substitute the value $x = 2$ into the linear equation to find y.

$$y - 2x = -2$$

$y - 2(2) = -2$	Substitute.
$y - 4 = -2$	Simplify.
$y - 4 + 4 = -2 + 4$	Add 4 to both sides.
$y = 2$	Simplify.

The linear and quadratic equations in the system share one point. The solution to the system is the ordered pair $(2, 2)$. ▪

EXAMPLE 3

Use substitution to find the solution to the linear/quadratic system.

$$y = x^2 + 3$$
$$y - x = -2$$

SOLUTION

Solve the linear equation for y.

$$y - x = -2$$

$y - x + x = -2 + x$	Add x to both sides.
$y = x - 2$	Simplify.

Substitute the value for y into the quadratic equation.

$$y = x^2 + 3$$

$x - 2 = x^2 + 3$	Substitute.
$x - 2 - x = x^2 + 3 - x$	Subtract x from both sides.
$-2 = x^2 - x + 3$	Simplify.
$-2 + 2 = x^2 - x + 3 + 2$	Add 2 to both sides.
$0 = x^2 - x + 5$	Simplify.

Use the quadratic formula.

$$x = \frac{-b \pm \sqrt{b^2 - 4ac}}{2a}$$

$a = 1, b = -1,$ and $c = 5$

$$x = \frac{-(-1) \pm \sqrt{(-1)^2 - 4(1)(5)}}{2(1)}$$ Substitute values for a, b, and c.

$$x = \frac{1 \pm \sqrt{1 - 20}}{2}$$ Simplify.

$$x = \frac{1 \pm \sqrt{-19}}{2}$$ Simplify.

The value under the radical is a negative number, so the value of x is not a real number. The system has no real solution. The two equations do not share any points. ■

Intersections of Graphs

The intersections of the graphs of $f(x)$ and $g(x)$ can help you determine the x-values where $f(x) = g(x)$.

Graphically Solving $f(x) = g(x)$

When two functions are graphed on the same set of axes, either they will not intersect or they will intersect at one or more points. The points of intersection determine the x-values for which the functions are equal.

▶ **Think About It** If the graphs of two functions don't intersect, then there is no x-value where the functions are equal.

EXAMPLE 1

Determine the solutions to $f(x) = g(x)$, where $f(x) = -x + 4$ and $g(x) = x^2 - 2$.

SOLUTION

Graph $f(x)$ and $g(x)$ on the same set of axes.

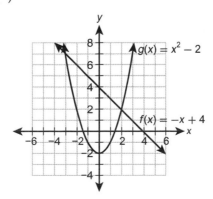

By inspection, it appears that the two graphs intersect at the points $(2, 2)$ and $(-3, 7)$. Substitute the x-value for each point into the functions to confirm that both $f(x)$ and $g(x)$ have the same values.

For $x = 2$:

$$f(x) = -x + 4 \qquad g(x) = x^2 - 2$$
$$f(2) = -(2) + 4 \qquad g(2) = (2)^2 - 2$$
$$f(2) = 2 \qquad g(2) = 4 - 2 = 2$$

For $x = -3$:

$$f(x) = -x + 4 \qquad g(x) = x^2 - 2$$
$$f(-3) = -(-3) + 4 \qquad g(-3) = (-3)^2 - 2$$
$$f(-3) = 3 + 4 = 7 \qquad g(-3) = 9 - 2 = 7$$

The functions have the same values at $x = 2$ and $x = -3$. The solutions to $f(x) = g(x)$ are $x = 2$ and $x = -3$. ▪

Using Technology to Find Intersections of Graphs

Suppose you're not able to determine the x-values at which two functions intersect by inspection. You can use technology to graph the functions and use trace and zoom features to approximate their intersection.

EXAMPLE 2

Determine the solutions to $f(x) = g(x)$: $\begin{cases} f(x) = \sqrt{x + 3} \\ g(x) = x^3 - 2x^2 - 3 \end{cases}$.

Round your answer to the nearest hundredth.

SOLUTION

Graph $f(x)$ and $g(x)$ on the same set of axes.

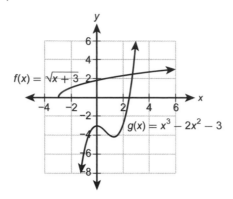

By inspection, it appears that the two graphs intersect when x is at slightly greater than 2. You can use technology (such as a zoom feature or setting a specific window on a graphing calculator) to get a closer look. This graph shows $f(x)$ and $g(x)$ with viewing window $2 < x < 3$ and $2 < y < 3$.

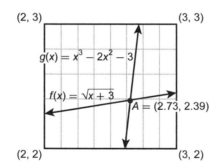

You can use the trace feature of your graphing technology to approximate the point of intersection. The graph shows the tracing of $f(x)$. The labeled point, which is very close to the point of intersection, shows a value of 2.73 for x where $f(x) = g(x)$. ∎

▶ **Think About It** Some CAS will automatically determine the best approximation of the coordinates of the points of intersection of two graphed objects.

Solving Problems Involving Intersections of Graphs

You can use graphing technology to solve problems involving the intersection of graphs.

EXAMPLE 3

After t seconds, the height, p, of a projectile (in feet) is given by the equation $p(t) = -16t^2 + 45t + 5$. After t seconds, the height, b, of a balloon (in feet) is given by the equation $b(t) = 6t + 3$. The projectile and the balloon are launched at the same time. After how many seconds (to the nearest hundredth) are the projectile and the balloon at the same height?

SOLUTION

Graph $p(t) = -16t^2 + 45t + 5$ and $b(t) = 6t + 3$ on the same set of axes.

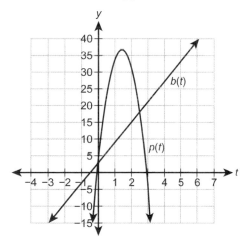

By inspection, it appears that the two graphs intersect when t is slightly less than zero and slightly greater than 2. Disregard the negative value of t for this problem, because time cannot be negative.

> ► **Think About It** The context of certain applications will eliminate some numbers as possible answers.

Use technology to confirm the point of intersection for the positive value of t. Set a specific window so that you can look at the graph closely. This graph shows viewing window $2 < t < 3$ and $15 < y < 20$.

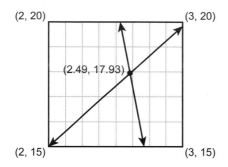

The labeled point is the approximate point of intersection with a value of 2.49 for the value of t. The projectile and the balloon will be the same height after about 2.49 s. ▪

Working with Function Models

Relative maximum and minimum points; increasing, decreasing, and constant intervals; and classification as even, odd, or neither are important features of functions.

The graph of a function can help you get an understanding of the relationships between two quantities. For example, the graph of the function $f(x) = x^2 - 2x$ shows that as the x-values increase, the values of $f(x)$ change from being positive values to being negative values and then return to positive values.

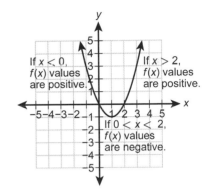

If $x < 0$, $f(x)$ values are positive.

If $x > 2$, $f(x)$ values are positive.

If $0 < x < 2$, $f(x)$ values are negative.

Finding Relative Maximum and Minimum Points

Definitions

A **relative maximum point** of a function is a point that has a greater function value than all the points on the function that are close to it.

A **relative minimum point** of a function is a point that has a value that is less than all the points on the function that are close to it.

EXAMPLE 1

The graph and table show the average cost of gasoline in the United States from 1918 to 2008 in 10-year intervals. The costs shown have been adjusted for inflation.

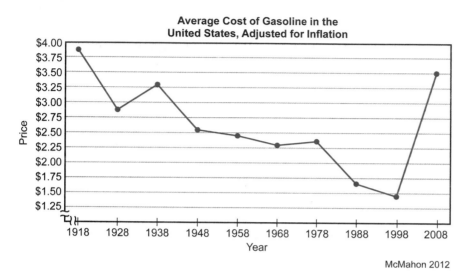

Average Cost of Gasoline in the United States, Adjusted for Inflation

McMahon 2012

Year	1918	1928	1938	1948	1958	1968	1978	1988	1998	2008
Average cost	$3.87	$2.87	$3.31	$2.52	$2.42	$2.28	$2.33	$1.89	$1.46	$3.49

A From 1928 to 1978, what was the relative maximum cost of gasoline?

SOLUTION

The relative maximum cost of gasoline from 1928 to 1978 was $3.31.

B From 1978 to 2008, what was the relative maximum cost of gasoline?

SOLUTION

The relative maximum cost of gasoline from 1978 to 2008 was $3.49.

C From 1918 to 2008, what year had the relative minimum cost of gasoline?

SOLUTION

From 1918 to 2008, the relative minimum cost of gasoline was in 1998. ▪

Determining Increasing, Decreasing, and Constant Intervals

Definitions
A function is **increasing** within an interval if the value of $f(x)$ increases as the value of x increases. A function is **decreasing** within an interval if the value of $f(x)$ decreases as the value of x increases. A function is **constant** within an interval if the value of $f(x)$ remains the same.

The graph shows a function that changes from increasing to constant to decreasing between different intervals.

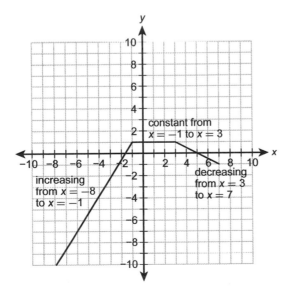

EXAMPLE 2

Consider the function $f(x) = x^2 - 4x$.

A Sketch the graph.

SOLUTION

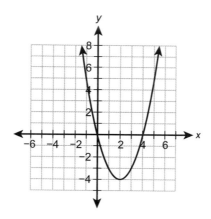

B Determine the intervals for which the function is positive or negative.

SOLUTION

From the graph, you can see that the value of the function is positive (above the x-axis) when $x < 0$ and when $x > 4$. The value of the function is negative when x is between 0 and 4.

C Determine any relative maximum and minimum points.

SOLUTION

From the graph, the point $(2, -4)$ is a relative minimum point.

D Determine the intervals for which the function is increasing, decreasing, or constant.

SOLUTION

The function is decreasing when $x < 2$. The function is increasing when $x > 2$. ▪

Classifying Functions as Even, Odd, or Neither

Definitions
A function $f(x)$ is **even** if $f(-x) = f(x)$ for all values of x. The graph of an even function is always symmetric about the y-axis.   A function $f(x)$ is **odd** if $f(-x) = -f(x)$ for all values of x. The graph of an odd function is always symmetric about the origin.

EXAMPLE 3

Determine whether the function is even, odd, or neither even nor odd.

A $f(x) = x^4 - 3x^2$

SOLUTION

Find $f(-x)$

$$f(-x) = (-x)^4 - 3(-x)^2$$
$$= x^4 - 3x^2$$

The function $f(x) - x^4 - 3x^2$ is even because $f(-x) = f(x)$.

B $f(x) = \sin x$

SOLUTION
Find $f(-x)$.

$$f(-x) = \sin(-x)$$
$$= -\sin x$$

The function $f(x) = \sin x$ is odd because $f(-x) = -f(x)$.

C $f(x) = 2x^3 - 3x^2 - 4x + 4$

SOLUTION
Find $f(-x)$.

$$f(-x) = 2(-x)^3 - 3(-x)^2 - 4(-x) + 4$$
$$= -2x^3 - 3x^2 + 4x + 4$$

The function $f(x) = 2x^3 - 3x^2 - 4x + 4$ is neither even nor odd because $f(-x) \neq f(x)$ and $f(-x) \neq -f(x)$. ■

Identifying Even and Odd Graphs

You can determine whether a function is even, odd, or neither even nor odd by inspecting the graph. The graph of an even function is always symmetric about the y-axis, and the graph of an odd function is always symmetric about the origin. The graph of a function that is neither even nor odd is not symmetric about the origin or the y-axis.

EXAMPLE 4

Determine whether the function is even, odd, or neither even nor odd by examining the graph.

A

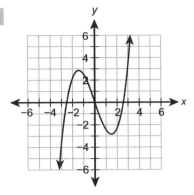

> ▶ **Think About It** If the point (x, y) is on the graph of an odd function, you will also find the point $(-x, -y)$ on the graph. If the point (x, y) is on the graph of an even function, you will also find the point $(-x, y)$ on the graph.

SOLUTION

The function is odd. The graph of an odd function is always symmetric about the origin. If you rotate the graph 180° about the origin, it is identical.

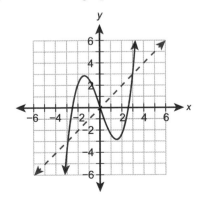

B

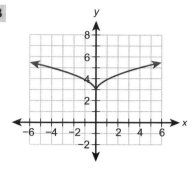

SOLUTION

The function is even. The graph of an even function is always symmetric about the y-axis. If you fold the graph along the y-axis, it is identical.

C

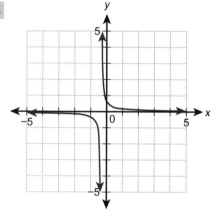

SOLUTION

The function is neither even nor odd. It is not symmetric about the origin or the y-axis. ■

Continuous and Discontinuous Functions

Definitions

A function is **continuous** if every value of x within the domain of the function has a corresponding value for $f(x)$.

A function is **discontinuous** if there are values of x for which $f(x)$ is undefined.

EXAMPLE 5

Determine whether the graph is continuous or discontinuous.

 A

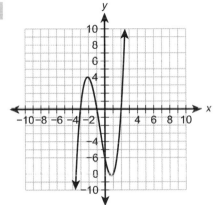

SOLUTION

This function is continuous over all real numbers. The graph of the function has no breaks, so every value of x has a corresponding value for $f(x)$.

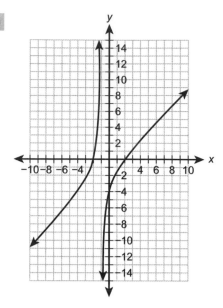

SOLUTION

This function is discontinuous over its domain. It has a vertical asymptote at $x = -1$, so the function is undefined for that point.

C

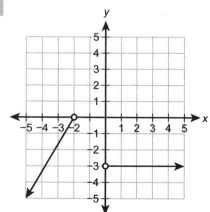

SOLUTION

This function is discontinuous over its domain because it is not defined for $-2 \leq x \leq 0$. ▪

Interpreting Real-World Polynomial Graphs

Real-world situations can be modeled with polynomial graphs. The features of polynomial graphs, including maximum or minimum points and x- and y-intercepts, can help interpret the data.

EXAMPLE 6

A software company tracked its profits each year from 2010 to 2014. The profits, in millions of dollars, are shown in the graph.

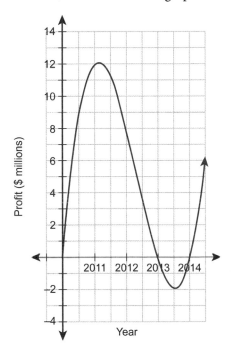

A Estimate the maximum and minimum points of the graph. What do they represent?

SOLUTION

The maximum point of the graph occurs at 2011, when the profit was $12 million. The minimum point occurs between 2013 and 2014, when the profit was –$2 million. These points represent the time periods when profits were highest and lowest.

B Locate the *x*- and *y*-intercepts and interpret what they mean in terms of profits.

SOLUTION

The *x*-intercepts are at $x = 2010$, $x = 2013$, and $x = 2014$, meaning that at the beginning of 2010, 2013, and 2014, the company's profits were at $0. Since $x = 2010$ has a *y*-value of 0, it is also the *y*-intercept of the graph.

C During what time period were the company's profits negative?

SOLUTION

The company's profits were negative between 2013 and 2014 because the graph drops below the *x*-axis. ▪

Thinking About Domain and Range

Sometimes, only some of the domain and range values of a function make sense for a given situation.

Two Types of Domains and Ranges

Definitions

The **theoretical domain and range** of a function are the sets of all allowable inputs and outputs. The **practical domain and range** of a function are the sets of all realistic inputs and outputs for a particular situation.

EXAMPLE 1

A vendor has 20 umbrellas to sell. He sells them for $15 each. The function $m(u) = 15u$ models the total amount of money the vendor makes from selling u umbrellas.

A What is the theoretical domain of the function?

SOLUTION
You can substitute any real number into the function rule, $15u$. The theoretical domain is the set of all real numbers.

B What is the practical domain of the function?

SOLUTION
The fewest number of umbrellas the vendor can sell is 0. The greatest number of umbrellas the vendor can sell is 20. It does not make sense for the vendor to sell part of an umbrella, so the practical domain is the set of all integers from 0 to 20, inclusive.

C What is the theoretical range of the function?

SOLUTION
Any real number could be the result of multiplying another real number by 15. The theoretical range is the set of all real numbers.

D What is the practical range of the function?

SOLUTION
The total amount of money the vendor makes is $15 times the number of umbrellas he sells. He can sell as few as 0 and as many as 20 umbrellas, so he can make as little as $0 and as much as $300. The practical range is the set of all multiples of 15 between 0 and 300, inclusive. ▪

> ▶ **Think About It** You can write the practical range as
> $\{m(u) \mid m(u) = 15k, k \in \mathbb{Z}, k \geq 0, k \leq 20\}$.

EXAMPLE 2

Graph $m(u)$ from Example 1 over its theoretical domain and over its practical domain.

A What is the theoretical domain of the function?

SOLUTION

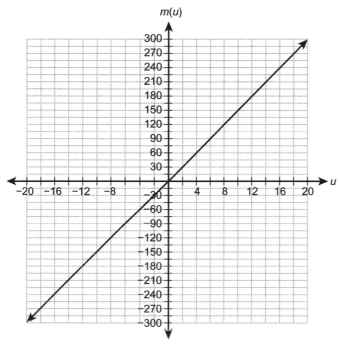

theoretical domain: $\{u \mid u \in \mathbb{R}\}$

B What is the practical domain of the function?

SOLUTION

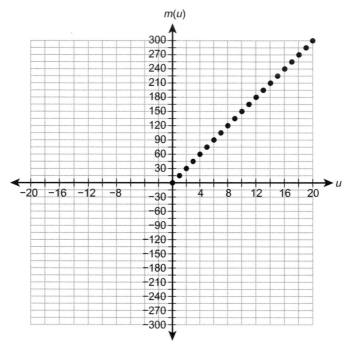

practical domain: $\{u \mid u \in \mathbb{Z}, u \geq 0, u \leq 20\}$ ▪

Comparing Models

To compare function models, you must identify key characteristics of the various models.

Using Multiple Representations

Function models can be represented algebraically, graphically, numerically, or verbally.

EXAMPLE 1

Give algebraic, graphic, and numerical representations of the verbal model: At Mug Manufacturing Inc., the total cost of production is based on a fixed overhead cost of $20 and a unit cost of $3/mug.

SOLUTION

The situation has a fixed unit cost, so a linear model makes sense. Specifically, the fixed overhead cost can be modeled with the y-intercept, and the unit cost can be modeled with the slope. An algebraic representation is $f(x) = 3x + 20$.

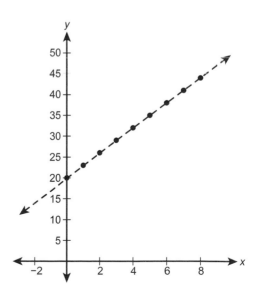

The model is a line with slope 3 and y-intercept 20, and the domain is nonnegative whole numbers. A graphical representation is shown.

A numerical representation is shown in the table.

x	0	1	2	3	5	10	20
f(x)	20	23	26	29	35	50	80

Describing Functions

All functions can be described by various characteristics. These characteristics focus on the relationship of the input and associated output of the function.

Characteristics of Function Models

A function model can be described with these characteristics:

- domain and range
- zeros
- *x*- and *y*-intercepts
- minimum and maximum values
- intervals of positive and negative values

- increasing, decreasing, and constant intervals
- lines of symmetry
- even and odd behavior
- rate of change
- amplitude and period

Comparing Function Models

When comparing function models, use characteristics that apply to the models being compared.

EXAMPLE 2

Model A and Model B are two quadratic models. Model A is represented graphically, and Model B is represented algebraically. Compare the two models.

Model A

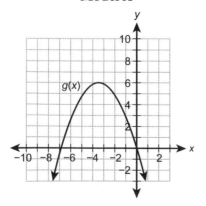

Model B

$$f(x) = 1 - x^2 + 4x$$

SOLUTION

For these models, compare domain and range, zeros, absolute maximum and minimum values, and intervals for which the models are positive and negative.

Because Model A is easier to interpret, focus on Model B.

Write $f(x) = 1 - x^2 + 4x$ as $f(x) = -(x-2)^2 + 5$ to find the vertex, which is the point $(2, 5)$.

Use the quadratic formula to find the zeros.

$$x = \frac{-b \pm \sqrt{b^2 - 4ac}}{2a} = \frac{-4 \pm \sqrt{4^2 - 4(-1)(1)}}{2(-1)} = \frac{-4 \pm \sqrt{20}}{-2} = \frac{-4 \pm 2\sqrt{5}}{-2} = 2 \pm \sqrt{5}$$

Compare the models using a table.

Characteristic	Model A	Model B
domain	all real numbers	all real numbers
range	$g(x) \le 6$	$f(x) \le 5$
zeros	$x = 0$ and $x = -7$	$x = 2 \pm \sqrt{5}$
absolute maximum and minimum values	maximum value of $y = 6$	maximum value of $y = 5$
intervals of positive and negative values	positive values: $-7 < x < 0$ negative values: $x < 7$ and $x > 0$	positive values: $2 - \sqrt{5} < x < 2 + \sqrt{5}$ negative values $x < 2 - \sqrt{5}$ and $x > 2 + \sqrt{5}$

Average Rate of Change

Logarithmic growth is characterized by a rate of change that decreases over time.

Finding the Rate of Change

A key feature for how a growth function behaves is the average rate of change from one point on the function to another.

Definition
The **average rate of change** of a function f from a to b is $$\frac{f(b) - f(a)}{b - a}.$$

EXAMPLE 1

What is the average rate of change of the function $f(x) = \ln x + 1$ from 1 to 4?

SOLUTION

Compute $f(1)$ and $f(4)$.

$f(1) = \ln 1 + 1 = 1$

$f(4) = \ln 4 + 1 \approx 2.39$

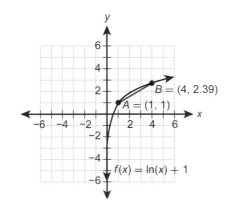

Substitute the values into the formula for average rate of change.

$$\frac{f(b) - f(a)}{b - a} = \frac{2.39 - 1}{4 - 1} \approx 0.46$$

The average rate of change from 1 to 4 is about 0.46. ∎

Visually, the average rate of change is the slope of the line connecting the two points.

EXAMPLE 2

What is the average rate of change of the graphed function from $x = -2$ to $x = -1$?

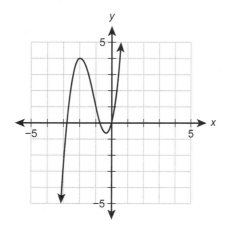

SOLUTION

Find $f(-2)$ and $f(-1)$ using the graph.

$$f(\ 2) = 4$$
$$f(-1)\ -1$$

Substitute the values into the formula for average rate of change.

$$\frac{f(b) - f(a)}{b - a} = \frac{1 - 4}{-1-(-2)} = \frac{-3}{1} = -3$$

The average rate of change from $x = -2$ to $x = -1$ is -3. ▪

EXAMPLE 3

A local high school hired a new basketball coach in 2008. To determine her effectiveness as a coach, the school looked at the number of games the team won each season. The results are summarized in the table. What is the average rate of change from 2011 to 2014?

Year	2008	2009	2010	2011	2012	2013	2014
Number of games won	1	7	8	10	15	21	25

SOLUTION

Find $f(2011)$ and $f(2014)$ using the table.

$$f(2011) = 10$$
$$f(2014) = 25$$

Substitute the values into the formula for average rate of change.

$$\frac{f(b) - f(a)}{b - a} = \frac{25 - 10}{2014 - 2011} = \frac{15}{3} = 5$$

The average rate of change from 2011 to 2014 is 5. This means that, on average, the basketball team is winning 5 more games each season between 2011 and 2014. ■

Analyzing Logarithmic Growth

The average rate of change will be different at different parts of the function.

EXAMPLE 4

For the function $f(x) = \ln x + 1$, compare the average rate of change from 0.25 to 0.75, from 1.5 to 2, and from 7 to 7.5.

SOLUTION

Notice that each interval is a distance of 0.5 along the x-axis. Computing the function values gives $f(0.25) \approx -0.38, f(0.75) \approx 0.71, f(1.5) \approx 1.41, f(2) \approx 1.69, f(7) \approx 2.95$, and $f(7.5) \approx 3.01$. Use the function values to compute the average rates of change.

$$\text{from } 0.25 \text{ to } 0.75: \frac{0.71 - (-0.38)}{0.75 - 0.25} = 2.18$$

$$\text{from } 1.5 \text{ to } 2: \frac{1.69 - 1.41}{2 - 1.5} = 0.56$$

$$\text{from } 7 \text{ to } 7.5: \frac{3.01 - 2.95}{7.5 - 7} = 0.12$$

As the x-values increase, the average rate of change decreases. ∎

In general, logarithmic growth means that the average rate of change decreases as x increases.

Combining Function Types

Functions can be combined using addition, subtraction, multiplication, and division.

Definitions

Functions can be combined using the four arithmetic operations.

Function Addition $(f+g)(x) = f(x) + g(x)$

Function Subtraction $(f-g)(x) = f(x) - g(x)$

Function Multiplication $(fg)(x) = f(x) \cdot g(x)$

Function Division $\left(\dfrac{f}{g}\right)(x) = \dfrac{f(x)}{g(x)}, g(x) \neq 0$

EXAMPLE 1

Write a rule for the indicated combination of the functions $f(x) = x^2 - 2x - 3$ and $g(x) = x + 1$.

A $(f+g)(x)$

SOLUTION

$$(f+g)(x) = f(x) + g(x)$$
$$= (x^2 - 2x - 3) + (x + 1) \qquad \text{Substitute the rules.}$$
$$= x^2 - 2x + x - 3 + 1 \qquad \text{Commutative Property}$$
$$= x^2 - x - 2 \qquad \text{Simplify.}$$

The rule is $(f+g)(x) = x^2 - x - 2$.

B $(f - g)(x)$

SOLUTION

$$(f - g)(x) = f(x) - g(x)$$

$$= \left(x^2 - 2x - 3\right) - (x + 1) \qquad \text{Substitute the rules.}$$

$$= \left(x^2 - 2x - 3\right) - x - 1 \qquad \text{Distributive Property}$$

$$= x^2 - 2x - x - 3 - 1 \qquad \text{Commutative Property}$$

$$= x^2 - 3x - 4 \qquad \text{Simplify.}$$

The rule is $(f - g)(x) = x^2 - 3x - 4.$

C $(fg)(x) = f(x) \cdot g(x)$

SOLUTION

$$(fg)(x) = f(x) \cdot g(x)$$

$$= \left(x^2 - 2x - 3\right)(x + 1) \qquad \text{Substitute the rules.}$$

$$= \left(x^3 - 2x^2 - 3x\right) + \left(x^2 - 2x - 3\right) \qquad \text{Distributive Property}$$

$$- x^3 - x^2 - 5x - 3 \qquad \text{Simplify.}$$

The rule is $(fg)(x) = x^3 - x^2 - 5x - 3.$

D $\left(\dfrac{f}{g}\right)(x) = \dfrac{f(x)}{g(x)}, \; g(x) \neq 0$

SOLUTION

$$\left(\frac{f}{g}\right)(x) = \frac{f(x)}{g(x)}$$

$$= \frac{x^2 - 2x - 3}{x + 1} \qquad \text{Substitute the rules.}$$

$$= \frac{(x - 3)(x + 1)}{x + 1} \qquad \text{Factor.}$$

$$= x - 3 \qquad \text{Divide out the common factor.}$$

Because $g(x)$ cannot be zero, x cannot be -1.

The rule is $\left(\dfrac{f}{g}\right)(x) = x - 3, x \neq -1.$ ∎

Evaluating Combined Functions

You can evaluate combined functions for specific values of x.

EXAMPLE 2

Given $f(x) = 2x - 3$ and $g(x) = 5 - x$, evaluate the function expression.

A $(f - g)(4)$

SOLUTION

$(f - g)(4) = f(4) - g(4)$

$\qquad\qquad = (2 \bullet 4 - 3) - (5 - 4)$ Substitute 4 for x in the rules.

$\qquad\qquad = (8 - 3) - 1$ Use the order of operations.

$\qquad\qquad = 4$ Simplify.

B $\left(\dfrac{g}{f}\right)(-1)$

SOLUTION

$\left(\dfrac{g}{f}\right)(-1) = \dfrac{g(-1)}{f(-1)}$

$\qquad\qquad = \dfrac{5 - (-1)}{2(-1) - 3}$ Substitute -1 for x in the rules.

$\qquad\qquad = -\dfrac{6}{5}$ Simplify. ▪

Sequences and Series

Topic List

Scientists use sequences and series to understand the abundance of species. These models of population data can help them understand whether a particular type of penguin is becoming endangered or is just going through normal periodic changes in population.

Arithmetic Sequences

Sequences with a constant difference between consecutive terms have interesting properties and come up in many situations.

Finding Common Differences

> ### Definitions
>
> A sequence is an **arithmetic sequence** if the difference between consecutive terms is a constant.
>
> $$d = a_n - a_{n-1}$$
>
> The constant d is called the **common difference** of the sequence.

To find the common difference of a given sequence, select any term of the sequence and subtract it from the next consecutive term.

▶ **Think About It** If the differences between consecutive terms in a sequence are not equal, the sequence is not arithmetic.

EXAMPLE 1

For the arithmetic sequence, find the common difference.

A $14, 11, 8, 5, 2, \ldots$

SOLUTION

Find the difference between c_3 and c_2.

$$d = 8 - 11 = -3$$

The common difference is -3.

B $-9, -7.5, -6, -4.5, -3, \ldots$

SOLUTION

Find the difference between h_2 and h_1.

$$d = -7.5 - (-9) = -7.5 + 9 = 1.5$$

The common difference is 1.5. ▪

Writing and Using Recursive Rules for Arithmetic Sequences

Recursive Rule for an Arithmetic Sequence

The formula for the common difference $d = a_n - a_{n-1}$ can be rearranged to obtain the following recursive rule for arithmetic sequences:

any term (after first) ⟵ $a_n = a_{n-1} + d$ ⟶ common difference

previous term

When you define an arithmetic sequence recursively, you also need to provide the value for a_1.

EXAMPLE 2

For the sequence $12, -3, -18, -33, -48, \ldots$:

A Find a recursive rule.

SOLUTION

Begin by finding the common difference.

$$d = -3 - 12 = -15$$

Substitute -15 for d in the equation $m_n = m_{n-1} + d$. The recursive rule is $m_n = m_{n-1} - 15$.

The sequence starts with 12, so $m_1 = 12$.

B Use the recursive rule to find the next two terms in the sequence.

SOLUTION

Find the next two terms, m_6 and m_7.

$$m_6 = m_{6-1} - 15 \qquad\qquad m_7 = m_{7-1} - 15$$
$$= m_5 - 15 \qquad\qquad\qquad = m_6 - 15$$
$$= -48 - 15 = -63 \qquad\qquad = -63 - 15 = -78$$

The next two terms of the sequence are −63 and −78. ■

▶ **Think About It** Note that an infinite number of sequences can be defined by the recursive rule $a_n = a_{n-1} - 15$, such as $-5, -20, -35, -50, \ldots$, and $47, 32, 17, 2, \ldots$, but only one has $a_1 = 12$.

Writing and Using Iterative Rules for Arithmetic Sequences

Using the recursive rule, you can see an iterative rule for jumping straight to the nth term in an arithmetic sequence.

$$a_1 = a_1 + 0d$$

$$a_2 = a_1 + d = a_1 + 1d$$

$$a_3 = a_2 + d = (a_1 + d) + d = a_1 + 2d$$

$$a_4 = a_3 + d = (a_1 + 2d) + d = a_1 + 3d$$

. . . and so on. Notice that each multiple of d is always 1 less than n.

Iterative Rule for an Arithmetic Sequence

The iterative rule for the nth term of an arithmetic sequence with first term a_1 and common difference d is

$$a_n = a_1 + (n-1)d.$$

This rule makes it possible to find any term of an arithmetic sequence if you know the first term and the common difference.

EXAMPLE 3

For the sequence 16, 20, 24, 28, 32, . . . :

A Find an iterative rule.

SOLUTION
The first term is $f_1 = 16$, and the common difference is $d = 20 - 16 = 4$. Substitute 16 for f_1 and 4 for d in the rule $f_n = f_1 + (n-1)d$, and then simplify.

$$
\begin{aligned}
f_n &= \mathbf{16} + (n-1)\mathbf{4} \\
&= 16 + 4n - 4 \\
&= 12 + 4n
\end{aligned}
$$

The iterative rule is $f_n = 12 + 4n$.

B Use the iterative rule to find the 82nd term in the sequence.

SOLUTION

To find the 82nd term, substitute 82 for n in the rule.

$$f_{82} = 12 + 4 \bullet 82 = 340$$

The 82nd term of the sequence is 340. ▪

Graphing Arithmetic Sequences

EXAMPLE 4

Graph the arithmetic sequence in the coordinate plane.

A $a_n = -5 + 4(n - 1)$

SOLUTION

The domain is the set of positive integers. Make a table of some points and plot those points to get a partial graph.

n	$a_n = -5 + 4(n - 1)$	a_n
1	$a_1 = -5 + 4(1 - 1) = -5 + 4 \bullet 0 = -5 + 0$	-5
2	$a_2 = -5 + 4(2 - 1) = -5 + 4 \bullet 1 = -5 + 4$	-1
3	$a_3 = -5 + 4(3 - 1) = -5 + 4 \bullet 2 = -5 + 8$	3
4	$a_4 = -5 + 4(4 - 1) = -5 + 4 \bullet 3 = -5 + 12$	7
5	$a_5 = -5 + 4(5 - 1) = -5 + 4 \bullet 4 = -5 + 16$	11

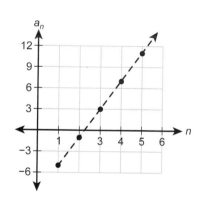

▶ **Think About It** The graph of any arithmetic sequence will consist of discrete points that lie on a line.

B $q_n = 12 + (-2)(n-1)$

SOLUTION

Find the first five terms.

n	$q_n = 12 + (-2)(n-1)$	q_n
1	$q_1 = 12 + (-2)(\mathbf{1}-1) = 12 + (-2)(0) = 12 + 0$	12
2	$q_2 = 12 + (-2)(\mathbf{2}-1) = 12 + (-2)(1) = 12 - 2$	10
3	$q_3 = 12 + (-2)(\mathbf{3}-1) = 12 + (-2)(2) = 12 - 4$	8
4	$q_4 = 12 + (-2)(\mathbf{4}-1) = 12 + (-2)(3) = 12 - 6$	6
5	$q_5 = 12 + (-2)(\mathbf{5}-1) = 12 + (-2)(4) = 12 - 8$	4

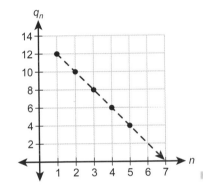

Geometric Sequences

Sequences for which consecutive terms have a constant ratio come up in many situations and have interesting properties.

Common Ratios

> ### Definitions
>
> A sequence is a **geometric sequence** if the ratio between consecutive terms is a constant.
>
> $$r = \frac{a_n}{a_{n-1}}$$
>
> The constant r is called the **common ratio** of the sequence.

EXAMPLE 1

Find the common ratio.

A 76, 38, 19, 9.5, 4.75, . . .

SOLUTION

To find the common ratio, select any term of the sequence except the first term. Then divide it by the previous term.

If you select 38, then $r = \frac{38}{76} = \frac{1}{2}$. The common ratio is $\frac{1}{2}$.

▶ **Think About It** If the common ratio is negative, then the terms of the sequence alternate between positive and negative values.

B $-3, 9, -27, 81, -243, \ldots$

SOLUTION

To find the common ratio, select any term of the sequence except the first term. Then divide it by the previous term.

If you select -27, then $r = -\dfrac{27}{9} = -3$. The common ratio is -3. ∎

Recursive Rules for Geometric Sequences

Recursive Rule for a Geometric Sequence

The formula for the common ratio $r = \dfrac{a_n}{a_{n-1}}$ can be rearranged to obtain the following recursive rule for geometric sequences:

$$\text{any term (after first)} \longleftarrow a_n = r \cdot a_{n-1} \longrightarrow \text{previous term}$$

$$\downarrow \text{common ratio}$$

When you define a geometric sequence recursively, you also need to provide the value for a_1.

▶ **Think About It** In the sequence $5, 15, 45, 135, 405, \ldots$

$$a_1 = \text{given}$$
$$a_2 = 3a_1$$
$$a_3 = 3a_2$$
$$a_4 = 3a_3$$

and so on.

EXAMPLE 2

For the sequence $8, -16, 32, -64, 128, \ldots$:

A Find a recursive rule.

SOLUTION

Begin by finding the common ratio.

$$r = \frac{g_2}{g_1} = \frac{-16}{8} = -2$$

Substitute -2 for r in the equation $g_n = r \cdot g_{n-1}$.

The recursive rule is $g_n = -2 \cdot g_{n-1}$.

The sequence starts with 8, so $g_1 = 8$.

B Use the recursive rule to find the next two terms in the sequence.

SOLUTION

The next two terms are g_6 and g_7.

$$
\begin{aligned}
g_6 &= -2 \cdot g_{6-1} \\
&= -2 \cdot g_5 \\
&= -2 \cdot 128 = -256
\end{aligned}
\qquad
\begin{aligned}
g_7 &= -2 \cdot g_{7-1} \\
&= -2 \cdot g_6 \\
&= -2 \cdot (-256) = 512
\end{aligned}
$$

The next two terms of the sequence are -256 and 512. ▪

▶ **Think About It** Note that an infinite number of sequences can be defined by the recursive rule $a_n = -2 \cdot a_{n-1}$, such as

$$-3, 6, -12, 24, \ldots, \text{and}$$

$$\frac{1}{16}, -\frac{1}{8}, \frac{1}{4}, -\frac{1}{2}, \ldots,$$

but only one of the sequences with this recursive definition has $a_1 = 8$.

$$8, -16, 32, -64, \ldots$$

Writing and Using Iterative Rules for Geometric Sequences

Using the recursive rule, you can see an iterative rule for jumping straight to the nth term in a geometric sequence.

$$a_1 = a_1 \cdot r^0$$

$$a_2 = a_1 \cdot r = a_1 \cdot r^1$$

$$a_3 = a_2 \cdot r = \left(a_1 \cdot r^1\right) \cdot r = a_1 \cdot r^2$$

$$a_4 = a_3 \cdot r = \left(a_1 \cdot r^2\right) \cdot r = a_1 \cdot r^3$$

. . . and so on. Notice that each power of r is always 1 less than n.

Iterative Rule for a Geometric Sequence

The iterative rule for the nth term of a geometric sequence with first term a_1 and common ratio r is

$$a_n = a_1 \cdot r^{n-1}.$$

This rule makes it possible to find any term of a geometric sequence, given the first term and the common ratio.

EXAMPLE 3

For the sequence $\dfrac{1}{64}, \dfrac{1}{16}, \dfrac{1}{4}, 1, 4, \ldots$:

A Find an iterative rule.

SOLUTION

Find the constant ratio, $r = c_2 \div c_1 = \dfrac{1}{16} \div \dfrac{1}{64} = \dfrac{1}{16} \cdot 64 = 4$.

Substitute $\dfrac{1}{64}$ for c_1 and 4 for r in the equation, $c_n = c_1 \cdot r^{n-1}$, to obtain the iterative rule.

$$c_n = \dfrac{1}{64} \cdot 4^{n-1}$$

B Use the iterative rule to find the 10th term in the sequence.

SOLUTION

To find the 10th term, substitute 10 for n.

$$c_{10} = \frac{1}{64} \cdot 4^{10-1}$$

$$= \frac{1}{64} \cdot 4^9$$

$$= 4096 \ \blacksquare$$

Graphing Geometric Sequences

EXAMPLE 4

Graph the geometric sequence in the coordinate plane.

A $b_n = 1 \cdot 3^{n-1}$

SOLUTION

The domain is the set of positive integers. Make a table of some points and plot those points to get a partial graph.

n	$b_n = 1 \cdot 3^{n-1}$	b_n
1	$b_1 = 1 \cdot 3^{1-1} = 1 \cdot 3^0 = 1 \cdot 1$	1
2	$b_2 = 1 \cdot 3^{2-1} = 1 \cdot 3^1 = 1 \cdot 3$	3
3	$b_3 = 1 \cdot 3^{3-1} = 1 \cdot 3^2 = 1 \cdot 9$	9
4	$b_4 = 1 \cdot 3^{4-1} = 1 \cdot 3^3 = 1 \cdot 27$	27
5	$b_5 = 1 \cdot 3^{5-1} = 1 \cdot 3^4 = 1 \cdot 81$	81

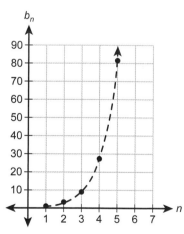

▶ **Think About It** The graph of any geometric sequence will consist of discrete points that lie on an exponential curve.

B $k_n = 32 \cdot \left(\frac{1}{2}\right)^{n-1}$

SOLUTION

n	$k_n = 32 \cdot \left(\frac{1}{2}\right)^{n-1}$	k_n
1	$k_1 = 32 \cdot \left(\frac{1}{2}\right)^{1-1} = 32 \cdot \left(\frac{1}{2}\right)^{0} = 32 \cdot 1$	32
2	$k_2 = 32 \cdot \left(\frac{1}{2}\right)^{2-1} = 32 \cdot \left(\frac{1}{2}\right)^{1} = 32 \cdot \frac{1}{2}$	16
3	$k_3 = 32 \cdot \left(\frac{1}{2}\right)^{3-1} = 32 \cdot \left(\frac{1}{2}\right)^{2} = 32 \cdot \frac{1}{4}$	8
4	$k_4 = 32 \cdot \left(\frac{1}{2}\right)^{4-1} = 32 \cdot \left(\frac{1}{2}\right)^{3} = 32 \cdot \frac{1}{8}$	4
5	$k_5 = 32 \cdot \left(\frac{1}{2}\right)^{5-1} = 32 \cdot \left(\frac{1}{2}\right)^{4} = 32 \cdot \frac{1}{16}$	2

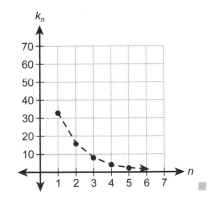

Applications: Sequences

You can use sequences to solve problems that involve number patterns.

A sequence may be arithmetic, geometric, or neither. For example, the sequence $1, -2, 3, -4, 5, \ldots$ is neither arithmetic nor geometric, but you can examine the pattern and predict that the 6th term is -6.

Determining Whether a Sequence Is Arithmetic, Geometric, or Neither

EXAMPLE 1

Decide whether the sequence is arithmetic, geometric, or neither.

A $-\dfrac{3}{2}, -\dfrac{3}{8}, -\dfrac{3}{32}, -\dfrac{3}{128}, \ldots$

SOLUTION

Is it arithmetic?

Test for a common difference by subtracting.

$$b_2 - b_1 = -\frac{3}{8} - \left(-\frac{3}{2}\right) = \frac{9}{8}$$

$$b_3 - b_2 = -\frac{3}{32} - \left(-\frac{3}{8}\right) = \frac{9}{32}$$

There is no common difference, so it is not arithmetic.

Is it geometric?

Test for a common ratio by dividing.

$$b_2 \div b_1 = -\frac{3}{8} \div \left(-\frac{3}{2}\right) = -\frac{3}{8} \cdot \left(-\frac{2}{3}\right) = \frac{1}{4}$$

$$b_3 \div b_2 = -\frac{3}{32} \div \left(-\frac{3}{8}\right) = -\frac{3}{32} \cdot \left(-\frac{8}{3}\right) = \frac{1}{4}$$

$$b_4 \div b_3 = -\frac{3}{128} \div \left(-\frac{3}{32}\right) = -\frac{3}{128} \cdot \left(-\frac{32}{3}\right) = \frac{1}{4}$$

The common ratio is $\frac{1}{4}$. The sequence is geometric.

> ▶ **Remember** In an arithmetic sequence, the difference between consecutive terms is the common difference.
>
> In a geometric sequence, the ratio between consecutive terms is the common ratio.

B $13, -8, -29, -50, \ldots$

SOLUTION

Is it arithmetic?

Test for a common difference by subtracting.

$$z_2 - z_1 = -8 - 13 = -21$$

$$z_3 - z_2 = -29 - (-8) = -21$$

$$z_4 - z_3 = -50 - (-29) = -21$$

The sequence is arithmetic.

C $6, 7, 9, 12, \ldots$

SOLUTION

Is it arithmetic?

Test for a common difference by subtracting.

$$t_2 - t_1 = 7 - 6 = 1$$

$$t_3 - t_2 = 9 - 7 = 2$$

There is no common difference, so it is not arithmetic.

Is it geometric?
Test for a common ratio by dividing.

$$t_2 \div t_1 = 7 \div 6 \approx 1.167$$

$$t_3 \div t_2 = 9 \div 7 \approx 1.286$$

There is no common ratio, so it is not geometric.
The sequence is neither arithmetic nor geometric. ▪

EXAMPLE 2

Decide whether the sequence is arithmetic, geometric, or neither. Find the common difference or the common ratio, if there is one. Use the sequence to answer the question.

A A display of soup cans in the grocery store is stacked so that the top layer has 1 can, the next layer is 2 by 2 and has 4 cans, the next layer is 3 by 3 and has 9 cans, and the next layer is 4 by 4 with 16 cans. How many cans are in the layer below that?

SOLUTION
Write the sequence of numbers.

$$1, 4, 9, 16, \ldots$$

Is it arithmetic?
Test for a common difference by subtracting.

$$4 - 1 = 3 \qquad 9 - 4 = 5$$

There is no common difference.

Is it geometric?
Test for a common ratio by dividing.

$$\frac{4}{1} = 4 \qquad \frac{9}{4} = 2.25$$

There is no common ratio.

The sequence is neither arithmetic nor geometric.

Use the pattern to find the next number in the sequence.

$$1^2 = 1 \qquad 2^2 = 4 \qquad 3^2 = 9 \qquad 4^2 = 16$$

The next layer will have 5^2 or 25 cans.

B Suppose you find 1 penny on Monday, 2 pennies on Tuesday, 4 pennies on Wednesday, 8 pennies on Thursday, and 16 pennies on Friday. If this pattern continues, how many pennies will you find on Saturday?

SOLUTION

Write the sequence of numbers.

$$1, 2, 4, 8, 16, \ldots$$

Is it arithmetic?
Test for a common difference.

$$2 - 1 = 1 \qquad 4 - 2 = 2$$

There is no common difference.

Is it geometric?
Test for a common ratio.

$$\frac{2}{1} = 2 \qquad \frac{4}{2} = 2 \qquad \frac{8}{4} = 2 \qquad \frac{16}{8} = 2$$

The common ratio is 2, so the sequence is geometric.

Use the common ratio to find the next number in the sequence.

$$16 \cdot 2 = 32$$

The next number in the pattern is 32. You will find 32 pennies on Saturday.

C Makena adds $15 every month to her savings jar. Every month, she counts the amount of money in the jar. What will her savings be after 6 months?

SOLUTION
Write the sequence of numbers.

$$15, 30, 45, 60, 75, \ldots$$

Is it arithmetic?
Test for a common difference.

$$30 - 15 = 15 \qquad 45 - 30 = 15 \qquad 60 - 45 = 15 \qquad 75 - 60 = 15$$

The common difference is $15, so it is an arithmetic sequence.

Use the common difference to find the next number in the sequence.

$$75 + 15 = 90$$

After 6 months, Makena will have $90. ▪

Application: Money

EXAMPLE 3

Suppose someone offers to pay you 1 penny on the first day, 2 pennies the second day, and so on, doubling the number of pennies each day. (This pattern is the same pattern as in Example 2B.) What is the first day on which your pay would be at least $10?

SOLUTION
Begin by changing $10 to pennies. So the question is, on which day would you be paid at least 1000 pennies?

Step 1 Write what you know, and what you are looking for, in terms of the sequence rules.

You know the common ratio: $r = 2$. You know the first term: $a_1 = 1$.

You will be paid 1000 pennies on Day n, so you know the value of the nth term: $a_n = 1000$.

What you don't know is the value of n.

Step 2 Substitute the known values into the iterative rule.

$a_n = a_1 \cdot r^{n-1}$ Iterative rule for a geometric sequence

$1000 = 1 \cdot 2^{n-1}$ Substitute.

$1000 = 2^{n-1}$ Simplify.

Step 3 Use the guess-and-check strategy to solve for n.

Try $n = 9: 2^{9-1} = 2^8 = 256$ too low

Try $n = 10: 2^{10-1} = 2^9 = 512$ too low

Try $n = 11: 2^{11-1} = 2^{10} = 1024$ too high

n is between 10 and 11. To determine if you should round up or down, think about what you are looking for: The first day, you earn at least 1000 pennies. On Day 10, your pay will be 512 pennies. On Day 11, your pay will be 1024 pennies, so the answer is Day 11. ■

▶ **Remember** When you know one term, a_n, of an arithmetic or a geometric sequence, use a recursive rule to find the next term.

For an arithmetic sequence:

$$a_n = a_{n-1} + d$$

For a geometric sequence:

$$a_n = r \cdot a_{n-1}$$

In both of these rules, a_n is any term after the first, called the nth term. The previous term is a_{n-1}. The common difference is d, and the common ratio is r.

Application: Population Growth

EXAMPLE 4

A small town had a population of 968 in 2000. By the next year, the population had grown to 1007. In 2002, there were 1047 people, and the next year there were 1089.

A What kind of sequence is this?

SOLUTION
Write the sequence of numbers.

$$968, 1007, 1047, 1089, \ldots$$

Step 1 Test for a common difference by subtracting.

$$1007 - 968 = 39 \qquad 1047 - 1007 = 40 \qquad 1089 - 1047 = 42$$

There is no common difference.

Step 2 Test for a common ratio by dividing.

$$\frac{1007}{968} \approx 1.04 \qquad \frac{1047}{1007} \approx 1.04 \qquad \frac{1089}{1047} \approx 1.04$$

There is a common ratio. This sequence is geometric.

Each year the population increases by about 4%.

▶ **Think About It** The ratios in Example 4A aren't exactly equal to each other, but they are pretty close, so a geometric sequence is a reasonable model.

B If this pattern continues, what will the population be after 15 years?

SOLUTION

Use the iterative rule, $a_n = a_1 \cdot r^{n-1}$, with the values you know.

$a_n = a_1 \cdot r^{n-1}$

$a_{15} \approx 968 \cdot 1.04^{15-1}$ Substitute.

$a_{15} \approx 968 \cdot 1.04^{14}$ Simplify.

$a_{15} \approx 1676$ Use a calculator to approximate the value.

After 15 years, the population will be about 1676. ■

Application: Finance

EXAMPLE 5

The balance on a car loan is $7600. The car owner makes a payment of $200 every month.

A Write a sequence showing the balance for the first 5 months. What kind of sequence is this?

SOLUTION

The sequence is $7600, $7400, $7200, $7000, ... There is a common difference of $200, so this is an arithmetic sequence.

B When will the balance be less than $600?

SOLUTION

Find the number of the term that is equal to $600.

$c_n = c_1 + (n-1) \cdot d$

$600 = 7600 + (n-1) \cdot -200$ Substitute.

$600 = 7600 - 200n + 200$ Distribute -200.

$-7200 = -200n$ Simplify.

$36 = n$ Divide both sides by -200.

Notice that the first term, c_1, is $7600, and the balance after 1 payment is c_2, or $7400. So c_{36} is the balance after 35 payments, and $c_{36} = 600$. The balance will be less than $600 after 36 payments. ■

Application: Physics

EXAMPLE 6

A ball is dropped from a height of 100 in. The ball bounces, each time reaching a lower and lower height. The height of each bounce is 80% of the height of the previous bounce.

A What height, rounded to the nearest inch, will the ball reach after bouncing 4 times?

SOLUTION

In this situation, the first height in this geometric sequence is 100 in., so $f_1 = 100$. The second height will be 80% of 100 in., and so forth. The height, after bouncing 4 times, is the fifth height in the sequence, f_5.

Step 1 Write what you know, and what you are looking for, in sequence notation.

The common ratio is 80%, or 0.8, so $r = 0.8$, and you know $f_1 = 100$.

You are looking for the value of the fifth term, f_5.

Step 2 Find f_n when $n = 5$.

$$f_n = f_1 \cdot r^{n-1}$$
$$f_5 = 100 \cdot 0.8^{5-1} \qquad \text{Substitute.}$$
$$f_5 = 100 \cdot 0.8^4 \qquad \text{Simplify.}$$
$$f_5 = 40.96 \qquad \text{Use a calculator to evaluate.}$$

After bouncing 4 times, the ball will reach a height of almost 41 in.

> ▶ **Think About It** Because the height of each successive bounce is 80% of a positive number, the ball's bounce, in theory, will never reach a zero height. In practice, however, the ball loses energy and does eventually stop bouncing.

> ▶ **Think About It** To be sure of the pattern in a sequence, you may need to know more than just three terms.

B How many bounces will it take for the ball to reach a height of less than 1 in.?

SOLUTION
You need to solve for n when the height f_n is 1 in.

$f_n = f_1 \cdot r^{n-1}$

$1 = 100 \cdot 0.8^{n-1}$ Substitute.

Use the guess-and-check strategy to solve for n.

Try $n = 23$: $100 \cdot 0.8^{23-1} = 100 \cdot 0.8^{22} \approx 0.7379$ too low

Try $n = 22$: $100 \cdot 0.8^{22-1} = 100 \cdot 0.8^{21} \approx 0.9223$ too low

Try $n = 21$: $100 \cdot 0.8^{21-1} = 100 \cdot 0.8^{20} \approx 1.153$ too high

n is between 21 and 22, but only whole number values make sense in this situation. Think about what you are looking for: the number of bounces it will take for the ball to reach a height of less than 1 in. Because $f_{21} > 1$, you want the bounce number that corresponds with f_{22}. The bounce number is 1 less than n, so the answer is 21 bounces. ■

Actually, if you try this with a real ball, the ball would probably not bounce as many as 21 times. It would lose energy and stop bouncing before that.

Series and Sigma Notation

The sum of the first four terms of the sequence 1, 3, 5, 7, . . . is represented by the sum $1 + 3 + 5 + 7$.

The expression $1 + 3 + 5 + 7$ is an example of a series.

Definition
A **series** is the sum of consecutive terms of a sequence.

The notation S_n represents the sum of the first n terms of a series.

Sequence: 2, 5, 8, 11, 14, . . .

Corresponding Series: $2 + 5 + 8 + 11 + 14 + \ldots$

$$S_1 = 2$$
$$S_2 = 2 + 5 = 7$$
$$S_3 = 2 + 5 + 8 = 15$$
$$S_4 = 2 + 5 + 8 + 11 = 26$$
$$S_5 = 2 + 5 + 8 + 11 + 14 = 40$$

. . . and so on. When a series has many terms, it can be convenient to use sigma notation, also known as summation notation. Sigma notation uses the Greek capital letter sigma: Σ.

▶ **Think About It** The sum of the first n terms of a series is called the nth partial sum.

Finding a Sum in Sigma Notation

Definitions

The sum S_n of the first n terms of a sequence can be represented as

$$S_n = \sum_{i=1}^{n} a_i = a_1 + a_2 + a_3 + \ldots + a_n.$$

S_n is equivalent to $\sum_{i=1}^{n} a_i$, which is read as "the sum from 1 to n of a_i."

In this notation, i is called the **index**, n is called the **upper limit**, and 1 is the **lower limit**.

▶ **Think About It** The lower limit of a series in sigma notation is not always equal to 1. The lower limit can be any whole number less than or equal to n.

To find the sum of a series given in sigma notation, begin by writing it in expanded form. You can then find the sum by adding the terms of the series.

EXAMPLE 1

Write the series in expanded form and find the sum.

A $\sum_{i=1}^{4} 6i$

SOLUTION

$$\sum_{i=1}^{4} 6i = 6 \cdot 1 + 6 \cdot 2 + 6 \cdot 3 + 6 \cdot 4 \qquad \text{Expanded form}$$

$$= 6 + 12 + 18 + 24 \qquad \text{Simplify.}$$

$$= 60$$

B $\displaystyle\sum_{k=1}^{6} k^2$

SOLUTION

$$\sum_{k=1}^{6} k^2 = 1^2 + 2^2 + 3^2 + 4^2 + 5^2 + 6^2 \qquad \text{Expanded form}$$

$$= 1 + 4 + 9 + 16 + 25 + 36 \qquad \text{Simplify.}$$

$$= 91 \; \blacksquare$$

Using Sigma Notation to Describe a Series

EXAMPLE 2

Write the series using sigma notation.

A $4 + 9 + 14 + 19 + 24 + 29 + 34$

SOLUTION

This series is arithmetic, with a first term of 4 and a common difference of 5. The iterative rule for the related sequence is $a_i = 5i - 1$. There are $n = 7$ terms in the series.

The answer is $\displaystyle\sum_{i=1}^{7} (5i - 1)$. You can check the answer by writing it in expanded form.

▶ **Remember** The iterative rule for an arithmetic sequence is $a_n = a_1 + (n-1)d$, and the iterative rule for a geometric sequence is $a_n = a_1 \cdot r^{n-1}$.

B $1 + \frac{1}{2} + \frac{1}{4} + \frac{1}{8}$

SOLUTION

This series is geometric, with a first term of 1 and a common ratio of $\frac{1}{2}$.

The iterative rule for the related sequence is $a_i = \left(\frac{1}{2}\right)^{i-1}$. There are $n = 4$ terms in the series.

The answer is $\sum_{i=1}^{4} \left(\frac{1}{2}\right)^{i-1}$. You can check the answer by writing it in expanded form. ■

Arithmetic Series

How quickly can you add the numbers from 1 to 100 in your head?

It is said that in elementary school, the famous mathematician Carl Friedrich Gauss added the integers from 1 to 100 in seconds by recognizing that the sum was 50 pairs of numbers, each of which added to 101.

Arithmetic Series

Definition

An **arithmetic series** is a series that results from adding the terms of an arithmetic sequence.

▶ **Remember** A **series** is the sum of consecutive terms of a sequence.

For example, if you start with the arithmetic sequence

$$5, 8, 11, 14, \ldots,$$

then you can define the corresponding series:

$$5 + 8 + 11 + 14 + \ldots.$$

Because the sequence goes on forever, the sum also goes on forever. In general, if a_n represents the terms of an arithmetic sequence, then the sum of all the terms of the sequence is

$$S = a_1 + a_2 + a_3 + a_4 + \ldots.$$

When you are interested in the sum of the first n terms of the arithmetic sequence, you can write the nth partial sum of the series as follows:

$$S_n = a_1 + a_2 + a_3 + a_4 + \ldots + a_{n-2} + a_{n-1} + a_n.$$

Finding the Sum of the First n Terms of an Arithmetic Series

A general formula for the sum, S_n, of the first n terms of an arithmetic series can be seen with the help of an example.

sums of pairs
$20 + 23 = 43$
$17 + 26 = 43$
$5 + 8 + 11 + 14 + 17 + 20 + 23 + 26 + 29 + 32 + 35 + 38$ $14 + 29 = 43$
$11 + 32 = 43$
$8 + 35 = 43$
$5 + 38 = 43$

You can see that each of these six pairs sums to 43. This is the type of pattern that Gauss recognized and used to calculate the sum so quickly.

Arithmetic Series Formula

The sum of the first n terms of an arithmetic series with first term a_1 and nth term a_n is given by

$$S_n = \frac{n}{2}(a_1 + a_n).$$

EXAMPLE 1

A Find the sum of the first 100 positive even integers.

SOLUTION
There are $n = 100$ terms. Also, $a_1 = 2$ and $a_n = 200$.

$$S_{100} = \frac{100}{2}(2 + 200)$$
$$= 50 \cdot 202 = 10{,}100$$

So the sum of the first 100 positive even integers is 10,100.

B Find the sum: $\displaystyle\sum_{i=1}^{17} 2i + 5$.

SOLUTION

There are $n = 17$ terms. Find a_1 and a_n.

$$a_1 = 2 \cdot 1 + 5 = 7$$

$$a_{17} = 2 \cdot 17 + 5 = 39$$

Now find S_{17}.

$$S_{17} = \frac{17}{2}\,(7 + 39)$$

$$= 8.5 \cdot 46 = 391$$

So $\displaystyle\sum_{i=1}^{17}(2i + 5) = 391.$ ■

▶ **Think About It** To find the sum of the first n terms of an arithmetic series by using the formula

$$S_n = \frac{n}{2}\big(a_1 + a_n\big),$$

you need to know the number of terms, n, the first term, a_1, and the last term, a_n.

An Alternate Formula for the Sum of the First n Terms of an Arithmetic Series

If you substitute $a_1 + (n - 1)d$ for a_n in the formula $S_n = \frac{n}{2}\,(a_1 + a_n)$, you get an alternate formula for the sum of the first n terms of an arithmetic series.

$$S_n = \frac{n}{2}\big(a_1 + a_n\big) = \frac{n}{2}\,\big(a_1 + a_1 + (n - 1)d\big) = \frac{n}{2}\big(2a_1 + (n - 1)d\big)$$

Alternate Arithmetic Series Formula

The sum of the first n terms of an arithmetic series with first term a_1 and common difference d is given by

$$S_n = \frac{n}{2}\left(2a_1 + (n-1)d\right).$$

EXAMPLE 2

A Find the sum of the first 20 terms: $-35 + (-30) + (-25) + (-20) + \ldots$.

SOLUTION

The first term is $b_1 = -35$, and the constant difference is $d = 5$. So the sum of the first 20 terms can be found as shown:

$$
\begin{aligned}
S_n &= \frac{n}{2}\left(2b_1 + (n-1)d\right) \\
&= \frac{20}{2}\left[2(-35) + (20-1)5\right] \\
&= 10(-70 + 19 \cdot 5) \\
&= 10 \cdot 25 \\
&= 250
\end{aligned}
$$

So the sum of the first 20 terms is 250.

▶ **Remember** The sum of the first n terms of a series is called the nth partial sum. In Example 2A, the 20th partial sum is 250.

B Find the sum of the first 14 terms of the arithmetic series where $c_1 = 32{,}000$ and common difference $d = 1500$.

SOLUTION

There are $n = 14$ terms in the series. The first term is $c_1 = 32{,}000$, and the constant difference is $d = 1500$. So the sum of the first 14 terms is

$$S_n = \frac{n}{2}\left(2c_1 + (n-1)d\right)$$

$$= \frac{14}{2}\left[2 \cdot \mathbf{32{,}000} + (\mathbf{14} - 1)\mathbf{1500}\right]$$

$$= 7\left(64{,}000 + 19{,}500\right)$$

$$= 7 \cdot 83{,}500$$

$$= 584{,}500$$

So the sum of the first 14 terms is 584,500. ■

Graphing the Partial Sums of an Arithmetic Series

EXAMPLE 3

Graph the first five partial sums of the arithmetic series.

$$1 + 2 + 3 + 4 + 5 + 6 + 7 + \ldots$$

SOLUTION

Make a table of the five partial sums and then plot the points.

n	S_n
1	1
2	$1 + 2 = 3$
3	$1 + 2 + 3 = 6$
4	$1 + 2 + 3 + 4 = 10$
5	$1 + 2 + 3 + 4 + 5 = 15$

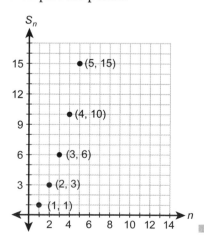

Geometric Series

The sum of the terms of an arithmetic sequence is an arithmetic series. Likewise, you can sum the terms of a geometric sequence to get a geometric series.

Definition

A **geometric series** is a series that results from adding the terms of a geometric sequence.

For example, if you start with the geometric sequence

$$2, -6, 18, -54, 162, \ldots,$$

then you can define the corresponding series.

$$2 + (-6) + 18 + (-54) + 162 + \ldots$$

▶ **Remember** The iterative rule for a geometric sequence is

$$a_n = a_1 \cdot r^{n-1}.$$

Finding the Sum of the First n Terms of a Geometric Series

A general formula for the sum, S_n, of the first n terms of a geometric series can be seen with the help of an example.

Consider a geometric series where $a_1 = 1$ and $r = 2$. Now consider the 8th partial sum.

$$S_8 = 1 + 2 + 4 + 8 + 16 + 32 + 64 + 128$$

Multiply both sides of the equation by 2, then subtract.

$$S_8 = 1 + 2 + 4 + 8 + 16 + 32 + 64 + 128$$
$$- \quad 2S_8 = - \quad (2 + 4 + 8 + 16 + 32 + 64 + 128 + 256)$$
$$\overline{(1-2)S_8 = 1 + 0 + 0 + 0 + \ 0 + \ 0 + \ 0 + \ 0 \ -256}$$

$$S_8 = \frac{1 - 256}{(1 - 2)}$$

In the numerator, notice that $1 = a_1$ and that $256 = a_9$. In the denominator, $2 = r$.

You can find the general rule for the sum of the first n terms of a geometric series as follows:

$$S_n = a_1 + a_1 r + a_1 r^2 + \ldots + a_1 r^{n-2} + a_1 r^{n-1}$$
$$- \quad rS_n = - \quad \left(a_1 r + a_1 r^2 + \ldots + a_1 r^{n-2} + a_1 r^{n-1} + a_1 r^n \right)$$
$$\overline{S_n - rS_n = a_1 - a_1 r^n}$$
$$S_n(1 - r) = a_1 - a_1 r^n$$

$$S_n = \frac{a_1 - a_1 r^n}{1 - r}$$

$$S_n = \frac{a_1 \left(1 - r^n \right)}{1 - r}, \text{ where } r \neq 1$$

Geometric Series Formula

The sum of the first n terms of a geometric series with first term a_1 and common ratio r is

$$S_n = \frac{a_1 \left(1 - r^n \right)}{1 - r}$$

where $r \neq 1$.

EXAMPLE 1

Find the indicated sum of the geometric series.

A S_7 for the series $400 + 200 + 100 + 50 + \ldots$

SOLUTION

Notice that $n = 7$, $a_1 = 400$, and $r = \dfrac{1}{2}$.

$$S_7 = \frac{400\left(1 - \left(\frac{1}{2}\right)^7\right)}{1 - \frac{1}{2}} = \frac{400\left(1 - \frac{1}{128}\right)}{\frac{1}{2}} = \frac{400 \cdot \frac{127}{128}}{\frac{1}{2}} = 793\frac{3}{4}$$

The sum is $793\dfrac{3}{4}$.

B $\displaystyle\sum_{i=2}^{6} 3^i$

SOLUTION

Here, $a_1 = 9$, $n = 6$ and $r = 3$.

$$S_6 = \frac{9\left(1 - 3^6\right)}{1 - 3} = \frac{9(1 - 729)}{-2} = \frac{-6552}{-2} = 3276$$

The sum is 3276. ▪

An Alternate Formula for the Sum of the First n Terms of a Geometric Series

You can see that, to use the formula for a geometric series, you need to know the first term, the common ratio, and the number of terms being summed.

With a little work, you can also derive a formula for the nth partial sum of a geometric series when you know the first term, the common ratio, and the value of the nth term.

Multiply both sides of the iterative rule for a geometric sequence by r.

$$a_n = a_1 r^{n-1}$$

$$a_n \cdot r = a_1 r^{n-1} \cdot r$$

$$a_n r = a_1 r^{n-1+1}$$

$$a_n r = a_1 r^n$$

Replacing $a_1 r^n$ with $a_n r$ in the formula $S_n = \dfrac{a_1 - a_1 r^n}{1 - r}$ yields the alternate geometric series formula.

Alternate Geometric Series Formula

The sum of the first n terms of a geometric series is given by

$$S_n = \frac{a_1 - a_n r}{1 - r}$$

where $r \neq 1$.

▶ **Think About It** This formula does not require you to know n.

EXAMPLE 2

Find the sum of the geometric series.

A $3 - 6 + 12 - 24 + \ldots + 192$

SOLUTION

Notice that $a_1 = 3$, $r = -2$, and $a_n = 192$. Use the formula that does not require knowing n.

$$S_n = \frac{a_1 - a_n r}{1 - r}$$

$$= \frac{3 - 192 \cdot (-2)}{1 - (-2)}$$

$$= \frac{3 + 384}{3}$$

$$= \frac{387}{3}$$

$$= 129$$

The sum of the series is 129.

B $2 + 1 + 0.5 + 0.25 + 0.125 + \ldots + 0.015625$

SOLUTION

Here, $a_1 = 2$, $r = 0.5$, and $a_n = 0.015625$. Use the formula that does not require knowing n.

$$S_n = \frac{a_1 - a_n r}{1 - r}$$

$$= \frac{2 - 0.015625 \cdot 0.5}{1 - 0.5}$$

$$= \frac{2 - 0.0078125}{0.5}$$

$$= \frac{1.9921875}{0.5}$$

$$= 3.984375$$

The sum of the series is 3.984375. ◼

Applications: Series

Series have many applications in everyday life.

Determining Whether a Series Is Arithmetic, Geometric, or Neither

Before you use series to solve problems, you should know how to tell whether a series is arithmetic, geometric, or neither.

A geometric series is a series for which the terms are the elements of a geometric sequence. An arithmetic series is a series for which the terms are the elements of an arithmetic sequence.

EXAMPLE 1

Determine whether the series is arithmetic, geometric, or neither.

A $4 + 12 + 36 + 108 + \ldots$

SOLUTION

Test to see if it is arithmetic.

$$a_2 - a_1 = 12 - 4 = 8 \qquad a_3 - a_2 = 36 - 12 = 24$$

The differences are not the same, so test to see if it is geometric.

$$\frac{a_2}{a_1} = \frac{12}{4} = 3 \qquad \frac{a_3}{a_2} = \frac{36}{12} = 3 \qquad \frac{a_4}{a_3} = \frac{108}{36} = 3$$

The ratios are the same, so the series is geometric.

B $1 + 2 + 6 + 24 + \ldots$

SOLUTION

Test to see if it is arithmetic.

$$a_2 - a_1 = 2 - 1 = 1 \qquad a_3 - a_2 = 6 - 2 = 4$$

The differences are not the same, so test to see if it is geometric.

$$\frac{a_2}{a_1} = \frac{2}{1} = 2 \qquad \frac{a_3}{a_2} = \frac{6}{2} = 3$$

The ratios are not the same, so the series is neither arithmetic nor geometric.

C $480 + 360 + 240 + 120 + \ldots$

SOLUTION

Test to see if it is arithmetic.

$$a_2 - a_1 = 360 - 480 = -120$$

$$a_3 - a_2 = 240 - 360 = -120$$

$$a_4 - a_3 = 120 - 240 = -120$$

The differences are the same, so the series is arithmetic.

D $-8 + 4 - 2 + 1 + \ldots$

SOLUTION

Test to see if it is arithmetic.

$$a_2 - a_1 = 4 - (-8) = 12 \qquad a_3 - a_2 = -2 - 4 = -6$$

The differences are not the same, so test to see if it is geometric.

$$\frac{a_2}{a_1} = \frac{4}{-8} = -\frac{1}{2} \qquad \frac{a_3}{a_2} = \frac{-2}{4} = -\frac{1}{2} \qquad \frac{a_4}{a_3} = \frac{1}{-2} = -\frac{1}{2}$$

The ratios are the same, so the series is geometric. ■

Application: Money

EXAMPLE 2

Brian and Kayla try different methods of saving money. Determine the total amount of money each will have after 10 days.

A Brian saves 51¢ on Day 1, 52¢ on Day 2, 53¢ on Day 3, ...

SOLUTION

The total amount of money Brian saves after 10 days, given 51¢ on Day 1, 52¢ on Day 2, 53¢ on Day 3, . . . , is an arithmetic series $51 + 52 + 53 + 54 + \ldots$, where $n = 10$, $a_1 = 51$, and $d = 1$.

$$S_n = \frac{n}{2}\left(2a_1 + (n-1)d\right)$$

$$S_{10} = \frac{10}{2}\left(2 \cdot 51 + (10-1) \cdot 1\right)$$

$$S_{10} = 5\left(102 + 9 \cdot 1\right)$$

$$S_{10} = 5 \cdot 111 = 555$$

The total amount of money Brian saves after 10 days is $5.55.

B Kayla saves 1¢ on Day 1, 2¢ on Day 2, 4¢ on Day 3, ...

SOLUTION

The total amount of money Kayla saves after 10 days, given 1¢ on Day 1, 2¢ on Day 2, 4¢ on Day 3, . . . , is a geometric series $1 + 2 + 4 + 8 + \ldots$, where $n = 10$, $a_1 = 1$, and $r = 2$.

$$S_n = \frac{a_1\left(1 - r^n\right)}{1 - r}$$

$$S_{10} = \frac{1\left(1 - 2^{10}\right)}{1 - 2}$$

$$S_{10} = \frac{1 \cdot (-1023)}{-1}$$

$$S_{10} = 1023$$

The total amount of money Kayla saves after 10 days is $10.23. Kayla saves more money with her method than Brian saves with his. ▪

Application: Seating Capacity

EXAMPLE 3

Suppose an auditorium has 30 rows of seats. There are 30 seats in the first row, 32 in the second row, 34 in the third row, and so on. How many seats are in all 30 rows?

SOLUTION

The total number of seats in the 30 rows form an arithmetic series with $n = 30$, $a_1 = 30$, and $d = 2$.

Step 1 Find the 30th term.

$$a_n = a_1 + (n-1)d$$
$$a_{30} = 30 + (30-1) \cdot 2$$
$$a_{30} = 30 + 29 \cdot 2$$
$$a_{30} = 30 + 58$$
$$a_{30} = 88$$

Step 2 Find the sum of the series.

$$S_n = \frac{n}{2}\left(a_1 + a_n\right)$$
$$S_{30} = \frac{30}{2}(30 + 88)$$
$$S_{30} = 15 \cdot 118$$
$$S_{30} = 1770$$

There are 1770 seats in the auditorium. ■

Application: Bouncing Distance

EXAMPLE 4

Silas drops a ball from a height of 25 ft. Each time it drops h feet, it rebounds to a height of $0.8h$ feet. How much vertical distance does the ball travel from the time he drops it until it reaches the peak after its 6th bounce?

SOLUTION

The ball travels 25 ft on the first drop. On each bounce after that, it goes up to its peak, and then back down the same distance, so it travels $2 \cdot 25 \cdot 0.8^k$ feet for $k = 1$ to 5. The ball then goes up after the 6th bounce.

$$25 \cdot 0.8^6 = 6.5536$$

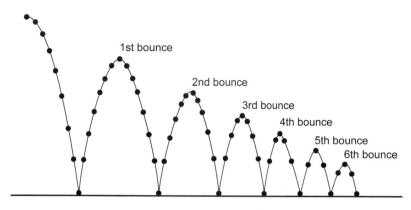

1st bounce

2nd bounce

3rd bounce

4th bounce

5th bounce

6th bounce

The five bounces, up and down, form the geometric series

$$2 \cdot 25 \cdot 0.8^1 + 2 \cdot 25 \cdot 0.8^2 + 2 \cdot 25 \cdot 0.8^3 + 2 \cdot 25 \cdot 0.8^4 + 2 \cdot 25 \cdot 0.8^5$$

where $n = 5$, $a_1 = 2 \cdot 25 \cdot 0.8^1 \approx 40$, and $r = 0.8$.

Substitute the values of n, a_1, and r into the formula,

$$S_n = \frac{a_1\left(1 - r^n\right)}{1 - r}$$

$$S_5 = \frac{40\left(1 - 0.8^5\right)}{1 - 0.8}$$

$$S_5 = \frac{40(0.67232)}{0.2}$$

$$S_5 = \frac{26.8928}{0.2}$$

$$S_5 = 134.464$$

The total vertical distance the ball travels is

$$25 + 134.464 + 6.5536 = 166.0176.$$

The ball travels a vertical distance of about 166 ft. ■

Application: Salary with Raises

EXAMPLE 5

Maya starts working for Titanium Works Company with a salary of $30,000. If she gets a 5% raise at the end of each year, what will Maya's total earnings be after 30 years on the job?

SOLUTION

The salaries form a geometric sequence with $a_1 = 30,000$ and $r = 1.05$.

Year	Raise from Previous Year	Salary
1		30,000
2	$30,000 \cdot 0.05 = 1500$	$30,000 \cdot 1.05^1 = 31,500$
3	$31,500 \cdot 0.05 = 1575$	$30,000 \cdot 1.05^2 = 33,075$
4	$33,075 \cdot 0.05 = 1653.75$	$30,000 \cdot 1.05^3 = 34,728.75$

To find Maya's total earnings, find the sum of the first 30 terms ($n = 30$) of the geometric series.

$$S_n = \frac{a_1\left(1 - r^n\right)}{1 - r}$$

$$S_{30} = \frac{30{,}000\left(1 - 1.05^{30}\right)}{1 - 1.05}$$

$$S_{30} \approx \frac{30{,}000(-3.32194)}{-0.05}$$

$$S_{30} \approx \frac{-99{,}658.27125}{-0.05}$$

$$S_{30} \approx 1{,}993{,}164.425$$

Maya's total earnings for 30 years will be about $1,993,164. ▪

Pronunciation Guide

The tables provide sample words to explain the sounds associated with specific letters and letter combinations used in the respellings in this book. For example, *a* represents the short "a" sound in *cat*, while *ay* represents the long "a" sound in *day*.

Letter combinations are used to approximate certain more complex sounds. For example, in the respelling of *trapezoid*—TRA-puh-zoyd—the letters *uh* represent the vowel sound you hear in *shut* and *other*.

VOWELS	
a	short a: **a**pple, c**a**t
ay	long a: c**a**ne, d**ay**
e, eh	short e: h**e**n, b**e**d
ee	long e: f**ee**d, t**ea**m
i, ih	short i: l**i**p, act**i**ve
iy	long i: tr**y**, m**i**ght
ah	short o: h**o**t, f**a**ther
oh	long o: h**o**me, thr**ow**
uh	short u: sh**u**t, **o**ther
yoo	long u: **u**nion, c**u**te

LETTER COMBINATIONS	
ch	**ch**in, an**ci**ent
sh	**sh**ow, mi**ss**ion
zh	vi**s**ion, a**z**ure
th	**th**in, heal**th**
th	**th**en, hea**th**er
ur	b**ir**d, f**ur**ther, w**or**d
us	b**us**, cr**us**t
or	c**our**t, f**or**mal
ehr	**err**or, c**are**
oo	c**oo**l, tr**ue**, r**u**le
ow	n**ow**, **ou**t
ou	l**oo**k, p**u**ll, w**ou**ld
oy	c**oi**n, t**oy**
aw	s**aw**, m**au**l, f**a**ll
ng	so**ng**, fi**ng**er
air	**A**ristotle, b**a**rrister
ahr	c**ar**t, m**ar**tyr

CONSONANTS	
b	**b**utter, **b**a**b**y
d	**d**og, cra**d**le
f	**f**un, **ph**one
g	**g**rade, an**g**le
h	**h**at, a**h**ead
j	**j**u**dg**e, **g**or**g**e
k	**k**ite, **c**ar, bla**ck**
l	**l**i**l**y, mi**l**e
m	**m**o**m**, ca**m**el
n	**n**ext, ca**n**did
p	**p**rice, co**pp**er
r	**r**ubbe**r**, f**r**ee
s	**s**mall, **c**ircle, ha**ss**le
t	**t**on, po**tt**ery
v	**v**ase, **v**i**v**id
w	**w**all, a**w**ay
y	**y**ellow, ka**y**ak
z	**z**ebra, ha**z**e

Glossary

absolute value function   a function whose rule contains an absolute value expression

accuracy   how close a measure is to its true value

acute angles   angles that measure less than 90°

addition counting principle   if there are m ways of doing one thing and n ways of doing another thing, then there are $m + n$ ways of doing one thing or the other

adjacent angles   angles that share a common side, have the same vertex, and do not share any interior common points

adjacent side of acute angle in a right triangle   the side next to the given angle in a right triangle but is not the hypotenuse

alternate exterior angles   angles outside the two lines that are not the transversal and are on diagonal opposite sides of the transversal

altitude of a pyramid   a perpendicular line segment that joins the vertex to the plane of the base; An altitude may lie inside, on, or outside a pyramid.

altitude of a triangle   a perpendicular segment from a vertex of the triangle to a line containing the base opposite the vertex

amplitude of a sinusoidal function   one-half the distance between the maximum value and the minimum value; the height of a sinusoidal function above the midline

analytic geometry   the study of geometry using the tools of algebra; also called coordinate geometry

angle   a figure formed by two rays, called sides, that share the same endpoint

angle bisector   a line or line segment or ray that divides an angle into two congruent angles

angle of depression of an object   the downward angle that the object makes with the horizontal

angle of elevation of an object   the upward angle that the object makes with the horizontal

annulus   the region between two concentric circles

arc   the set of points on a circle between two points on the circle

arc length   a part of the circumference of a circle; It can be found by writing the part as a fraction over 360° and multiplying by the circumference.

arccosine (arccos) function $y = \arccos x$ if and only if $\cos y = x$ where $-1 \leq x \leq 1$ and $0 \leq y \leq \pi$

arcsine (arcsin) function $y = \arcsin x$ if and only if $\sin y = x$ where $-1 \leq x \leq 1$ and $-\frac{\pi}{2} \leq y \leq \frac{\pi}{2}$

area   the number of square units contained in the interior of a figure

argument   a set of statements, called premises, which are needed to reach a conclusion; Both the premise and the conclusion are considered to be part of the argument.

arithmetic sequence   a sequence in which the difference between consecutive terms is a constant

association   the relationship between two variables

asymptote   a line that a graph of a given function approaches without touching

average rate of change in a quantity   the ratio of the change in a quantity to the change in time

axis of a cylinder   the line connecting the centers of the bases

axis of a double-napped cone   the line about which a generating line revolves to produce a double-napped cone

axis of symmetry   a line drawn through a figure so that one side is a reflection of the image on the opposite side; also called a line of symmetry

base   a number raised to an exponent; For example, in 5^2, 5 is the base.

base edges of pyramid   edges that form the base of a pyramid; A base edge is formed when a lateral face and the base meet.

bell-shaped distribution   a type of symmetric distribution of data sets that is nearly bell-shaped, where the mean and median are nearly equal

bi–   prefix that means "two"

biased sample   a sample that is not representative of its population

binomial   a polynomial with two terms

bivariate data   data that show the relationship between paired variables

boundary line   a line that divides the coordinate plane into two half-planes

bounded closed interval   an interval that includes both endpoints

bounded half-open interval   an interval that includes one and only one endpoint

bounded interval   the set of all real numbers between two numbers, called endpoints; The endpoints may or may not be included.

bounded open interval   an interval that does not include either endpoint

box-and-whisker plot   a diagram that shows the distribution or spread of data with the minimum, the maximum, and the three quartiles of the data; The box extends from Q_1 to Q_3. The median is on the vertical line in the box. The whiskers extend from the first quartile to the minimum and from the third quartile to the maximum.

ceiling function   another name for the least integer function

center of a circle   the point inside a circle that is an equal distance from every point on the circle

center of a polygon   the point inside a polygon that is equidistant from each vertex

center of a sphere   the point inside a sphere from which all points on the surface of the sphere are an equal distance

center of dilation   the point where the lines connecting each point on the pre-image with its corresponding point on the image intersect

central angle of a circle   an angle that has its vertex at the center of a circle and its sides as radii of the circle

central angle of a polygon   an angle formed by line segments drawn from the center to two consecutive vertices

central limit theorem   when several random samples of size n are taken from a population and n is sufficiently large, then the means of the samples will have a distribution that is approximately normal

centroid   the point where all three medians of a triangle intersect

chord   a segment that connects any two points on a circle

circle   the set of all points in a plane that are a fixed distance r (the radius) from a given point (the center)

circle (as a conic section)   a conic section formed when a plane intersects only one nappe, perpendicular to the axis

circle graph   a graph that uses sectors of a circle to display and compare data that can be broken down into separate categories

circumcenter   the point where the perpendicular bisectors on each side of a triangle intersect

circumscribed circle   for a given triangle, the circle that contains each vertex of the triangle; The circumcenter of the triangle is the center of the circumscribed circle.

classes   equal-sized groups used to separate and categorize data; also called intervals

closed half-plane   a half-plane in a nonstrict inequality where the boundary line is a solid line

closed set a set such that, under an operation, the result of the operation on any two elements of the set is also an element of the set

coefficient the nonvariable factor of a term

coefficient of determination the square of the correlation coefficient; written r^2

coincident system a system with infinitely many solutions

collinear points that lie on the same line

common difference the difference between a term and the previous term; the constant difference d in an arithmetic sequence such that $d = a_n - a_{n-1}$

common factor a factor shared by two or more numbers

common logarithm a logarithm with base 10; Common logarithms, such as $\log_{10} x$, are usually written without the base, as $\log x$.

common logarithmic function with base 10 $f(x) = \log x$ when x is a positive real number; The domain is $x > 0$ and the vertical asymptote is $x = 0$.

common ratio of a geometric sequence the ratio of a term to the previous term; the constant r in a geometric sequence such that $r = \dfrac{a_n}{a_{n-1}}$

complementary angles angles whose measures sum to 90°

completing the square the process of transforming an expression of the form $x^2 + bx$ into a perfect square trinomial by adding the term $\left(\dfrac{b}{2}\right)^2$ to it

complex conjugates two complex numbers of the form $a + bi$ and $a - bi$

complex numbers numbers of the form $a + bi$ where a is the real part and b is the imaginary part and a and b are real numbers; denoted $\mathbb{C}$

complex plane the plane on which every complex number can be graphed; The horizontal axis is the real axis and the vertical axis is the imaginary axis.

compound event an event that consists of two or more simple events

compound inequality a pair of inequalities joined by the word *and* or the word *or*; a type of compound statement

computer algebra system (CAS) a computer program that performs algebraic manipulations such as simplifying algebraic expressions and solving equations

conclusion of a conditional statement the part of a conditional statement that includes the words following *then*

conclusion of an argument the end part of an argument that follows the premises

conditional probability the probability of an event given that another event has already happened; The conditional probability that event B occurs after event A has already occurred can be represented as $P(B \mid A)$, which is read as "the probability of B given A."

conditional statement a statement that has two parts; The first part begins with the word *if* and the second part begins with the word *then*.

cone a solid with a circular base, a vertex, and a curved surface

confidence interval an interval estimate that is likely to contain a population parameter being estimated

confidence level the percent chance that a population parameter falls inside the confidence interval

congruent line segments line segments that have equal length

congruent polygons polygons that are the same size and shape

conic section a two-dimensional graph that can be formed by the intersection of a plane with a double-napped cone

conjecture a statement that is thought to be true but is yet to be proven

conjugate binomials two binomials with the same terms but opposite signs; for example, $(a + b)$ and $(a - b)$

conjugate pair a pair of expressions of the form $a + bi$ and $a - bi$

conjunction a compound statement that uses the word *and*

consistent dependent system of equations a system with infinitely many solutions

consistent independent system of equations a system with exactly one solution

consistent system of equations a system with exactly one solution or infinitely many solutions

constant a term that has no variables

constant function a function is constant within an interval if the value of $f(x)$ remains the same

constraint a necessary condition in a problem, often written in the form of an inequality

continuous function a function with a connected graph

continuous random variable a variable whose outcomes are both random and continuous

contraction a dilation for which the absolute value of the scale factor is between 0 and 1

contradiction (equation) an equation that is true for no values of the variable; A contradiction has no solutions, represented by the null set: $\{\ \}$ or $\varnothing$.

contradiction (statement) a statement that is logically at odds with a previous statement that was assumed to be true

converse a conditional statement that switches the hypothesis and the conclusion of the original conditional statement

conversion factor a fraction that is used to convert measures and rates and that has a numerator and denominator of the same quantity written in different units

coordinate the number on a number line that gives the location of a point

coordinate plane a plane in which the coordinates of any point are the point's distances from two intersecting perpendicular lines called axes (the x-axis and y-axis)

coplanar points that lie on the same plane

corollary a proposition that follows directly from a postulate or theorem and can be easily proven

correlation coefficient written as r, describes the strength and direction of the association between two variables; Values for r range from 1 (perfect positive correlation) to 0 (no correlation) to -1 (perfect negative correlation).

corresponding angles of figures the angles that lie in the same position or match up when a transversal intersects two lines

corresponding sides of figures the sides that lie in the same position or match up when a transversal intersects two lines

cosine function $\cos x = a$ is a trigonometric function of x when x is a radian measure of the angle that intercepts the unit circle at (a, b)

cosine of an angle the ratio of the length of the leg that is adjacent to that angle to the length of the hypotenuse; abbreviated cos

coterminal angles angles in standard position that have the same terminal side but have different amounts of rotation; Their angles differ by a multiple of 360°, or 2π radians.

counterexample an example that shows that a statement is false

critical z-scores z-scores for the upper limit and lower limit of the confidence interval

cylinder a solid with two parallel, congruent, circular bases joined by a curved surface

decreasing function a function is decreasing within an interval if the value of $f(x)$ decreases as the value of x increases

deductive reasoning a type of reasoning that uses previously proven or accepted properties to reach conclusions

degenerate conic section a conic section formed when a plane intersects the vertex of the double-napped cone

degree of a monomial the sum of the exponents of the variable factors

degree of a polynomial the degree of the monomial with the greatest degree

density the ratio of the mass of an object to its volume; density = mass ÷ volume

dependent events events in which knowing one outcome has an effect on the probability of the other event(s)

dependent variable the output variable of a function

descriptive statistics statistics that are used to numerically summarize or represent a set of data

deviation in a data set, the difference between a data value x_i and the mean $\overline{x}$ of the data set; $x_i - \overline{x}$

diagonals line segments with endpoints on nonconsecutive vertices

diameter a line segment that connects two points on a circle and contains the center of the circle; also the length of any diameter of a given circle

dilation a transformation that changes the size but not the shape of a figure, either by enlarging it or shrinking it

dimensional analysis the process of multiplying by conversion factors and dividing out common units

directed line segment a segment between two points A and B with a specified direction from A to B or from B to A and a standard distance between the two points

directrix one of two references in the definition of a parabola; The distance from any point on the parabola to the directrix (a line) is equal to the distance from that same point to the parabola's focus (a point).

discrete function a function with a graph that is disconnected

discriminant the radicand $b^2 - 4ac$ in the quadratic formula

disjunction a compound statement that uses the word *or*

dividend the number being divided by the divisor

divisor the number that divides the dividend

domain the set of all allowable inputs for a relation or function

double-napped cone cone formed by the generating line that intersects and revolves around another line called the axis; The axis is stationary and the two lines cannot be perpendicular.

element a member of a set

ellipse a conic section formed when a plane intersects only one nappe, not parallel to the generating line

end behavior how a function behaves when the domain values increase or decrease without bound

endpoints of an interval the minimum and maximum real numbers on a bounded interval

endpoints of an intercepted arc the points where the sides of an inscribed angle meet the circle

equal complex numbers complex numbers with real parts that are equal and with imaginary parts that are equal; $a + bi = c + di$ if and only if $a = c$ and $b = d$

equation a number sentence that indicates that two expressions have the same value

equiangular polygon a polygon with all angles congruent

equilateral triangle a triangle that has three congruent sides

equivalent equations equations with the same solution or solutions

equivalent fractions fractions that have the same value

equivalent inequalities inequalities with the same solutions

even function a function in which $f(-x) = f(x)$; The graph of an even function is symmetric about the y-axis.

event any particular subset of a sample space

expanded form of a sum a representation of a sum as every term added or subtracted to create the sum

expansion   a dilation for which the absolute value of the scale factor is greater than 1

experiment   any process that results in one or more results

explanatory variable   the variable graphed along the horizontal axis in a scatter plot; the independent variable in a statistical analysis

exponent   in a power, a number used to indicate the number of factors of the base that should be multiplied; For example, in 5^2, 2 is the exponent.

exponential equation   an equation with variable expressions as exponents

exponential function   an equation of the form $f(x) = b^x + k$ where $b > 0$ and $b \neq 1$

expression   a number, a variable, or a combination of numbers, variables, and operations

exterior angle of a triangle   an angle formed by one side of the triangle and another side of the triangle when it is extended

extremes   the exterior variables of a proportion

factor   one of two or more quantities that are multiplied together

factor of a number   a number that divides into the given number without a remainder

factorial of a positive integer n   the product of all the positive integers less than or equal to n; written $n!$

family of functions   a group of functions with the same fundamental characteristics

feasible region   the set of all ordered pairs that satisfy the constraints of an optimization problem and are possible solutions to the problem

Fermi estimate   an estimate of a very large number using the Fermi process; This process involves being able to estimate quantities and then round the estimates to the nearest number that is a product of a counting number less than 10 and a power of 10.

finite set   a set that has a number of elements that can be described with a whole number

first quartile, Q_1   the median of the lower subset of a data set

five-number summary   the minimum, the maximum, and the three quartiles of a data set

floor function   another name for the greatest integer function

flowchart proof   a graphical representation of the logical flow of a proof; In a flowchart proof, statements and conclusions are connected with arrows.

focus for a parabola   one of two references in the definition of a parabola; The distance from any point on the parabola to the focus (a point) is equal to the distance from that same point to the parabola's directrix (a line).

FOIL   a mnemonic used for a method to perform the distributive property when multiplying binomials; first-outer-inner-last

frequency distribution   a table or graph that describes the number of times a value or interval of values occurs in a data set

frequency of a sinusoidal function   the number of periods per unit; A function's frequency is the reciprocal of its period.

frequency table   a table that describes the number of times a value or interval of values occurs in a data set

function   a relation in which each member of the domain is assigned to exactly one member of the range

function composition   a mapping in which each element of the range of one function is the domain of another function; If f and g are functions of x, the composition of the f with g is denoted by fg and is defined as $f(g)$. The domain of $f(g(x))$ is the set of the domain values of g with range values that are in the domain of f.

function notation   a function equation written so that the dependent variable is replaced with $f(x)$; for example, $f(x) = 2x + 4$

generating line of a double-napped cone
the line that revolves about another line, called the axis, to produce a double-napped cone

geometric sequence   a sequence in which the ratio between consecutive terms is a constant

geometric series   a series that results from adding the terms of a geometric sequence

graph of an inequality   a display of all possible solutions of the inequality

greatest integer function   a function that assigns the greatest integer less than or equal to each real number in an interval; denoted by $f(x) = \lfloor x \rfloor$ or $f(x) = \text{int}(x)$; also called the floor function

half-life   the length of time it takes for one-half of a radioactive substance to decay

half-plane   a plane that has been divided in half by a boundary line

height   the length of the altitude

histogram   a bar graph that displays the frequency of data values that occur within certain intervals; The height of each bar gives the frequency in the respective interval.

horizontal asymptote   the line $y = b$ for the graph of the function f if $f(x)$ approaches b as x approaches ∞ or $-\infty$

horizontal line test   a test to determine whether a function f is invertible; If a horizontal line intersects a function more than once, then the function is not invertible. If every horizontal line intersects a function only once, then the function is invertible.

hyperbola   a conic section formed when a plane intersects both nappes

hypotenuse   the side opposite the right angle of a right triangle

hypothesis   the part of a conditional statement that includes the words following *if*

identity   an equation that is true for all values of the variable; It has infinitely many solutions and is often represented as $\{x \mid x \in \mathbb{R}\}$.

image   a figure after transformation

imaginary axis   the vertical axis of a complex plane along which the imaginary part of a complex number is graphed

imaginary number   any number that can be written in the form ai where a is any real number and i is the imaginary unit

imaginary unit i where $i^2 = -1$ and $i = \sqrt{-1}$

improper fraction   a fraction in which the numerator is greater than or equal to the denominator

incenter of a triangle   the point where the angle bisectors drawn through each vertex intersect

included angle of a triangle   an angle formed by two sides of a triangle

included side of a triangle   a side of a triangle that lies between two specific angles

inconsistent system of equations   a system with no solutions

increasing function   a function is increasing within an interval if the value of $f(x)$ increases as the value of x increases

independent events   two events in which knowing one outcome has no effect on the probability of the other event

independent variable   the input variable of a function

index in sigma notation   the variable i in sigma notation $\sum\limits_{i=0}^{3} a_i$; the variable that takes on all integer values from the lower limit to the upper limit of the summation

index of a radical n in a radical expression $\sqrt[n]{b}$; The index is always greater than 1.

inductive reasoning   a type of reasoning that starts with observation and moves from a specific observation to a general conclusion

inequality   a statement formed by placing one of the inequality symbols $<, >, \leq, \geq,$ or $\neq$ between two expressions

inferential statistics   statistics used to draw conclusions or make predictions by taking the information gained from the sample and generalizing it to the population it came from

infinite set   a set with a boundless number of elements

initial side of angle   the ray from which the rotation of an angle starts

inscribed angle   an angle that has its vertex on a circle and its sides as chords of the circle

inscribed circle   for a given triangle, a circle in the interior of the triangle that touches each side of the triangle at a single point; The incenter is the center of the inscribed circle.

integers   all the natural numbers, their opposites, and zero; denoted $\mathbb{Z} = \{\ldots, -2, -1, 0, 1, 2, \ldots\}$

intercepted arc   the arc opposite an inscribed angle

interior angles of a triangle   the three angles inside the triangle

interquartile range (IQR)   the difference between the third and first quartiles of a data set; $\text{IQR} = Q_3 - Q_1$

interval estimate   a range of values that contains the point estimate and is likely to contain the population parameter

inverse functions   two functions f and g that "undo" each other; If you start with a value x, apply f, and then apply g, the result is the original value x: $(f \circ g)(x) = x$ and $(g \circ f)(x) = x$. The inverse of a function f is denoted by f^{-1} ("f inverse"). For every pair of inverse functions, if $f^{-1} = g$, then $g^{-1} = f$.

inverse of a function   a relationship that interchanges the members of the ordered pairs of the original function; denoted by f^{-1}; The domain of the inverse function is the range of the original function. The range of the inverse function is the domain of the original function.

inverse of a relation   a relationship that switches the x- and y-values of the ordered pairs of the original relation; The domain of the inverse relation is the range of the original relation. The range of the inverse relation is the domain of the original relation. The graph of the inverse of a relation is its reflection over the line $y = x$.

inverse tangent   the angle that has a given value as its tangent ratio; abbreviated $\tan^{-1}$

invertible function   a function f whose inverse is also a function

irrational number   a real number that cannot be written in the form $\frac{a}{b}$ for any integers a and b

isometric transformation   any transformation that results in an image that is congruent to the pre-image; also called an isometry

isosceles triangle   a triangle that has at least two congruent sides

iterative rule   a rule that can be used to find the nth term of a sequence without calculating previous terms of the sequence

lateral edges of a pyramid   the edges of a pyramid that do not form the base; A lateral edge is formed when two lateral faces meet.

lateral side of an angle   the ray from which the rotation of an angle starts

lateral surface   the curved surface of a cylinder

law of detachment   an argument that has two true premises and a valid conclusion; The premises and conclusion have the following form:

> premise − If a, then b.
> premise − a is true.
> conclusion − Therefore, b is true.

law of syllogism   a logical argument that always contains two premises and a conclusion; The premises and conclusion have the following form:

> premise − If a, then b.
> premise − If b, then c.
> conclusion − Therefore, if a, then c.

leading coefficient of a polynomial in simplified form   the coefficient of the first term

leaf   the digits on the right side of a stem-and-leaf plot

least common denominator (LCD)   the least common multiple of two or more denominators

least integer function   a function that assigns the least integer greater than or equal to each real number in an interval; denoted by $f(x) = \lceil x \rceil$; also called the ceiling function

least squares regression line   the line that makes the sum of the squares of the vertical distances from each data point to the line as small as possible

length of a line segment   the distance between the endpoints of a line segment

like radicals   two or more square root expressions that have the same radicand

like terms   terms that contain the same variable factors taken to the same powers

line   a collection of points arranged in a straight path

line of best fit   a least squares regression equation

line of symmetry   a line over which you can flip a given figure, leaving the figure unchanged; A line of symmetry divides a figure into two congruent (mirror-image) halves.

line segment   a part of a line that consists of any two points on the line and all the points in between those two points

line symmetry   a characteristic of a figure in which there is at least one line such that when the figure is folded over the line, the two halves are mirror images that match up perfectly; also called reflection symmetry

linear equation   an equation whose graph in a coordinate plane is a line

linear inequality   an inequality that has terms with degree zero or one and an inequality symbol to relate two variables

linear pair of angles   two angles that have a common side and the same vertex with their other sides point in opposite directions

linear programming   the process of maximizing or minimizing a linear function subject to a set of conditions, called constraints, that are linear inequalities

logarithm   the exponent to which a base would have to be raised to result in a given value; The logarithm of a with base b, $\log_b a$, where $b > 0$, $b \neq 1$, and $a > 0$, is defined as $\log_b a = x$ if and only if $b^x = a$.

logistic growth function   a function of the form $f(x) = \dfrac{C}{1 + Ae^{-Bx}}$ where A, B, and C are all positive constants

lower limit   in sigma notation, the starting value for the index n; In $\sum\limits_{n=1}^{n} a_n$, the lower limit is 1.

major arcs   arcs larger than a semicircle

margin of error   the greatest likely difference between the point estimate and the parameter

marginal frequency   the ratio of the total for a particular column or row to the overall total in a two-way table

mean   the statistical average of a data set

means of a proportion   the middle variables of a proportion

median of a data set   the middle value when the values are ordered; If the data set has an even number of values, the median is the mean of the two middle values.

median of a triangle   a segment from the vertex of a triangle to the midpoint of its opposite side

midline of a sinusoidal function   the horizontal line that is halfway between the maximum and the minimum; The equation of the midline of a sinusoidal function is $y = \dfrac{\text{maximum} + \text{minimum}}{2}$.

midpoint   a point that divides a line segment into two congruent parts

minor arcs   arcs smaller than a semicircle

mixed number   a number consisting of both a whole number and a fraction or the opposite of such a number

mode   the value that occurs most frequently

model parameter   a value that is held constant for a specific model

model variable   a variable that takes on different values for a particular model

modified box-and-whisker plot a box-and-whisker plot in which outliers are shown with dots and the whiskers extend to the least and greatest values in the data set that are not outliers

monomial a number, a variable, or the product of a number and one or more variables

multiplication counting principle if a task can be broken into two stages and there are m ways of doing the first stage and n ways of doing the second stage, then there are $m \cdot n$ ways of doing one thing and the other

multiplicity for a root a of $p(x) = 0$, the number of times the factor $x - a$ occurs in the factorization of any polynomial $p(x)$

nappe one of two equal pieces of a cone where the cone is divided at the vertex by a plane perpendicular to the axis

natural logarithm a logarithm with a base e; Natural logarithms, such as $\log_e x$, are often written using the notation $\ln x$.

natural logarithmic function with base e $g(x) = \ln x$ where x is a positive real number; The domain is $x > 0$, and the vertical asymptote is $x = 0$.

natural numbers the set of numbers $\mathbb{N} = \{1, 2, 3, \ldots\}$; also called counting numbers or positive integers

nearest integer function a function that assigns the nearest integer to each real number in an interval; denoted by $\text{nint}(x)$; also called the round function

negative association when comparing two data sets, as the data from one set increase, the data from the second set decrease; In a scatter plot, the data points decrease from left to right.

noncollinear points that do not lie on the same line

nonstrict inequality an inequality that uses $\leq$ or $\geq$

normal distribution a bell-shaped distribution, centered on the mean

nth root of b a when $a^n = b$, a and b are both real numbers, and n is a positive integer

number line a line with equally spaced intervals that are labeled with numbers

numerical expression an expression that consists of numbers, operations, and sometimes grouping symbols

objective function a linear function that models a quantity that is to be optimized in a linear programming problem

oblique cone a cone with an axis that is not an altitude

oblique cylinder a cylinder with an axis that is not an altitude

obtuse angles angles that measure greater than 90° and less than 180°

odd function a function in which $f(-x) = -f(x)$; The graph of an odd function is symmetric about the origin.

one-to-one function a function in which every element of the domain corresponds to exactly one element on the range

open half-plane a half plane in a strict inequality where the boundary line is dashed

open sentence an equation or inequality containing one or more variables

opposite side of an acute angle in a right triangle the side across from the given angle

ordered pair a pair of numbers on a coordinate plane, in which the first number is the x-coordinate the second is the y-coordinate

origin the intersection of the x- and y-axes

outcomes the results of an experiment

outlier a value far away from most other values in a data set

parabola a symmetric curve that is the graph of a quadratic function

parabola (conic section) a conic section formed when a plane intersects only one nappe, parallel to the generating line

parabola (locus of points) the set of all points in a plane that are equidistant from a fixed line (the directrix) and a fixed point (the focus)

paragraph proof a proof in the form of a paragraph

parallel lines coplanar lines that never intersect

parallelogram a quadrilateral with two pairs of parallel sides

parameter a measurement that describes a population

parent function the most basic function in a family of functions

partition a directed line segment to divide a directed line segment into segments based on a given ratio

percentile rank the percentage of data that falls below a particular value

perfect square a rational number with a square root that is also rational

perimeter the distance around a figure

period the length of each interval in a periodic function

period of a sinusoidal graph the interval over which a sinusoidal graph repeats itself

periodic function a function that repeats itself in regular intervals

perpendicular bisector a line, line segment, or ray that passes through the midpoint of a line segment and forms a right angle with the segment

perpendicular lines lines that meet at right angles

piecewise function a function defined using different rules for different intervals of the domain

plane a flat surface that has infinite length and width but no thickness

point references a location in space; It has no length, width, or depth.

point estimates statistics, such as $\hat{p}$ and $\hat{x}$, that are used to estimate population parameters

point of tangency a point where a circle and one of its tangents intersect

point-slope form of a linear equation an equation of the form $y - y_1 = m(x - x_1)$ where m is the slope and (x_1, y_1) is a point on the corresponding line

polygon a closed figure in a plane formed by three or more line segments, such that each line segment intersects exactly two other line segments at their endpoints only

polynomial a monomial or the sum of monomials

polynomial in x a polynomial of the form $a_n x^n + a_{n-1} x^{n-1} + \ldots + a_2 x^2 + a_1 x + a_0$ where the exponents are all whole numbers, the coefficients are all real numbers, and $a_n \neq 0$

population an entire set of members that you want to know something about

positive association when comparing two data sets, if the data from one set increase, the data from the second set also increase; In a scatter plot, data points increase from left to right.

postulates mathematical statements that are accepted as true without proof

power a number that is, or could be, represented by a base with an exponent

power function any function that can be written in the form $f(x) = ax^2 + b$ when n is a positive integer, a is any nonzero real number, and b is any real number

practical domain and range of a function the sets of all realistic inputs and outputs for a particular situation

pre-image the original figure before a transformation

premises statements that are presumed to be true in the course of a logical argument

prime polynomial a polynomial that cannot be factored

principal of a loan the amount of money actually borrowed

principal square root another name for a positive square root; indicated by the radical sign $\sqrt{}$

probability distribution table a frequency table where each frequency is replaced by the probability of the outcome

probability of an event a measure of the likelihood that an event will occur; Probability is always a number between 0 and 1 (inclusive) that can be written as a fraction, a decimal, or a percent.

product of the functions f and g
$(fg)(x) = f(x) \cdot g(x)$

proof a clear, logical structure of reasoning that begins from accepted ideas and proceeds through logic to reach a conclusion

proper fraction a fraction in which the numerator is less than the denominator

proportion an equation that states that two ratios are equal; often written as $a : b = c : d$ or $\frac{a}{b} = \frac{c}{d}$

pyramid a polyhedron with a polygonal base and lateral faces; The faces are triangles that meet at a common vertex.

Pythagorean identity for any angle θ, $\sin^2 \theta + \cos^2 \theta = 1$

quadrantal angles angles in standard position that have their terminal sides along the horizontal or vertical axis

quadrants the sections of a coordinate plane; The first quadrant is between the positive horizontal axis and the positive vertical axis. The second, third, and fourth quadrants are located counterclockwise from the first quadrant, respectively.

quadratic formula a formula for finding the solutions of a quadratic equation in the form
$ax^2 + bx + c = 0$ where $a \neq 0$; $x = \dfrac{-b \pm \sqrt{b^2 - 4ac}}{2a}$

quadratic function a second-degree polynomial function

quadrilateral a four-sided polygon

quotient the number of times the divisor goes into the dividend evenly

quotient of the functions f and g $\dfrac{f}{g}(x) = \dfrac{f(x)}{g(x)}$, $g(x) \neq 0$

radian measure of a central angle of a circle the quotient of the angle's arc length and the circle's radius

radian measure of an angle the length of the arc on a unit circle subtended (intercepted) by the angle

radical equation an equation that contains at least one radical expression with a variable in the radicand

radical expression an expression that contains a radical sign $\sqrt{}$

radical function a function of the form $f(x) = a\sqrt{x - h} + k$ where n is an integer greater than 1

radicand the expression under a radical sign; For example, in the expression $\sqrt[n]{b}$, b is the radicand.

radius a line segment that connects the center of a circle to a point on the circle; also the length of all radii of a given circle

range of a data set the difference between its greatest value (maximum) and its least value (minimum)

range of a relation the set of possible outputs

rational expression a ratio with a numerator and a denominator that are polynomials and with a denominator that is nonzero

rational function any function that can be written as the quotient of two polynomials

rational number any number that can be expressed as a ratio $\frac{a}{b}$, where a and b are integers and $b \neq 0$; denoted $\mathbb{Q}$

raw score an original data value

ray part of a line that starts at an endpoint and extends infinitely in one direction

real axis the horizontal axis of a complex plane along which the real part of a complex number is graphed

real numbers the set of numbers that can be written as decimals; the combined set of the rational and irrational numbers; denoted $\mathbb{R}$

reciprocal power function a function that has the power of x in the denominator of a rational function; The functions $f(x) = \frac{1}{x}$, $g(x) = \frac{1}{x^2}$, and $h(x) = \frac{1}{x^3}$ are reciprocal power functions.

rectangle a parallelogram with four right angles

recursive rule a rule for generating terms of a sequence that depends on one or more previous terms of the sequence

reference angle for an acute angle x, the positive acute angle made by the terminal side of x and the horizontal axis

reflection an isometric transformation that flips a figure across a line or line segment, creating a mirror image of the figure

reflection symmetry when a figure that has at least one axis of symmetry; The figure can be folded along the axis of symmetry so that both halves match up.

regression line a line drawn through the points of a scatter plot to summarize the straight line pattern that the points fit

regular hexagon a six-sided polygon with congruent sides and congruent angles

regular polygon a polygon that is both equiangular and equilateral

regular pyramid a pyramid whose base is a regular polygon and whose lateral faces are congruent isosceles triangles

relation a mapping from one set, called the domain, to another set, called the range

relative frequency the ratio of the value of a subtotal to the value of the total

relative maximum point of a function a point that has a greater function value than all the points on the function that are close to it

relative minimum point a point that has a value that is less than all the points on the function that are close to it

remainder the amount left over after evenly dividing a dividend by a divisor

remote interior angles the angles that are inside the triangle and are not adjacent to a given exterior angle

repeating decimal a decimal that does not end but shows a repeating of digits (not made up of all zeros) that goes on forever after the decimal point

residual the difference between an observed value and the predicted value from a model; residual (e) = observed (y) − predicted $(\hat{y})$; the vertical distance between a point on the scatter plot and the point on the linear model directly above or below the point

residual plot a graph that shows the residual for each value of the explanatory variable

response variable the variable graphed along the vertical axis in a scatter plot; the independent variable(s) in a statistical analysis

rhombus a parallelogram with four congruent sides

right angle an angle that measures exactly 90°

right cone a cone with an axis that is also an altitude

right cylinder a cylinder with an axis that is also an altitude

rigid motion motion that relocates a figure while preserving its shape and size

roots of a polynomial the solutions to a polynomial equation in which one side of the equation is a factored polynomial and the other side of the equation is equal to zero

rotation an isometric transformation that turns a figure a certain number of degrees, called the angle of rotation, around a central point, called the center of rotation

rotation symmetry when a figure can be rotated around its center less than one full turn so that the rotated figure looks exactly like the original figure

round function another name for the nearest integer function

same-side interior angles angles in between the two lines that are not the transversal and are on the same side of the transversal

sample a subset of a population

sample space the set of all possible outcomes of an experiment

scale factor *t* of a dilation the ratio of the length of any side of on an image to the length of its corresponding side on the pre-image

scalene triangle a triangle that has no congruent sides

scatter plot a graph that displays a set of bivariate data

secant a line that intersects a circle in two points

second quartile, Q$_2$ the median of the entire data set that separates the ordered data set into a lower subset and an upper subset

sector a region whose boundaries are two radii and part of the circle

segment bisector a line, line segment, or ray that passes through the midpoint of a line segment

semicircle an arc with endpoints that are also the endpoints of a diameter

sequence a function whose domain is the set of natural numbers

series the sum of consecutive terms of a sequence

set a collection of objects

sides the line segments that form a polygon

sigma notation a way to write a sum as sum as $\sum_{i=1}^{n} a_i = a_1 + a_2 + a_3 + \ldots + a_n$; $\sum_{i=1}^{n} a_i$, read as "the sum from 1 to *n* of a_i," where *i* is the index, *n* is the upper limit, and 1 is the lower limit; The right side of the equation is the expanded form of the sum.

similar figures figures that are the same shape but are not necessarily the same size; The symbol ∼ means "is similar to."

similar solids solids that have the same shape and all the corresponding dimensions are proportional

similar triangles two triangles with congruent corresponding angles and proportional corresponding side lengths

simple event a single outcome of an experiment; a single element of a sample space

simplified form of a polynomial a polynomial that has no like terms, every term is in simplest form, and its terms are in order of decreasing degree with respect to a variable

simplified radical form of a square root expression a square root expression in which the radicand is not a fraction, there are no radicals in the denominator, and no factor is a perfect square other than 1

sine of an angle the ratio of the length of the leg opposite the angle to the length of the hypotenuse; abbreviated sin

sine function $\sin x = b$ is a trigonometric function of *x* when *x* is a radian measure of the angle that intercepts the unit circle at (a, b)

sinusoidal function a function that has the equation $f(x) = A \sin Bx + C$ or $f(x) = A \cos Bx + C$ where $A \neq 0$ and $B \neq 0$

skewed distribution one side has lower frequencies than the other side

slope a number that describes the steepness of a line; the ratio of the vertical change, or rise, to the horizontal change, or run, between any two points on a line

slope of a line the ratio of the vertical change, or rise, to the horizontal change, or run, between any two points on the line

slope-intercept form of a linear equation an equation of the form $y = mx + b$ where *m* is the slope and *b* is the *y*-intercept of the corresponding line

solution a value for the variable that makes the equation or open sentence a true statement

solve to find all the solutions for an equation

sphere the set of all points in space that are a given distance from a point called the center

square a parallelogram with four congruent sides and four right angles

square root a factor of a number that, when multiplied by itself, results in the number

standard deviation a measure of spread of a data set; the standard deviation $s = \sqrt{\dfrac{\Sigma(x - \overline{x})^2}{n - 1}}$ where x is a data value, $\overline{x}$ is the mean of the data set, and n is the number of data values in the set

standard form of a linear equation an equation of the form $Ax + By = C$ where A, B, and C are integers, and A and B are both nonzero

standard form of a polynomial the form of a polynomial in which every term is simplified and its terms are listed by decreasing degree

standard normal curve a probability distribution where the mean is 0, the standard deviation is 1, and the total area under the curve is 1

standard position of an angle an angle on coordinate plane that has its vertex is at the origin and its initial side along the positive horizontal axis

statement a sentence that is either true or false

statistic a measurement that describes a sample

stem leftmost digit of data values in a stem-and-leaf plot

stem-and-leaf plot a data display that lists the last digits (leaves) of the data values to the right of the earlier digits (stems)

step function a function defined using a rule that produces a constant value for each designated interval of the domain

straight angles angles that measure exactly 180°; A straight angle is a line.

strength of association how closely the data points on a scatter plot fit a straight line pattern

strict inequality inequality that uses $<$ or $>$

substitute to replace

sum of the functions f and g $(f + g)(x) = f(x) + g(x)$

supplementary angles angles with measures that sum to 180°

system of equations a group of two or more equations in the same variables

system of linear equations two or more linear equations with the same variables

system of linear inequalities a set of two or more linear inequalities using the same variables

tangent function $\tan x = \dfrac{\sin x}{\cos x}$; a trigonometric function of x in which x is the radian measure of the angle that intercepts the unit circle at (a, b); The value of x may not result in the cosine being zero.

tangent of an angle the ratio of the length of the leg opposite the angle to the length of the leg adjacent to the angle; abbreviated tan

tangent to a circle a line in the plane of the circle that intersects the circle in exactly one point

terminal side of angle the ray at which the rotation of an angle stops

terms the parts of an expression that are added or subtracted

terms of a sequence the values of a function whose domain is the set of natural numbers; the range of a sequence

theorem a mathematical statement that has been proven to be true

theoretical domain and range of a function the sets of all allowable inputs and outputs

third quartile, Q_3 the median of the upper subset

transformation a one-to-one mapping between two sets of points

translate (a figure) the sliding of a figure in a straight path without rotating or reflecting it

translation a transformation that slides a figure in a straight path without rotation or reflection

transversal a line that intersects two or more lines in a plane

trapezoid a quadrilateral with exactly one pair of parallel sides

triangle a three-sided polygon

trigonometric functions of angle θ $\sin \theta = \dfrac{b}{r}$, $\cos \theta = \dfrac{a}{r}$, $\tan \theta = \dfrac{b}{a}$ $(a \neq 0)$ where (a, b) is a point other than the origin on the terminal side of an angle θ in standard position, and r is the distance $\sqrt{a^2 + b^2}$ from the point to the origin

trigonometric identity   an equation containing a trigonometric ratio that is true for all values of the variable

trigonometric ratio   the ratio of two sides of a right triangle

trinomial   a polynomial with three terms

two-column proof   a proof shown in two columns; The first column sows the steps and the second column shows the justification for each step.

two-way table   a table that shows data from one sample group as it relates to two different categories

unbounded interval   the set of all real numbers on one side of a number, called an endpoint; The endpoint may or may not be included.

uniform distribution   a type of symmetric distribution of data sets where all intervals have the same frequency

uniform probability distribution   the probability distribution resulting when all values of a random variable X are equally likely to occur

unit circle   circle with a radius of one unit

upper limit   in sigma notation $\sum\limits_{i=1}^{n} a_i$, the variable n, which indicates the maximum value for the index i

valid argument   an argument in which, if the premises are all true, then the conclusion must also be true

variable   a symbol that represents a value

variable expression   a combination of variables, numbers, and operations

variance   a measure of variability of a set relative to its mean; For a data set with values $x_1, x_2, \ldots, x_n$, the variance is $s^2 = \dfrac{\sum\limits_{i=1}^{n}(x_i - \overline{x})^2}{n-1}$ where each difference $x_i - \overline{x}$ is called a deviation and s is called the standard deviation

vertex form of a quadratic function $f(x) = a(x - h)^2 + k$ where $a \neq 0$

vertex of a double-napped cone   the point where the axis and the generating line of a double-napped cone intersect

vertex of a parabola   the highest or lowest point on a parabola that opens down or up

vertex of a polygon   a point where the sides of a polygon meet

vertex of a pyramid   the common vertex where the triangular faces of a pyramid meet

vertex of an angle   the common endpoint of two rays that form an angle

vertex points   corner points of the feasible region

vertical angles   nonadjacent angles formed by intersecting lines; Vertical angles are congruent.

vertical asymptote   the line $x = a$ of the graph of the function f if $f(x)$ approaches ∞ or $-\infty$ as x approaches a, either from the left or the right

vertical line test   a test used to determine whether a graphed relation is a function; If the graph is a function, then there is no vertical line that passes through the graph more than once.

volume   the measure of the space inside (or the space occupied by) a three-dimensional figure; expressed in cubed units

volume of rectangular prism   the product of the rectangular prism's length, width, and height

whole number   a number in the set $\{0, 1, 2, 3, \ldots\}$

x-coordinate   the first number in an ordered pair

x-intercept   the x-coordinate of a point where a graph intersects the x-axis

y-coordinate   the second number in an ordered pair

y-intercept   the y-coordinate of a point where a graph intersects the y-axis

zeros of a polynomial function $f(x)$ the roots (solutions) of the equation $f(x) = 0$

z-score   the number of standard deviations that a data value is from the mean

Symbols

	such that	a_n	nth element of a sequence
$\in$	is an element of	π	pi
$\varnothing$ or $\{\ \}$	null or empty set	σ	standard deviation of a population
$\subset$	is a proper subset of	S_n	the sum of the first n terms of a series
$\subseteq$	is a subset of	$\displaystyle\sum_{i=1}^{n} a_i$	the sum from 1 to n of a_i
$\cap$	intersection	$n!$	factorial of a nonnegative integer n
$\cup$	union	$\overline{x}$	sample mean
$-a$	the opposite of a	$\approx$	is approximately equal to
∞	infinity	$=$	is equal to
$\sqrt{}$	radical sign; the principal square root	$\neq$	is not equal to
$\sqrt[n]{x}$	nth root of x	$<$	is less than
i	imaginary unit	$>$	is greater than
$\mathbb{N}$	the set of natural numbers	$\leq$	is less than or equal to
$\mathbb{Z}$	the set of integers	$\geq$	is greater than or equal to
$\mathbb{Q}$	the set of rational numbers	$f(x)$	f is a function of x
$\mathbb{R}$	the set of real numbers	$\lfloor x \rfloor$	greatest integer function; floor function
$\mathbb{I}$	the set of irrational numbers		
$\mathbb{W}$	the set of whole numbers	$\lceil x \rceil$	least integer function; ceiling function
$\mathbb{C}$	the set of complex numbers	$\text{nint}(x)$	nearest integer function; round function
e	base of the natural logarithm		
$\ln x$	logarithm with base e; natural logarithm	$f \circ g$	the composition of function f with function g
$\log x$	logarithm with base 10	f^{-1}	inverse of a function f
$\log_b a$	log base b of a	$|x|$	absolute value of x
		$\{\ldots\}$	description or list of all elements in a set; roster notation

$\{x \mid \text{condition}\}$	the set of all x that satisfy the given condition; set-builder notation	$\perp$	is perpendicular to
$P(A)$	the probability of event A	$\therefore$	therefore
$P(A \mid B)$	the conditional probability of A given B	$\angle$	angle
ϕ	phi; the golden ratio	$\triangle$	triangle
$'$	prime	$\overleftrightarrow{AB}$	line AB
$\circ$	degree	$\overline{AB}$	line segment AB
$\ldots$	continues	$\overrightarrow{AB}$	ray AB
$\sim$	is similar to	$m\angle CAB$	measure of angle CAB
$\cong$	is congruent to	$\overset{\frown}{AB}$	arc AB
$\parallel$	is parallel to	$m\overset{\frown}{AB}$	measure of arc AB

Properties

Real Number Properties

Let a, b, and c be any real numbers.

Addition Property of Equality	If $a = b$, then $a + c = b + c$ and $c + a = c + b$.
Addition Property: Addends with Like Signs	For all $a > 0$ and $b > 0$, $a + b = \|a\| + \|b\|$. For all $a < 0$ and $b < 0$, $a + b = -\|a\| + \|b\|$.
Addition Property: Addends with Unlike Signs	For all $a > 0$ and $b < 0$, $\quad$ If $\|a\| > \|b\|$, then $a + b = \|a\| - \|b\|$. $\quad$ If $\|a\| < \|b\|$, then $a + b = -\|b\| - \|a\|$.
Subtraction Property of Equality	If $a = b$, then $a - c = b - c$.
Substitution Property of Equality	If $a = b$, then a may be replaced with b in any expression or equation.
Multiplication Property of Equality	If $a = b$, then $c \bullet a = c \bullet b$ and $a \bullet c = b \bullet c$.
Division Property of Equality	If $a = b$ and $c \neq 0$, then $\dfrac{a}{c} = \dfrac{b}{c}$.
Distributive Property	$a(b + c) = ab + ac$

	Addition	Multiplication
Commutative Properties	$a + b = b + a$	$a \bullet b = b \bullet a$
Associative Properties	$(a + b) + c = a + (b + c)$	$(a \bullet b) \bullet c = a \bullet (b \bullet c)$
Inverse Properties	$a + (-a) = 0$ and $(-a) + a = 0$	$a \bullet \dfrac{1}{a} = 1$ and $\dfrac{1}{a} \bullet a = 1$, $a \neq 0$
Identity Properties	$a + 0 = a$ and $0 + a = a$	$a \bullet 1 = a$ and $1 \bullet a = a$

Absolute Value Equations

If $\|x\| = a$ for some positive number a, then $x = a$ or $x = -a$.

Properties of Exponents

Let a and b be nonzero real numbers. Let m and n be integers.

If n is a positive integer, then $a^n = a \cdot a \cdot a \cdot \ldots \cdot a$ (n factors).

Zero Exponent Property	$a^0 = 1, a \neq 0$
Negative Exponent Property	$a^{-m} = \dfrac{1}{a^m}, a \neq 0$
Product of Powers Property	$a^m \cdot a^n = a^{m+n}$

Square Root Properties

For nonnegative values of m, n, and p, if $m < n < p$, then $\sqrt{m} < \sqrt{n} < \sqrt{p}$.

Product Property	For real numbers a and b, $\sqrt{ab} = \sqrt{a} \cdot \sqrt{b}$ and $\sqrt{a} \cdot \sqrt{b} - \sqrt{ab}$.
Quotient Property	For real numbers a and b with $b \neq 0$, $\sqrt{\dfrac{a}{b}} = \dfrac{\sqrt{a}}{\sqrt{b}}$.

Reciprocal Properties

Reciprocal Property of Multiplication	For any nonzero real number a, $a \cdot \dfrac{1}{a} = 1$.

For all nonzero real numbers a and b, the reciprocal of $\dfrac{a}{b}$ is $\dfrac{b}{a}$.

For any nonzero real number a, $\dfrac{1}{-a} = \dfrac{-1}{a} = -\dfrac{1}{a}$.

For all nonzero real numbers a and b, $\dfrac{1}{ab} = \dfrac{1}{a} \cdot \dfrac{1}{b}$.

Division Properties

For any real number a and nonzero real number b, $a \div b = a \cdot \dfrac{1}{b}$.

For all real numbers a and b and nonzero real number c, $a + \dfrac{b}{c} = \dfrac{a}{c} + \dfrac{b}{c}$.

For all $a > 0$ and $b > 0$, $a \div b > 0$.

For all $a < 0$ and $b < 0$, $a \div b > 0$.

For all $a < 0$ and $b > 0$, $a \div b < 0$.

Properties of Order

Comparison Property of Order	If $a > b$, then $b < a$. If $a < b$, then $b > a$.
Transitive Property of Order	If $a > b$ and $b > c$, then $a > c$. If $a < b$ and $b < c$, then $a < c$.
Addition Property of Order	If $a > b$, then $a + c > b + c$. If $a < b$, then $a + c < b + c$.
Subtraction Property of Order	If $a > b$, then $a - c > b - c$. If $a < b$, then $a - c < b - c$.
Multiplication Property of Order, Positive Multiplier	If $a > b$ and $c > 0$, then $ca > cb$ and $ac > bc$. If $a < b$ and $c > 0$, then $ca < cb$ and $ac < bc$.
Multiplication Property of Order, Negative Multiplier	If $a > b$ and $c < 0$, then $ca < cb$ and $ac < bc$. If $a < b$ and $c < 0$, then $ca > cb$ and $ac > bc$.
Division Property of Order, Positive Multiplier	If $a > b$ and $c > 0$, then $\frac{a}{c} > \frac{b}{c}$. If $a < b$ and $c > 0$, then $\frac{a}{c} < \frac{b}{c}$.
Division Property of Order, Negative Multiplier	If $a > b$ and $c < 0$, then $\frac{a}{c} < \frac{b}{c}$. If $a < b$ and $c < 0$, then $\frac{a}{c} > \frac{b}{c}$.

Comparison Property of Rational Numbers

For nonzero integers a and c and positive integers b and d,

$\frac{a}{b} > \frac{c}{d}$ if, and only if, $ad > bc$.

$\frac{a}{b} < \frac{c}{d}$ if, and only if, $ad < bc$.

Properties of Proportions

Let a, b, c, and d be real numbers.

Means-Extremes Product Property	$\frac{a}{b} = \frac{c}{d}$ if, and only if, $ad = bc$, given that b and d are not 0.
Reciprocal Property	If $\frac{a}{b} = \frac{c}{d}$, then $\frac{b}{a} = \frac{d}{c}$, given that a, b, c, and d are all nonzero.

Formulary

Real, Imaginary, and Complex Numbers

RATIONAL EXPONENTS

$$x^{\frac{a}{b}} = \sqrt[b]{x^a}$$

POWERS OF i

$$i = \sqrt{-1}$$
$$i^2 = -1$$
$$i^3 = -i$$
$$i^4 = 1$$

ADDING COMPLEX NUMBERS

For any real a, b, c, and d, if $w = a + bi$ and $z = c + di$, then $w + z = (a + c) + (b + d)i$.

Factoring Patterns

PERFECT SQUARE TRINOMIAL PATTERNS

$$a^2 + 2ab + b^2 = (a + b)^2$$

DIFFERENCE OF SQUARES PATTERNS

$$a^2 - b^2 = (a + b)(a - b)$$

$$a^3 + b^3 = (a + b)\left(a^2 - ab + b^2\right)$$

DIFFERENCE OF CUBES

$$a^3 - b^3 = (a - b)\left(a^2 + ab + b^2\right)$$

Plane Geometry

CIRCLE

circumference $\quad C = \pi d = 2\pi r$

area $\quad A = \pi r^2$

length of an arc with degree measure m $\quad L = \left(\frac{m}{360°}\right) 2\pi r$

equation with center (h, k) on a coordinate plane $\quad (x - h)^2 + (y - k)^2 = r^2$

PARALLOGRAM

area $\quad A = bh$

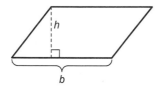

REGULAR POLYGON WITH n SIDES

sum of interior angles $\quad I = (n - 2)180°$

interior angle of regular polygon $\quad i = \dfrac{(n - 2)180°}{n}$

perimeter of regular polygon $\quad P = ns$

area of regular polygon $\quad A = \frac{1}{2}aP$

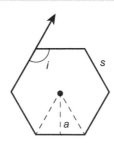

RECTANGLE

area $A = lw$

perimeter $P = 2l + 2w$

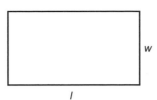

TRAPEZOID

length of midsegment $\text{length} = \dfrac{b_1 + b_2}{2}$

area $A = \dfrac{1}{2}h(b_1 + b_2)$

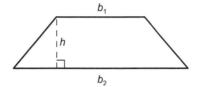

TRIANGLE: GENERAL

sum of interior angles $m\angle A + m\angle B + m\angle C = 180°$

area $A = \dfrac{1}{2}bh$

length of midsegment $\text{length} = \dfrac{1}{2}$ length of parallel side

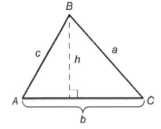

TRIANGLE: RIGHT

Pythagorean theorem $a^2 + b^2 = c^2$

Solid Geometry

CONE

volume $\quad V = \frac{1}{3}Bh = \frac{1}{3}\pi r^2 h$

surface area $\quad S = L + B = \pi r l + \pi r^2$

CYLINDER

volume $\quad V = Bh = \pi r^2 h$

surface area $\quad S = L + 2B$

$\qquad\qquad S = 2\pi r h + 2\pi r^2$

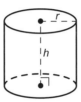

PRISM: CUBE

volume $\quad V = s^3$

surface area $\quad S = 6s^2$

PRISM: GENERAL

volume $\quad V = Bh$

surface area $\quad S = 2B + L$

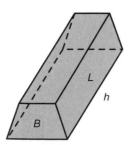

PRISM: RIGHT RECTANGULAR

volume $V = lwh$

surface area $S = 2lw + 2lh + 2wh$

length of diagonal $d = \sqrt{l^2 + w^2 + h^2}$

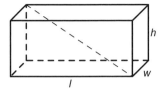

PYRAMID

volume $V = \frac{1}{3}Bh$

surface area $S = \frac{1}{2}lP + B$

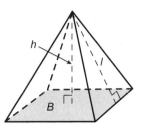

SPHERE

volume $V = \frac{4}{3}\pi r^3$

surface area $S = 4\pi r^2$

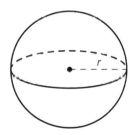

Coordinate Geometry

LINE AND SEGMENT

slope $m = \dfrac{\text{rise}}{\text{run}} = \dfrac{y_2 - y_1}{x_2 - x_1}$

coordinates of midpoint $M = \left(\dfrac{x_1 + x_2}{2}, \dfrac{y_1 + y_2}{2} \right)$

distance $d = \sqrt{(x_2 - x_1)^2 + (y_2 - y_1)^2}$

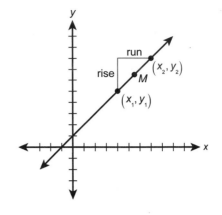

LINEAR EQUATION FORMS

standard $Ax + By = C$

slope-intercept $y = mx + b$

point-slope $y - y_1 = m(x - x_1)$

CIRCLE

equation in graphing form $(x - h)^2 + (y - k)^2 = r^2$

center (h, k) and radius r

PARABOLA GRAPHING FORMS

vertical axis of symmetry
$y - k = a(x - h)^2$ (axis of symmetry $x = h$)

horizontal axis of symmetry
$x - h = a(y - k)^2$ (axis of symmetry $y = k$)

vertex (h, k)

focal distance $f = \dfrac{1}{4a}$

eccentricity $e = 1$

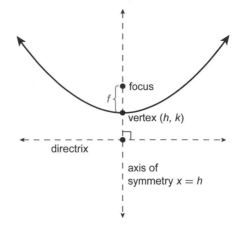

THREE-DIMENSIONAL SPACE

distance between points $\quad d = \sqrt{(x_2 - x_1)^2 + (y_2 - y_1)^2 + (z_2 - z_1)^2}$

coordinates of midpoint $\quad \left(\dfrac{x_1 + x_2}{2}, \dfrac{y_1 + y_2}{2}, \dfrac{z_1 + z_2}{2} \right)$

general equation of a line $\quad Ax + By + Cz - D$

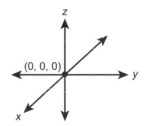

FUNCTIONS

average rate of change $\quad \dfrac{f(b) - f(a)}{b - a}$

axis of symmetry for $f(x) = ax^2 + bx + c \quad x = -\dfrac{b}{2a}$

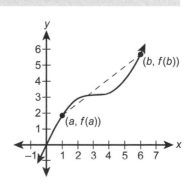

Solving Equations

completing the square   Given the equation $ax^2 + bx = c$, add $\left(\dfrac{b}{2a}\right)^2$ to both sides.

discriminant   Given the equation $ax^2 + bx + c = 0$, the discriminant is $b^2 - 4ac$.

quadratic formula   The solutions of the equation $ax^2 + bx + c = 0$, where $a \neq 0$,

are $x = \dfrac{-b \pm \sqrt{b^2 - 4ac}}{2a}$.

EXPONENTS AND LOGARITHMS

$$x^a \cdot x^b = x^{a+b}$$

$$\frac{x^a}{x^b} = x^{a-b}$$

$$x^0 = 1$$

$$x^1 = x$$

For any $a > 0$ and $b > 0$, $b \neq 1$: $\log_b a = x$ if and only if $b^x = a$.

$$\log mn = \log m + \log n$$

$$\log\left(\frac{m}{n}\right) = \log m - \log n$$

$$\log m^a = a \log m$$

Counting and Probability

FACTORIAL

$$n! = n \cdot (n - 1) \cdot (n - 2) \cdot \ldots \cdot 1 \ (n \text{ factors})$$
$$0! = 1$$

SIMPLE THEORETICAL PROBABILITY

$$P(E) = \frac{\text{number of outcomes in event } E}{\text{total number of outcomes in sample space } S} = \frac{n(E)}{n(S)}$$

PROBABILITY OF DEPENDENT EVENTS

$$P(A \text{ and } B) = P(A) \bullet P(B|A)$$

PROBABILITY OF INDEPENDENT EVENTS

$$P(A \text{ and } B) = P(A) \bullet P(B)$$

PROBABILITY OF MUTUALLY EXCLUSIVE EVENTS

$$P(A \text{ or } B) = P(A) + P(B)$$

PROBABILITY OF COMPLEMENTARY EVENTS

$$P(A) = 1 - P(B)$$

EXPERIMENTAL PROBABILITY OF EVENT E

$$P(E) = \frac{\text{number of times event } E \text{ has occurred}}{n}$$

Statistics

MEAN

For a data set with n elements, the mean is

$$\bar{x} = \frac{x_1 + x_1 + \ldots + x_n}{n}.$$

MEDIAN

Arrange the values in order from least to greatest. For an

Odd number of values, use the middle value.

Even number of values, use the average of the middle two values.

MODE

The mode is the value that occurs most often in a set of data. If no one value occurs most often, then there is no mode for the set.

STANDARD DEVIATION

To find the standard deviation s of a data set with n values, where x is the data value and $\overline{x}$ is the mean, use the formula

$$s = \sqrt{\frac{\Sigma(x - \overline{x})^2}{n - 1}}.$$

z-SCORE

If x is a raw data value from a normally distributed data set with mean μ and standard deviation σ, then

$$z = \frac{x - \mu}{\sigma}$$

is the number of standard deviations x is from the mean.

SAMPLING STANDARD DEVIATION

If random samples of size n are taken from a distribution with poplation standard deviation σ, then the sampling distribution will have standard deviation approximately equal to

$$\frac{\sigma}{\sqrt{n}}.$$

STANDARD DEVIATION OF A SAMPLING DISTRIBUTION OF A PROPORTION

If a sample of size n is drawn from a population with proportion p, then the sampling distribution of the proportion will have standard deviation approximately equal to

$$\sqrt{\frac{p(1 - p)}{n}}.$$

Sequences and Series

common difference of an arithmetic sequence $\quad d = a_n - a_{n-1}$

iterative rule for an arithmetic sequence $\quad a_n = a_1 + (n-1)d$

recursive rule for an arithmetic sequence $\quad a_n = a_{n-1} + d$

common ratio of a geometric sequence $\quad r = \dfrac{a_n}{a_{n-1}}$

iterative rule for a geometric sequence $\quad a_n = a_1 \cdot r^{n-1}$

recursive rule for a geometric sequence $\quad a_n = r \cdot a_{n-1}$

sigma notation   The sum of the first n terms of a sequence can be written as

$$S_n = \sum_{i=0}^{n} a_i = a_1 + a_2 + a_3 + \ldots + a_n$$

where i is the index, 1 is the lower limit, and n is the upper limit.

arithmetic series   The nth partial sum of an arithmetic series a with common difference d is

$$S_n = \frac{n}{2}(a_1 + a_2) \text{ or } S_n = \frac{n}{2}(2a_1 + (n-1)d).$$

geometric series   The nth partial sum of a geometric series a with common ratio r is

$$S_n = \frac{a_1(1 - r^n)}{1 - r}, \text{ or } S_n = \frac{a_1 - a_n r}{1 - r} \text{ where } r \neq 1.$$

Exponential Growth and Decay

If a quantity is decaying exponentially from initial amount b and with decay rate r, then the amount y remaining after t time periods is

$$y = b(1 - r)^t.$$

EXPONENTIAL GROWTH FORMULA

If a quantity is growing exponentially from the initial amount b where r is the fixed percent expressed as a decimal, then the total amount y after t time periods is

$$y = b(1 + r)^t.$$

COMPOUND INTEREST FORMULA

The total amount A of an investment with initial principal P, earning compound interest at an annual interest rate r and compounded n times per year for t years, is

$$A = P\left(1 + \frac{r}{n}\right)^{nt}.$$

HALF-LIFE FORMULA

The amount y of a radioactive substance after t time periods, where b is the initial amount and h is the half-life, is

$$y = b\left(\frac{1}{2}\right)^{\frac{t}{h}}.$$

Trigonometry

RIGHT TRIANGLE RATIOS

tangent: $\tan A = \dfrac{\text{opposite}}{\text{adjacent}} = \dfrac{a}{b}$

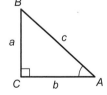

cosine: $\cos A = \dfrac{\text{adjacent}}{\text{hypotenuse}} = \dfrac{b}{c}$

sine: $\sin A = \dfrac{\text{opposite}}{\text{hypotenuse}} = \dfrac{a}{c}$

SPECIAL RIGHT TRIANGLES

Angle measure	Sine	Cosine	Tangent
30°	$\dfrac{1}{2}$	$\dfrac{\sqrt{3}}{2}$	$\dfrac{\sqrt{3}}{3}$
45°	$\dfrac{\sqrt{2}}{2}$	$\dfrac{\sqrt{2}}{2}$	1
60°	$\dfrac{\sqrt{3}}{2}$	$\dfrac{1}{2}$	$\sqrt{3}$

UNIT CIRCLE ON THE COORDINATE PLANE

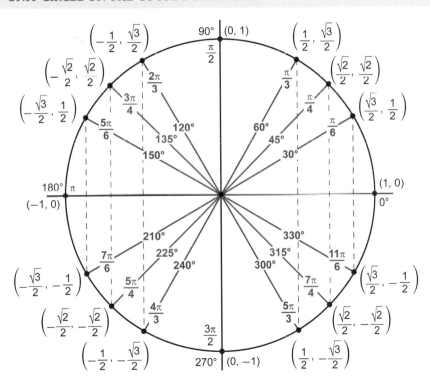

TRIGONOMETRIC IDENTITIES

$$\sin^2 x + \cos^2 x = 1$$

$$\tan x = \frac{\sin x}{\cos x}$$

$$\sin x = \cos(90° - x)$$

$$\cos x = \sin(90° - x)$$

General Applications

DISTANCE

For uniform motion, where d is distance, r is rate, and t is time,

$$d = rt.$$

PROJECTILE MOTION

The height of an object, in meters, after t seconds, with initial vertical velocity v_0 and initial height h_0, is given by

$$h(t) = -4.9t^2 + v_0 t + h_0.$$

The height of an object, in feet, after t seconds, with initial vertical velocity v_0 and initial height h_0, is given by

$$h(t) = -16t^2 + v_0 t + h_0.$$

SIMPLE INTEREST

The amount of simple interest I earned, where P is the principal (amount borrowed, deposited, or invested), r is the annual interest rate, and t is the time in years, is given by

$$I = Prt.$$

TEMPERATURE CONVERSION

$$F = \frac{9}{5}C + 32$$

where F is degrees Fahrenheit and C is degrees Celsius.

Postulates and Theorems

Euclid's Postulates

POSTULATE EUC-1

Any two points can be connected with a line segment.

POSTULATE EUC-2

Any line segment can be extended indefinitely in two directions to make a line.

POSTULATE EUC-3

Given any line segment, a circle can be drawn that has the segment as its radius and one endpoint as its center.

POSTULATE EUC-4

All right angles are equivalent to each other.

POSTULATE EUC-5

Given any straight line and a point not on the line, there is exactly one line through the point that is parallel to the line.

General

POSTULATE GEN-1

Two points determine a line.

POSTULATE GEN-2

Three noncollinear points determine a plane.

Measurement

POSTULATE MEAS-1

Ruler Postulate   The points on a line can be numbered so that positive number differences measure distances.

POSTULATE MEAS-2

Segment Addition Postulate   If B is between A and C, then $AB + BC = AC$. Also, if $AB + BC = AC$ and A, B, and C are collinear, then B is between A and C.

POSTULATE MEAS-3

Segment Congruence Postulate   If two segments have the same length as measured by a fair ruler, then the segments are congruent ($\cong$). Also, if two segments are congruent, then they have the same length as measured by a fair ruler.

POSTULATE MEAS-4

Angle Addition Postulate   If point D lies in the interior of $\angle ABC$, then $m\angle ABD + m\angle DBC = m\angle ABC$.

POSTULATE MEAS-5

Angle Congruence Postulate   If two angles have the same measure as measured by a protractor, then the angles are congruent. Also, if two angles are congruent, then they have the same measure as measured by a protractor.

POSTULATE MEAS-6

Linear Pair Postulate   If two angles form a linear pair, then they are supplementary angles.

THEOREM MEAS-1

Vertical Angles Theorem   If two angles form a pair of vertical angles, then they are congruent.

Parallels

POSTULATE PAR-1

Corresponding Angles Postulate   If two parallel lines are intersected by a transversal, then corresponding angles are congruent.

POSTULATE PAR-2

Converse of the Corresponding Angles Postulate   If two coplanar lines are intersected by a transversal and the corresponding angles are congruent, then the lines are parallel.

THEOREM PAR-1

Alternate Interior Angles Theorem   If two parallel lines are intersected by a transversal, then the alternate interior angles are congruent.

THEOREM PAR-2

Alternate Exterior Angles Theorem   If two parallel lines are intersected by a transversal, then the alternate exterior angles are congruent.

THEOREM PAR-3

Same-Side Interior Angles Theorem   If two parallel lines are intersected by a transversal, then the same-side interior angles are supplementary.

THEOREM PAR-4

Converse of the Alternate Interior Angles Theorem   If two coplanar lines are intersected by a transversal and the alternate interior angles are congruent, then the lines are parallel.

THEOREM PAR-5

Converse of the Alternate Exterior Angles Theorem   If two coplanar lines are intersected by a transversal and the alternate exterior angles are congruent, then the lines are parallel.

THEOREM PAR-6

Converse of the Same-Side Interior Angles Theorem   If two coplanar lines are intersected by a transversal and the same-side interior angles are supplementary, then the lines are parallel.

Lines

POSTULATE LINES-1

Parallel Postulate   Given a line and a point not on the line, there is one and only one line that contains the given point and is parallel to the given line.

THEOREM LINES-1

If two coplanar lines are perpendicular to ($\perp$) the same line, then the two lines are parallel.

THEOREM LINES-2

If two coplanar lines are parallel to the same line, then the two lines are parallel.

Coordinate

THEOREM COORD-1

Parallel Lines Theorem   Two coplanar nonvertical lines are parallel if and only if they have the same slope. Any two vertical lines are parallel.

THEOREM COORD-2

Perpendicular Lines Theorem   Two coplanar nonvertical lines are perpendicular if and only if the product of their slopes equals -1. Any vertical line is perpendicular to any horizontal line.

Congruence

POSTULATE CONG-1

Polygon Congruence Postulate   Two polygons are congruent if and only if there is a correspondence between their sides and angles so that all pairs of corresponding angles are congruent and all pairs of corresponding sides are congruent.

POSTULATE CONG-2

Side-Side-Side (SSS) Congruence Postulate   If the three sides of one triangle are congruent to the three sides of another triangle, then the two triangles are congruent.

POSTULATE CONG-3

Side-Angle-Side (SAS) Congruence Postulate   If two sides and the included angle in one triangle are congruent to two sides and the included angle in another triangle, then the two triangles are congruent.

POSTULATE CONG-4

Angle-Side-Angle (ASA) Congruence Postulate   If two angles and the included side in one triangle are congruent to two angles and the included side in another triangle, then the two triangles are congruent.

THEOREM CONG-1

Hypotenuse-Leg (HL) Congruence Theorem   If the hypotenuse and a leg of one right triangle are congruent to the hypotenuse and corresponding leg of another right triangle, then the two triangles are congruent.

Triangles

THEOREM TRI-1

Triangle Sum Theorem   The sum of the measures of the interior angles of a triangle is 180°.

THEOREM TRI-2

Exterior Angle Theorem   The measure of an exterior angle of a triangle is equal to the sum of the measures of the remote interior angles.

THEOREM TRI-3

Isosceles Triangle Theorem   If two sides of a triangle are congruent, then the angles opposite those sides are congruent.

THEOREM TRI-4

Converse of the Isosceles Triangle Theorem   If two angles of a triangle are congruent, then the sides opposite those angles are congruent.

Quadrilaterals

THEOREM QUAD-1

In a parallelogram, the opposite sides are congruent.

THEOREM QUAD-2

In a rectangle, the diagonals are congruent.

THEOREM QUAD-3

If two pairs of opposite sides of a quadrilateral are congruent, then the quadrilateral is a parallelogram.

THEOREM QUAD-4

If two opposite sides of a quadrilateral are parallel and congruent, then the quadrilateral is a parallelogram.

THEOREM QUAD-5

If the diagonals of a quadrilateral bisect each other, then the quadrilateral is a parallelogram.

THEOREM QUAD-6

If the diagonals of a parallelogram are congruent, then the parallelogram is a rectangle.

THEOREM QUAD-7

If the diagonals of a parallelogram are perpendicular, then the parallelogram is a rhombus.

THEOREM QUAD-8

If two adjacent sides of a parallelogram are congruent, then the parallelogram is a rhombus.

THEOREM QUAD-9

If the diagonals of a parallelogram bisect the angles of the parallelogram, then the parallelogram is a rhombus.

THEOREM QUAD-10

If one angle of a parallelogram is a right angle, then the parallelogram is a rectangle.

Right Triangles

THEOREM RIGHT-1

Pythagorean Theorem For all right triangles, the square of the length of the hypotenuse c equals the sum of the squares of the lengths of the legs a and b.

$$c^2 = a^2 + b^2$$

THEOREM RIGHT-2

Converse of the Pythagorean Theorem If the square of the length of the longest side of a triangle equals the sum of the squares of the lengths of the other two sides, then the triangle is a right triangle.

THEOREM RIGHT-3

45°-45°-90° Triangle Theorem In any 45°-45°-90° triangle, the length of the hypotenuse is $\sqrt{2}$ times the length of a leg.

THEOREM RIGHT-4

30°-60°-90° Triangle Theorem In any 30°-60°-90° triangle, the length of the hypotenuse is 2 times the length of the shorter leg, and the length of the longer leg is $\sqrt{3}$ times the length of the shorter leg.

Similarity

POSTULATE SIM-1

Polygon Similarity Postulate   Two polygons are similar if and only if there is a correspondence between their angles and their sides so that all corresponding angles are congruent and all corresponding sides are proportional.

POSTULATE SIM-2

Angle-Angle (AA) Similarity Postulate   If two angles of a triangle are congruent to two angles of another triangle, then the triangles are similar.

COROLLARY SIM-1

Two-Transversal Proportionality Corollary   Three or more parallel lines divide two intersecting transversals proportionally.

THEOREM SIM-1

Side-Side-Side (SSS) Similarity Theorem   If the three sides of a triangle are proportional to the three sides of another triangle, then the triangles are similar.

THEOREM SIM-2

Side-Angle-Side (SAS) Similarity Theorem   If two sides of a triangle are proportional to two sides of another triangle and if their included angles are congruent, then the triangles are similar.

THEOREM SIM-3

Triangle Proportionality Theorem   A line parallel to one side of a triangle divides the other two sides proportionally.

THEOREM SIM-4

Angle Bisector Theorem   An angle bisector of an angle of a triangle divides the opposite side in two segments that are proportional to the other two sides of the triangle.

Circles

COROLLARY CIRC-1

Right-Angle Corollary   An angle that is inscribed in a semicircle is a right angle.

COROLLARY CIRC-2

Arc-Intercept Corollary   Two inscribed angles that intercept the same arc have the same measure.

COROLLARY CIRC-3

Converse of the Right-Angle Corollary   If an inscribed angle is a right angle, then the intercepted arc is a semicircle.

THEOREM CIRC-1

Chords and Arcs Theorem   In a circle or in congruent circles, the arcs of congruent chords are congruent.

THEOREM CIRC-2

Converse of the Chords and Arcs Theorem   In a circle or in congruent circles, the chords of congruent arcs are congruent.

THEOREM CIRC-3

Tangent Theorem   A line that is tangent to a circle is perpendicular to a radius of the circle at the point of tangency.

THEOREM CIRC-4

Converse of the Tangent Theorem   A line that is perpendicular to a radius of a circle at its endpoint on the circle is tangent to the circle.

THEOREM CIRC-5

Radius and Chord Theorem   A radius that is perpendicular to a chord of a circle bisects the chord.

THEOREM CIRC-6

Inscribed Angle Theorem   An angle inscribed in a circle has a measure that equals one-half the measure of its intercepted arc.

THEOREM CIRC-7

Inscribed Quadrilateral Theorem   If a quadrilateral is inscribed in a semicircle, then the opposite angles are supplementary.

THEOREM CIRC-8

If a tangent and a secant or chord intersect on a circle at the point of tangency, then the measure of the angle formed equals one-half the measure of the intercepted arc.

THEOREM CIRC-9

The measure of a secant-tangent angle with its vertex outside the circle equals one-half of the difference of the measures of the intercepted arcs.

THEOREM CIRC-10

The measure of an angle that is formed by two secants that intersect in the exterior of a circle equals one-half of the difference of the measures of the intercepted arcs.

THEOREM CIRC-11

The measure of a tangent-tangent angle with its vertex outside the circle equals one-half of the difference of the measures of the intercepted arcs, or the measure of the major arc minus 180°.

THEOREM CIRC-12

The measure of an angle that is formed by two secants or chords that intersect in the interior of a circle equals one-half the sum of the measures of the arcs intercepted by the angle and its vertical angle.

Illustrations Credits

All illustrations © K12 Inc. unless otherwise noted

Cover Blue fish background. © Dobrynina Elena/Shutterstock.com

Back Cover Blue, white, and green background. © Dobrynina Elena/Shutterstock.com

K¹² Summit Curriculum Computer monitor. © antpkr/Shutterstock; Tablet and phone. © Radu Bercan/Shutterstock

Probability Distributions Ladybugs on leaf. © caia image/Alamy Stock Photo

Data Gathering and Analysis Bees working on honeycomb. © Grafissimo/iStockphoto.com

Systems of Linear Equations and Inequalities Paint. © Subbotina Anna/Shutterstock

Radicals and Complex Numbers Fractals. © clawan/BigStock

Polynomials Launch of the *Atlantis* space shuttle. © Scott Andrews/Getty Images

Polynomial Functions Fountains. © Pongmanat/BigStockPhoto

Rational Expressions Monsoon storm. © Tim Martin/Getty Images

Exponential and Logarithmic Functions Photographer. © Taxi/Getty Images

Radians and Trigonometric Functions Canadarm 2. © Stocktrek Images, Inc./Alamy Stock Photo

Graphs of Sinusoidal Functions NAVSEA Maneuvering and Seakeeping Basin facility. © Ryan Hanyok/U.S. Navy

More Function Types Coronal mass ejection in suns atmosphere. NASA/GSFC/SDO

Using Function Models Clay model car. © Car Culture/Getty Images

Sequences and Series Snares crested penguins. © Janelle Lugge/Shutterstock

Data Sources

GRAPHS OF SINUSOIDAL FUNCTIONS

Tide High and Low, Inc. 2013. "Regions with Tide Predictions." Accessed September 17, 2013. http://www.saltwatertides.com/pickpred.html.

WORKING WITH FUNCTION MODELS

McMahon, Tim. 2012. "Gasoline 20 Cents a Gallon?" InflationData.com. Accessed March 27, 2015. http://inflationdata.com/articles/inflation-adjusted-prices/gasoline/.

Table of z-Scores for Normal Distribution

This portion of the z-distribution table gives areas under the standard normal curve for negative z-values.

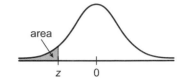

z	.00	.01	.02	.03	.04	.05	.06	.07	.08	.09
−3.5	0.0002	0.0002	0.0002	0.0002	0.0002	0.0002	0.0002	0.0002	0.0002	0.0002
−3.4	0.0003	0.0003	0.0003	0.0003	0.0003	0.0003	0.0003	0.0003	0.0003	0.0002
−3.3	0.0005	0.0005	0.0005	0.0004	0.0004	0.0004	0.0004	0.0004	0.0004	0.0003
−3.2	0.0007	0.0007	0.0006	0.0006	0.0006	0.0006	0.0006	0.0005	0.0005	0.0005
−3.1	0.0010	0.0009	0.0009	0.0009	0.0008	0.0008	0.0008	0.0008	0.0007	0.0007
−3.0	0.0013	0.0013	0.0013	0.0012	0.0012	0.0011	0.0011	0.0011	0.0010	0.0010
−2.9	0.0019	0.0018	0.0018	0.0017	0.0016	0.0016	0.0015	0.0015	0.0014	0.0014
−2.8	0.0026	0.0025	0.0024	0.0023	0.0023	0.0022	0.0021	0.0021	0.0020	0.0019
−2.7	0.0035	0.0034	0.0033	0.0032	0.0031	0.0030	0.0029	0.0028	0.0027	0.0026
−2.6	0.0047	0.0045	0.0044	0.0043	0.0041	0.0040	0.0039	0.0038	0.0037	0.0036
−2.5	0.0062	0.0060	0.0059	0.0057	0.0055	0.0054	0.0052	0.0051	0.0049	0.0048
−2.4	0.0082	0.0080	0.0078	0.0075	0.0073	0.0071	0.0069	0.0068	0.0066	0.0064
−2.3	0.0107	0.0104	0.0102	0.0099	0.0096	0.0094	0.0091	0.0089	0.0087	0.0084
−2.2	0.0139	0.0136	0.0132	0.0129	0.0125	0.0122	0.0119	0.0116	0.0113	0.0110
−2.1	0.0179	0.0174	0.0170	0.0166	0.0162	0.0158	0.0154	0.0150	0.0146	0.0143
−2.0	0.0228	0.0222	0.0217	0.0212	0.0207	0.0202	0.0197	0.0192	0.0188	0.0183
−1.9	0.0287	0.0281	0.0274	0.0268	0.0262	0.0256	0.0250	0.0244	0.0239	0.0233
−1.8	0.0359	0.0351	0.0344	0.0336	0.0329	0.0322	0.0314	0.0307	0.0301	0.0294
−1.7	0.0446	0.0436	0.0427	0.0418	0.0409	0.0401	0.0392	0.0384	0.0375	0.0367
−1.6	0.0548	0.0537	0.0526	0.0516	0.0505	0.0495	0.0485	0.0475	0.0465	0.0455
−1.5	0.0668	0.0655	0.0643	0.0630	0.0618	0.0606	0.0594	0.0582	0.0571	0.0559
−1.4	0.0808	0.0793	0.0778	0.0764	0.0749	0.0735	0.0721	0.0708	0.0694	0.0681
−1.3	0.0968	0.0951	0.0934	0.0918	0.0901	0.0885	0.0869	0.0853	0.0838	0.0823
−1.2	0.1151	0.1131	0.1112	0.1093	0.1075	0.1056	0.1038	0.1020	0.1003	0.0985
−1.1	0.1357	0.1335	0.1314	0.1292	0.1271	0.1251	0.1230	0.1210	0.1190	0.1170
−1.0	0.1587	0.1562	0.1539	0.1515	0.1492	0.1469	0.1446	0.1423	0.1401	0.1379
−0.9	0.1841	0.1814	0.1788	0.1762	0.1736	0.1711	0.1685	0.1660	0.1635	0.1611
−0.8	0.2119	0.2090	0.2061	0.2033	0.2005	0.1977	0.1949	0.1922	0.1894	0.1867
−0.7	0.2420	0.2389	0.2358	0.2327	0.2296	0.2266	0.2236	0.2206	0.2177	0.2148
−0.6	0.2743	0.2709	0.2676	0.2643	0.2611	0.2578	0.2546	0.2514	0.2483	0.2451
−0.5	0.3085	0.3050	0.3015	0.2981	0.2946	0.2912	0.2877	0.2843	0.2810	0.2776
−0.4	0.3446	0.3409	0.3372	0.3336	0.3300	0.3264	0.3228	0.3192	0.3156	0.3121
−0.3	0.3821	0.3783	0.3745	0.3707	0.3669	0.3632	0.3594	0.3557	0.3520	0.3483
−0.2	0.4207	0.4168	0.4129	0.4090	0.4052	0.4013	0.3974	0.3936	0.3897	0.3859
−0.1	0.4602	0.4562	0.4522	0.4483	0.4443	0.4404	0.4364	0.4325	0.4286	0.4247
−0.0	0.5000	0.4960	0.4920	0.4880	0.4840	0.4801	0.4761	0.4721	0.4681	0.4641

This portion of the z-distribution table gives areas under the standard normal curve for positive z-values.

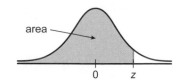

area

0   z

z	.00	.01	.02	.03	.04	.05	.06	.07	.08	.09
0.0	0.5000	0.5040	0.5080	0.5120	0.5160	0.5199	0.5239	0.5279	0.5319	0.5359
0.1	0.5398	0.5438	0.5478	0.5517	0.5557	0.5596	0.5636	0.5675	0.5714	0.5753
0.2	0.5793	0.5832	0.5871	0.5910	0.5948	0.5987	0.6026	0.6064	0.6103	0.6141
0.3	0.6179	0.6217	0.6255	0.6293	0.6331	0.6368	0.6406	0.6443	0.6480	0.6517
0.4	0.6554	0.6591	0.6628	0.6664	0.6700	0.6736	0.6772	0.6808	0.6844	0.6879
0.5	0.6915	0.6950	0.6985	0.7019	0.7054	0.7088	0.7123	0.7157	0.7190	0.7224
0.6	0.7257	0.7291	0.7324	0.7357	0.7389	0.7422	0.7454	0.7486	0.7517	0.7549
0.7	0.7580	0.7611	0.7642	0.7673	0.7704	0.7734	0.7764	0.7794	0.7823	0.7852
0.8	0.7881	0.7910	0.7939	0.7967	0.7995	0.8023	0.8051	0.8078	0.8106	0.8133
0.9	0.8159	0.8186	0.8212	0.8238	0.8264	0.8289	0.8315	0.8340	0.8365	0.8389
1.0	0.8413	0.8438	0.8461	0.8485	0.8508	0.8531	0.8554	0.8577	0.8599	0.8621
1.1	0.8643	0.8665	0.8686	0.8708	0.8729	0.8749	0.8770	0.8790	0.8810	0.8830
1.2	0.8849	0.8869	0.8888	0.8907	0.8925	0.8944	0.8962	0.8980	0.8997	0.9015
1.3	0.9032	0.9049	0.9066	0.9082	0.9099	0.9115	0.9131	0.9147	0.9162	0.9177
1.4	0.9192	0.9207	0.9222	0.9236	0.9251	0.9265	0.9279	0.9292	0.9306	0.9319
1.5	0.9332	0.9345	0.9357	0.9370	0.9382	0.9394	0.9406	0.9418	0.9429	0.9441
1.6	0.9452	0.9463	0.9474	0.9484	0.9495	0.9505	0.9515	0.9525	0.9535	0.9545
1.7	0.9554	0.9564	0.9573	0.9582	0.9591	0.9599	0.9608	0.9616	0.9625	0.9633
1.8	0.9641	0.9649	0.9656	0.9664	0.9671	0.9678	0.9686	0.9693	0.9699	0.9706
1.9	0.9713	0.9719	0.9726	0.9732	0.9738	0.9744	0.9750	0.9756	0.9761	0.9767
2.0	0.9772	0.9778	0.9783	0.9788	0.9793	0.9798	0.9803	0.9808	0.9812	0.9817
2.1	0.9821	0.9826	0.9830	0.9834	0.9838	0.9842	0.9846	0.9850	0.9854	0.9857
2.2	0.9861	0.9864	0.9868	0.9871	0.9875	0.9878	0.9881	0.9884	0.9887	0.9890
2.3	0.9893	0.9896	0.9898	0.9901	0.9904	0.9906	0.9909	0.9911	0.9913	0.9916
2.4	0.9918	0.9920	0.9922	0.9925	0.9927	0.9929	0.9931	0.9932	0.9934	0.9936
2.5	0.9938	0.9940	0.9941	0.9943	0.9945	0.9946	0.9948	0.9949	0.9951	0.9952
2.6	0.9953	0.9955	0.9956	0.9957	0.9959	0.9960	0.9961	0.9962	0.9963	0.9964
2.7	0.9965	0.9966	0.9967	0.9968	0.9969	0.9970	0.9971	0.9972	0.9973	0.9974
2.8	0.9974	0.9975	0.9976	0.9977	0.9977	0.9978	0.9979	0.9979	0.9980	0.9981
2.9	0.9981	0.9982	0.9982	0.9983	0.9984	0.9984	0.9985	0.9985	0.9986	0.9986
3.0	0.9987	0.9987	0.9987	0.9988	0.9988	0.9989	0.9989	0.9989	0.9990	0.9990
3.1	0.9990	0.9991	0.9991	0.9991	0.9992	0.9992	0.9992	0.9992	0.9993	0.9993
3.2	0.9993	0.9993	0.9994	0.9994	0.9994	0.9994	0.9994	0.9995	0.9995	0.9995
3.3	0.9995	0.9995	0.9995	0.9996	0.9996	0.9996	0.9996	0.9996	0.9996	0.9997
3.4	0.9997	0.9997	0.9997	0.9997	0.9997	0.9997	0.9997	0.9997	0.9997	0.9998
3.5	0.9998	0.9998	0.9998	0.9998	0.9998	0.9998	0.9998	0.9998	0.9998	0.9998

Table of Random Digits

This table was created by randomly generating the digits 0, 1, 2, 3, 4, 5, 6, 7, 8, and 9. Individual digits, as well as groups of digits, are independent of each other and are equally likely to appear in any given location.

Line								
101	61948	03027	33141	63157	78772	21836	90510	61655
102	91620	74848	70363	06857	52569	06161	86277	49814
103	85979	01365	65281	74386	34312	99968	25273	04716
104	46945	50613	58782	15470	55432	11517	45082	93068
105	06857	83023	69347	25426	16372	97610	31833	35017
106	85569	48307	19604	46319	34885	86291	15291	17576
107	62482	49347	21366	73056	42193	34996	34437	45965
108	01136	12428	34626	91253	58427	75229	10693	32036
109	34710	56471	29761	35322	15799	15728	72632	85452
110	47942	57768	13870	71092	96351	16392	98138	16154
111	58043	39340	71797	19710	31745	69753	59189	21854
112	37697	24731	53600	43295	83819	49237	67017	17926
113	10311	43137	24736	90584	43692	48335	98715	10551
114	19724	50552	14851	69355	37856	20190	07579	99328
115	64628	88781	35241	19739	31439	55383	59304	07965
116	84307	05017	79713	19252	39557	15608	90737	81430
117	43887	37323	47413	50487	23703	66932	09024	19395
118	01178	69415	09264	17728	58858	76330	57712	66411
119	36748	24247	75430	36452	95641	00723	22490	51418
120	66805	86573	49093	14317	20330	09825	36777	82572
121	61353	72890	49782	17351	25752	97463	13848	55997
122	47711	89200	20408	90226	48337	78474	56670	32427
123	19674	79436	62849	82534	53308	15043	73660	67276
124	76158	36233	90485	63091	07415	62319	34251	94438
125	08447	27851	60051	33465	16523	35981	41028	47113

Line								
126	47934	01885	20967	94841	27015	44184	05108	86788
127	73786	87922	17887	03752	70494	09483	34655	28603
128	53537	96428	40115	27467	90826	52358	14570	54184
129	20266	49844	35186	57228	65170	85907	44662	91487
130	89214	31076	93733	30746	44086	20432	94732	78616
131	91027	18200	74536	83514	90127	17369	63329	42042
132	64590	25562	53991	84693	23729	07208	48253	49181
133	20139	41704	10931	04546	15698	00496	80875	97746
134	84973	67235	37150	68126	73940	24012	55792	90144
135	97462	29957	45238	15720	29586	99668	58850	17145
136	19860	28864	90400	74509	62772	25553	14361	09172
137	68481	45032	22849	87727	43979	12720	30551	80164
138	63029	54834	18922	86434	10098	12231	44527	70725
139	83771	23744	35849	93987	39059	21814	31364	65209
140	19860	77985	17729	05037	84795	46237	08049	27047
141	96408	03766	36932	41651	08410	56191	95729	39544
142	40267	28369	76635	58250	49655	34511	47379	17246
143	31932	66602	84722	66425	73843	66245	05042	11491
144	21890	58696	35514	22300	40904	10963	87658	98571
145	35126	85093	96751	88858	34777	00778	35831	76274
146	52297	42906	34100	94089	64070	44916	73935	24790
147	99920	01124	56018	28674	70123	32165	28422	63118
148	24463	92048	77004	64139	59183	97109	49671	85516
149	85978	69330	82882	91190	42772	83313	38828	57345
150	08070	40853	77914	34718	65143	70394	92396	41075
151	03450	56097	32265	10902	61142	09589	79854	88509
152	28966	67648	92558	52609	75466	88029	68994	57520
153	31068	29401	07709	85428	66715	59246	18439	32775
154	90347	13546	69472	97378	30982	97578	28718	40431
155	17264	64009	96465	16538	44789	92369	06771	61720
156	18547	91013	04346	55848	67969	66506	07975	86217
157	11892	76592	62064	09841	85676	92839	66320	90037
158	68046	54031	75840	06637	23138	01003	89362	25922
159	36912	12426	85437	07756	72542	54834	60424	76333
160	43968	29533	99011	79325	17191	04644	30827	92697